Prentice Hall
WRITING and GRAMMAR
Communication in Action

Platinum Level

Grammar Exercise Workbook

TEACHER'S EDITION

Prentice Hall

Upper Saddle River, New Jersey
Glenview, Illinois
Needham, Massachusetts

Teacher's Edition

ISBN 0-13-043483-3

6 7 8 9 10 07

Contents

Note: This workbook supports Chapters 16–28 (Part 2: Grammar, Usage, and Mechanics) of Prentice Hall *Writing and Grammar*.

Chapter 21: Writing Effective Sentences

Chapter 22: Verb Usage

Diagraming

16.1 Nouns (Names, Compound Nouns) • Practice 1

Nouns as Names   A *noun* is the name of a person, place, or thing. Nouns that name things that can be seen, touched, or recognized through any of the five senses are called concrete nouns. Nouns that name things that cannot be recognized through any of the five senses are called abstract nouns.

Concrete Nouns		Abstract Nouns	
beach	tree	dismay	happiness
moose	Judy	wisdom	courage
hotel	sand	treatment	honor
Europe	table	decision	oppression

Compound Nouns   A compound noun is a noun that is made up of more than one word.

TYPES OF COMPOUND NOUNS		
Separate Words	Hyphenated Words	Combined Words
soap opera	Jack-of-all-trades	dishwasher
fire engine	Commander-in-Chief	toothbrush

▷**Exercise 1**   **Identifying Nouns.**   Underline each concrete noun. Circle each abstract noun. The number in parentheses tells how many nouns there are.

EXAMPLE: Erica has high (hopes) for her (future). (3)

1. The Constitution guarantees many different (rights.) (2)

2. The biggest (concern) of the hikers was (time). (3)

3. The (grace) of the long-legged birds surprised the tourists. (3)

4. Paula overcame her (fear) of (success.) (3)

5. The (difference) between Lou and Len is their (attitude.) (4)

6. Several hunters came back with deer, elk, and moose. (4)

7. Has the doctor given Sherry any good (advice?) (3)

8. An article in the newspaper describes the (opening) of Marvelle Park. (4)

9. A sign outside the auditorium listed the soloists. (3)

10. A nurse at the hospital put a splint on my arm. (4)

▷**Exercise 2**   **Recognizing Compound Nouns.**   Circle each compound noun. Underline all other nouns.

EXAMPLE: Andrew's favorite thing at the (playground) is the (seesaw).

1. The scientist had a (breakthrough) in her research.

2. The birdwatcher made his way through the (underbrush.)

3. That player hit two (home runs) in the same game.

4. The host was unable to seat all the guests in the (dining room.)

5. My (stepmother) is recovering well from her (heart attack.)

6. A (jack-in-the-box) is a perfect toy for a (two-year-old.)

7. The recent (heat wave) broke all previous records.

8. What are your plans after (high school?)

9. (Spring cleaning) is a chore that few people like.

10. The actor stepped into the (spotlight.)

16.1 Nouns (Names, Compound Nouns) • Practice 2

> **Exercise 1** | **Identifying Nouns.** Underline the two nouns in each sentence. Then, label one *concrete* and one *abstract*.

EXAMPLE: My <u>mother</u> admired your <u>honesty</u>. ___*concrete/abstract*___

1. An inventor must have a good imagination. _____
2. Their excitement at the zoo was expected. _____
3. The election was held in the auditorium. _____
4. Poor health made the frail child sad. _____
5. Wild animals in captivity often seem pathetic. _____
6. The artist thought about her plan. _____
7. The young boy wanted to know about his future. _____
8. The average of his tests was not satisfactory. _____
9. Amazingly, our team won the championship. _____
10. Her memories of Italy were fading. _____
11. The hunger of the children is amazing. _____
12. He has a terrible fear of airplanes. _____
13. The quarterback demonstrated great courage. _____
14. She used green ink to write her memoirs. _____
15. The clown's mask showed sadness. _____

> **Exercise 2** | **Recognizing Compound Nouns.** Underline three nouns in each sentence. Then circle each compound noun.

EXAMPLE: <u>Smoke</u> from the (<u>campfire</u>) drifted toward the <u>trees</u>.

1. The maid-of-honor at the wedding cried during the ceremony.
2. The back of the station wagon was loaded with luggage.
3. The gardener and his son filled the trash bags.
4. Ed enjoyed his visit with his mother-in-law.
5. Three planes awaited the signal for takeoff.
6. In the attic, the children found a lampshade.
7. This railroad has many bridges and tunnels.
8. Most families still have an ironing board and iron.
9. The young cook put too much salt on the lima beans.
10. Laura held the position of editor-in-chief.
11. John acted as a go-between during the transaction.
12. It was quite a milestone when the baby took her first step.
13. Janice shared her watermelon with six friends.
14. The car Frank bought has bucket seats.
15. Sara joined a book club this year.

16.1 Nouns (Common and Proper Nouns) • Practice 1

Common and Proper Nouns   A *common noun* names any one of a class of people, places, or things. A *proper noun* names a specific person, place, or thing. Each important word in a proper noun begins with a capital letter.

Common Nouns		Proper Nouns	
book	desert	Statue of Liberty	Asia
holiday	leader	Gettysburg Address	Texas
car	composer	*Jane Eyre*	Lassie
country	horse	Mercury	Canada

▶ **Exercise 1**   **Recognizing Proper Nouns.**   Write the proper noun in each sentence in the blank at the right, adding the missing capitalization.

EXAMPLE: My favorite poet is emily dickinson.   ___*Emily Dickinson*___

1. The brooklyn bridge has been featured in many movies. _____
2. Many famous prisoners have been held in the tower of london. _____
3. The bulldogs are the leading team in our league. _____
4. My cousin is a senior at jackson high school. _____
5. At this time of year, tomatoes come from california. _____
6. Have you been in the new shop on willow street? _____
7. This book is a biography of abigail adams. _____
8. I hope uncle mike will visit this weekend. _____
9. Do you know the capital of montana? _____
10. Whose faces appear on mount rushmore? _____

▶ **Exercise 2**   **Adding Proper Nouns to Sentences.**   Fill in each blank with a proper noun.

EXAMPLE: I bought an album by ___*Elton John*___ .

1. Have you eaten at the new restaurant on _____?
2. At the end of the close game, the _____ were the winners.
3. Last summer we visited _____ on vacation.
4. The _____ is a famous landmark in our nation's capital.
5. Didn't you lend that book to _____?
6. The new bridge will cross the _____.
7. Our next-door neighbors are moving to _____.
8. The chef has opened a health-food restaurant called _____.
9. Our new car is a _____.
10. An author I admire is _____.

16.1 Nouns (Common and Proper Nouns) • Practice 2

▶ **Exercise 1** **Distinguishing Between Common and Proper Nouns.** Determine which words are common nouns and which are proper. If a word is a *common noun*, write a *proper noun* that falls into the same category. If a word is a *proper noun*, write a *common noun* of the same category.

EXAMPLE: language _____French_____

1. town _____
2. dog _____
3. author _____
4. Labor Day _____
5. state _____
6. woman _____
7. Sahara _____
8. river _____
9. George III _____
10. organization _____
11. boy _____
12. planet _____
13. relative _____
14. building _____
15. Asia _____
16. toothpaste _____
17. mountain _____
18. United States _____
19. animal _____
20. country _____
21. holiday _____
22. Caroline _____
23. Queen Elizabeth _____
24. doctor _____
25. ship _____
26. Mark Twain _____
27. actor _____
28. Elvis Presley _____
29. religion _____
30. Lake Erie _____

▶ **Writing Application** **Writing Sentences with Nouns.** Use the following instructions to write five sentences of your own.

EXAMPLE: Write a sentence about plants that includes two common nouns.

_____Crocuses bloom in the early spring._____

1. Write a sentence about school activities that includes one common noun and one compound common noun.

   _____

2. Write a sentence about a city or town that includes one common noun and one compound proper noun.

   _____

3. Write a sentence about a person that includes one concrete noun and one abstract noun.

   _____

4. Write a sentence about food that includes one common noun and one compound common noun.

   _____

5. Write a sentence about another country that includes two proper nouns.

   _____

16.2 Pronouns (Antecedents of Pronouns) • Practice 1

Antecedents of Pronouns   A *pronoun* is a word used to take the place of a noun (or group of words acting as a noun). An *antecedent* is the noun (or group of words acting as a noun) which a pronoun stands for in a sentence.

PRONOUNS AND ANTECEDENTS
ANTECEDENT PRONOUN   PRONOUN The Hobsons built *their* back porch *themselves*.
PRONOUN ANTECEDENT *That* is the house Jim hopes to buy.
ANTECEDENT   PRONOUN ANTECEDENT PRONOUN Jonathan, please pass *some* of the salad *you* made.

▶ **Exercise 1**   **Identifying Antecedents.**   Circle the antecedent of each underlined pronoun.

EXAMPLE: (Jill) will let you have some of the (milkshake) if you ask her.

1. Without his parents' permission, Al could not go on the field trip.
2. Most of the critics liked the play.
3. The man who greeted Sally at the door asked to see her ticket.
4. Hannah, have you decided which of the bikes to buy?
5. Climbing to the top of the Washington Monument was fun, but it tired us.
6. The huge old trunk was something the bride and groom never expected.
7. Several of the students completed their papers early.
8. Which of the twins was that?
9. Anthony quickly told Mrs. Lee how much he appreciated her kindness.
10. The senator who introduced the bill worked hard for its passage.

▶ **Exercise 2**   **Adding Pronouns to Match Antecedents.**   Find the antecedent for a pronoun that could fill in each blank. Then write the appropriate pronoun for that antecedent.

EXAMPLE: The Hornets owe much of ____their____ success to Coach Maloney.

1. Paul went to school without ____his____ lunch money.
2. To find the area of a rectangle, multiply ____it's____ length by ____it's____ width.
3. Jenny, would ____you____ like ____some____ of this cake?
4. Although the leaves are changing later this year, ____their____ colors are more vivid than usual.
5. Without ____your____ help, Pete, we would still be working.
6. Mayor Anita Rimirez announced ____her____ plans to seek a second term.
7. The woman ____who____ once baby-sat for my brother still sends ____him____ a Christmas card every year.
8. Two robins made ____their____ nest in the maple tree.
9. One explanation for the show's success is ____it's____ appeal to teenagers.
10. If ____some____ of the players show confidence, the other players are likely to follow ____their____ example.

16.2 Pronouns (Antecedents of Pronouns) • Practice 2

Exercise 1 **Recognizing Antecedents.** Circle the antecedent of each underlined pronoun.

EXAMPLE: My (brothers) cooked all of the (food) by themselves.

1. Betty accomplished all of this work herself.

2. The doll was one that had been made in England. It was painted by hand.

3. Mr. Jenkins gave a bonus to all of the employees and to himself as well.

4. The audience was disappointed with the play, and many left before it was over.

5. Magnolias are trees that grow in the South. They produce beautiful white blossoms.

6. The class gave their petitions to the senator, who was glad to receive them.

7. Joe, these are great potatoes. Where did you buy them?

8. Many of the people rose from their seats.

9. The group gave themselves credit for their hard work.

10. How could Matt prove he wrote that paper himself?

11. Mel bought an orchid for his mother, but she did not wear it.

12. When Carlito saw the dance steps, he just had to learn them.

13. Diane, how will you be able to duplicate the recipe if you don't have all of the ingredients it calls for?

14. When Pamela heard her brother crying, she tried to help him.

15. Walt wanted to take the pictures of his brother's soccer game himself.

16. Pat gave the money to Sam, who deposited it in the bank.

17. If you need more time, Jon, let the teacher know. She will probably allow another day.

18. Sue walked onto the stage, fussing with her hair before facing all the other students.

19. "Dina herself volunteered to help me," said Pablo.

20. Joanne bought herself some birthday candles that relight when they are blown out.

Exercise 2 **Writing Sentences with Pronouns and Antecedents.** Write a sentence that uses the given antecedent and an appropriate pronoun for that antecedent.

EXAMPLE: library _____Justine went to the library, but it was closed._____

1. kitten _____

2. Marion _____

3. roses _____

4. bananas _____

5. tree _____

6. skateboard _____

7. guests _____

8. photographs _____

9. water _____

10. moonlight _____

16.2 Pronouns (Personal, Reflexive, and Intensive Pronouns) • Practice 1

Personal, Reflexive, and Intensive Pronouns   *Personal pronouns* refer to the person speaking, the person spoken to, or the person, place, or thing spoken about. A *reflexive* pronoun ends in *-self* or *-selves* and adds information to a sentence by pointing back to a noun or pronoun earlier in the sentence. An *intensive* pronoun ends in *-self* or *-selves* and simply adds emphasis to a noun or pronoun in the same sentence.

Personal Pronouns		Reflexive and Intensive Pronouns	
Singular	**Plural**	**Singular**	**Plural**
I, me, my, mine	we, us, our, ours	myself	ourselves
you, your, yours	you, your, yours	yourself	yourselves
he, him, his, she	they, them	himself, herself	themselves
her, hers, it, its	their, theirs	itself	

EXAMPLES: *She* and *I* will help *you* with that job. (personal pronouns)
Tom fixed *himself* a bedtime snack. (reflexive pronoun)
Mom fixed the car *herself.* (intensive pronoun)

▶ **Exercise 1**   Identifying Personal, Reflexive, and Intensive Pronouns.   Underline the pronoun in each sentence. In the blank, write whether it is *personal, intensive,* or *reflexive.*

EXAMPLE: Pam and I enjoyed the concert. ____*personal*____

1. The tourists suddenly found themselves in a strange part of town. _____
2. The loud music from next door interrupted my studying. _____
3. The neighbors cleaned up the block themselves. _____
4. Mom, prepare yourself for some exciting news. _____
5. The star made his way through the crowd of screaming fans. _____
6. Jillian packed the footlocker herself. _____
7. The salad dressing has too much vinegar in it. _____
8. The President himself will greet the Prime Minister. _____
9. The children amused themselves by playing checkers. _____
10. Please complete your assignment by Friday. _____

▶ **Exercise 2**   Adding Personal, Reflexive, and Intensive Pronouns to Sentences.   Fill in each blank with an appropriate pronoun of the kind called for in parentheses.

EXAMPLE: Ladies and gentlemen, please help ____*yourselves*____ . (reflexive)

1. Do all these candles have coconut inside _____? (personal)
2. We told _____ that we were imagining things. (reflexive)
3. The news show has changed _____ format this season. (personal)
4. I _____ favor a dress code. (intensive)
5. After the first few seconds, Kathy regained _____ confidence. (personal)
6. In spite of all _____ studying, Ken was nervous about the test. (personal)
7. We found _____ wondering what to do next. (reflexive)
8. Mike and I gave _____ reports. (personal)
9. The committee members decided among _____ on the date. (reflexive)
10. The poet read her newest work _____ . (intensive)

16.2 Pronouns (Personal, Reflexive, and Intensive Pronouns) • Practice 2

▶ **Exercise 1** **Identifying Personal, Reflexive, and Intensive Pronouns.** Underline the pronoun in each sentence. Then label each as *personal, reflexive,* or *intensive.*

EXAMPLE: Abby taught <u>herself</u> to play the piano. ____*reflexive*____ .

1. Grandfather wrote you a letter yesterday. _____
2. Laura made herself a white dress for the dance. _____
3. I can't study while the radio is playing. _____
4. If the bus does not arrive soon, we will be late. _____
5. The Queen herself is coming to launch the ship. _____
6. Jim promised himself a reward for working so hard. _____
7. A flying squirrel uses its tail as a rudder. _____
8. The family harvested the wheat themselves. _____
9. Louise's good judgment saved their lives. _____
10. The sun itself provides energy, light, and warmth. _____
11. Isadora Duncan is remembered for her fresh approach to dancing. _____
12. Jamie hurt himself while cutting the roses. _____
13. My grandfather himself built the house. _____
14. Cindy didn't realize that I had arranged a surprise. _____
15. Give yourself credit for an amazing accomplishment. _____
16. The clubhouse was painted by the children themselves. _____
17. The greedy child wanted all the marbles for himself. _____
18. Has the police officer given them the news yet? _____
19. Of course, she had no idea what to expect. _____
20. Margaret herself wishes to thank the members of the academy. _____

▶ **Exercise 2** **Writing Sentences with Personal, Reflexive, and Intensive Pronouns.** Write a sentence for each given pronoun. Use each intensive or reflexive pronoun in the manner shown in parentheses.

EXAMPLE: himself (reflexive pronoun) ____*He allowed himself ten minutes to eat lunch.*____

1. mine _____
2. yourself (intensive pronoun) _____
3. him _____
4. themselves (reflexive pronoun) _____
5. we _____
6. hers _____
7. myself (intensive pronoun) _____
8. his _____
9. our _____
10. ourselves (reflexive pronoun) _____

16.2 Pronouns (Demonstrative, Relative, and Interrogative Pronouns) • Practice 1

Demonstrative, Relative, and Interrogative Pronouns   *Demonstrative pronouns* direct attention to specific people, places, or things.

DEMONSTRATIVE PRONOUNS			
this	that	these	those

A *relative* pronoun begins a subordinate clause and connects it to another idea in the sentence.

RELATIVE PRONOUNS				
that	which	who	whom	whose

An *interrogative* pronoun is used to begin a question.

INTERROGATIVE PRONOUNS				
what	which	who	whom	whose

▷ **Exercise 1**   **Recognizing Demonstrative, Relative, and Interrogative Pronouns.**   On the blank at the right, write whether each sentence contains a *demonstrative*, *relative*, or *interrogative* pronoun.

EXAMPLE: What shall we do? ___*interrogative*___

1. That was a wonderful movie. _____
2. Here is a person whom I want you to meet. _____
3. Who told you the password? _____
4. The article, which was written by a senator, was interesting. _____
5. Which of the notebooks is yours? _____
6. These are excellent baked apples. _____
7. Whom did you meet at the library? _____
8. Do you know anyone who can help us? _____
9. This is the author's first book. _____
10. Where is the picture that you painted? _____

▷ **Exercise 2**   **Adding Demonstrative, Relative, and Interrogative Pronouns to Sentences.**   Fill in each blank with an appropriate *demonstrative*, *relative*, or *interrogative* pronoun.

EXAMPLE: This package feels heavier than ____*that*____ .

1. _____ of the colors do you prefer?
2. Are _____ the right glasses?
3. The family from _____ we bought the house had owned it for years.
4. Alice made the decision _____ she thought was best.
5. _____ is bringing the salad?
6. _____ is slightly lighter than that.
7. _____ gave you the application forms?
8. Is there anyone _____ can advise you?
9. Behind _____ of the doors is the treasure chest?
10. _____ are you going to do next?

16.2 Pronouns (Demonstrative, Relative, and Interrogative Pronouns) • Practice 2

Exercise 1 **Recognizing Demonstrative, Relative, and Interrogative Pronouns.** Underline the pronoun in each of the following sentences. Then label each as *demonstrative*, *relative*, or *interrogative*.

EXAMPLE: <u>What</u> is known about planetary rings? _____*interrogative*_____

(1) Who first discovered rings around a planet? (2) In the early 1600's, Galileo, who was an Italian astronomer, first saw rings around Saturn. (3) With a small telescope, Galileo could not see clearly and thought the things that appeared were satellites. (4) Later, other astronomers, using more powerful telescopes, saw these were rings. (5) In 1980, scientists discovered the true nature of the rings, which are actually made up of thousands of pieces of ice. (6) Which of the other planets are known to have rings? (7) Uranus has nine thin rings, fainter than those of Saturn. (8) Jupiter's one thin ring, which appears to be made of rock fragments, was discovered by the *Jupiter I* space probe in 1980. (9) Who knows why the rings around planets are always parallel to the planets' equators? (10) This and other questions may be answered by future space probes.

1. _____   6. _____
2. _____   7. _____
3. _____   8. _____
4. _____   9. _____
5. _____   10. _____

Exercise 2 **Writing Sentences with Pronouns.** Write a sentence using the kind of pronoun given in parentheses. Underline the pronoun in your sentence.

EXAMPLE: (demonstrative pronoun) Would you like to try some of <u>these</u>?

1. (demonstrative pronoun) _____
2. (relative pronoun) _____
3. (interrogative pronoun) _____
4. (demonstrative pronoun) _____
5. (relative pronoun) _____
6. (interrogative pronoun) _____
7. (demonstrative pronoun) _____
8. (relative pronoun) _____
9. (interrogative pronoun) _____
10. (demonstrative pronoun) _____
11. (relative pronoun) _____
12. (interrogative pronoun) _____
13. (demonstrative pronoun) _____
14. (relative pronoun) _____
15. (interrogative pronoun) _____

16.2 **Pronouns** (Indefinite Pronouns) • **Practice 1**

Indefinite Pronouns   *Indefinite pronouns* refer to people, places, or things, often without specifying which ones.

INDEFINITE PRONOUNS			
Singular		**Plural**	**Singular or Plural**
another	much	both	all
anybody	neither	few	any
anyone	nobody	many	more
anything	no one	others	most
each	nothing	several	none
either	one		some
everybody	other		
everyone	somebody		
everything	someone		
little	something		

▶ **Exercise 1**   **Recognizing Indefinite Pronouns.**   Underline each indefinite pronoun in the sentences below.

EXAMPLE: If neither of these scarves is acceptable, I can show you others.

1. Everyone on the team had the same goals.
2. Someone has already eaten most of the cookies.
3. Each of the actors was nervous about dress rehearsal.
4. None of the guests had much to eat.
5. Few of the officials would admit that anything was wrong.
6. Does either of the candidates seem better than the other?
7. Both of the twins fool everyone by switching places.
8. Several of the speakers suggested that much remained to be done.
9. No one denied that something definite should be done.
10. Many of my classmates find fault with everything.

▶ **Exercise 2**   **Adding Indefinite Pronouns to Sentences.**   Fill in each blank with an indefinite pronoun that makes sense.

EXAMPLE: Has ____*anyone*____ called for me?

1. _____ of my friends plan to go to college.
2. Is _____ of these the style you had in mind?
3. Mike's size is surprising, considering how _____ he eats.
4. The mayor said _____ about her future plans.
5. This book tells _____ you will ever need to know about seashells.
6. These boots are more expensive than _____.
7. _____ about that house is very attractive.
8. Would you like to have _____ of this pie?
9. Tonight's paper says _____ about the election returns.
10. _____ in the new park is appealing to children.

16.2 Pronouns (Indefinite Pronouns) • Practice 2

Exercise 1 **Supplying Indefinite Pronouns.** Complete each sentence by writing one indefinite pronoun in each blank.

EXAMPLE: Did you eat ___*any*___ of the apples?

1. Jonathan has forgotten _____ he learned.
2. _____ has been done to inform _____.
3. Does _____ know where the supplies are?
4. You may take _____ of the packages.
5. We sent _____ of the invitations to our friends.
6. As a visitor to this country, she knew _____ of the customs, but _____ of the language.
7. Are _____ of the guests here yet?
8. Rebecca has lost _____ of her charm.
9. He shares his ideas with _____.
10. _____ of the boys looks a lot like his father.
11. These peaches are good—would you like _____?
12. Duane joined _____ of his friends at the baseball field.
13. The damage was done by _____.
14. _____ of you know what I mean.
15. Brittany did not want to go to _____ of those stores.
16. Brandon's talents are _____.
17. _____ will make Ryan change his mind about this.
18. _____ of the boys refused to go into the cold pool.
19. If it's not one thing, it's _____.
20. "_____ of you will pay for this," screamed the angry neighbor.

Writing Application **Writing Sentences with Pronouns.** Use the following instructions to write sentences of your own.

EXAMPLE: Write a sentence that includes two personal pronouns.

___*I have finished my homework.*___

1. Write a sentence that includes a demonstrative pronoun followed by the word *were* and a personal pronoun.

_____

2. Write a sentence that includes an interrogative pronoun followed by the word *is* and a personal pronoun.

_____

3. Write a sentence that includes a personal pronoun and an intensive pronoun.

_____

4. Write a sentence that includes an indefinite pronoun followed by the word *of* and a personal pronoun.

_____

5. Write a sentence that includes a reflexive pronoun and a relative pronoun.

_____

16.3 Action Verbs and Linking Verbs (Action Verbs, Transitive and Intransitive Verbs) • Practice 1

Action Verbs   A *verb* is a word that expresses time while showing an action, a condition, or the fact that something exists. An *action verb* is a verb that tells what action someone or something is performing.

Visible Action	Mental Action
Jeremy *ate* the whole pizza.	Elena *wondered* about her future.

Transitive and Intransitive Verbs   An action verb is *transitive* if it directs action toward someone or something named in the same sentence. An action verb is *intransitive* if it does not direct action toward someone or something named in the same sentence. The word that receives the action of a transitive verb is the object of the verb.

Transitive	Intransitive
The host *interviewed* Sue. (interviewed *whom?*) Sue	She *smiled* when she won. (smiled what?) no answer

▶Exercise 1   **Recognizing Action Verbs.**   Underline the action verb in each sentence. In the blank, write whether the action is *V* (visible) or *M* (mental).

EXAMPLE: Tristan forgot the assignment. ___M___

1. Wendy thought about the puzzle for hours. __M__
2. The auctioneer pointed toward the woman in the back row. __V__
3. The pendulum of the grandfather's clock swung rhythmically. __V__
4. Dana decided early on the topic for her essay. __M__
5. The committee made posters to announce the next dance. __V__
6. Betsy plays golf every weekend. __V__
7. The tennis players sipped lemonade between sets. __V__
8. Both politicians considered withdrawing from the campaign. __M__
9. Tracy drew up a plan for us to follow. __V__
10. The star, with dignity, entered the room. __V__

▶Exercise 2   **Adding Transitive and Intransitive Verbs to Sentences.**   In each blank, write a verb that logically completes the sentence. In the blank after the sentence, write *I* (intransitive) or *T* (transitive) to describe the verb you wrote.

EXAMPLE: The harpist ___plucked___ the shortest string. ___T___

1. My parents _____ a new dresser for my bedroom. _____
2. The car _____ into the parking space easily. _____
3. A strong friendship _____ between the two families. _____
4. Benedict Arnold _____ the plans for West Point to the British. _____
5. The shop _____ beautiful floral centerpieces. _____
6. Please _____ those cabbages on the counter. _____
7. High winds _____ throughout the night. _____
8. The plane finally _____ after a three-hour delay. _____
9. The receptionist _____ another appointment in six weeks. _____
10. Linda _____ that article for the school paper. _____

16.3 Action Verbs and Linking Verbs (Action Verbs, Transitive and Intransitive Verbs) • Practice 2

▶ **Exercise 1** **Supplying Action Verbs.** Complete each sentence by adding an action verb for each blank. Then label each verb as *visible* or *mental*.

EXAMPLE: The stars _____twinkled_____ in the dark sky. _____visible_____

1. They _____ about life on the planet Mars. _____
2. Someone _____ it was almost midnight. _____
3. The ping-pong ball _____ off the table. _____
4. A dog house _____ its occupant from the rain. _____
5. The gardener _____ the thick green lawn. _____
6. Why don't you _____ for a few minutes? _____
7. No one _____ the dismal weather. _____
8. The carpenter _____ the pine boards. _____
9. The waitress _____ at the soggy mess. _____
10. How did the pilot _____ where to land? _____
11. Anne _____ the strawberries in the garden. _____
12. Margaret _____ the dinner for her family. _____
13. The frog _____ from one lily pad to another. _____
14. Did you _____ the beautiful sunset? _____
15. The girls _____ all afternoon. _____
16. Please _____ the gloves on the counter. _____
17. Sandra _____ the prettiest goldfish for her collection. _____
18. Pierre _____ a salad for lunch. _____
19. Roxanne _____ her bike to the mall. _____
20. The queen _____ to the crowd. _____

▶ **Exercise 2** **Distinguishing Between Transitive and Intransitive Verbs.** Underline the verb in each sentence. Then, label the verb *transitive* or *intransitive*. Finally, write the object of each transitive verb.

EXAMPLE: We prepared sandwiches for our lunch. _____(transitive) sandwiches_____

1. The bird cage swung from a golden chain. _____(intransitive)_____
2. Margaret angrily crumpled her letter in her fist. _____(transitive) letter_____
3. Someone answered that question. _____(transitive) question_____
4. He shuddered with fright during the scary movie. _____(intransitive)_____
5. The rats chewed their way into the old house. _____(transitive) way_____
6. Acorns drop from the trees every fall. _____(intransitive)_____
7. Charlie combed his hair before the dance. _____(transitive) hair_____
8. We made lemonade for the picnic. _____(transitive) lemonade_____
9. Zelda smiled gleefully at the thought of a parade. _____(intransitive)_____
10. Fish and potatoes sizzled in the pan. _____(intransitive)_____

16.3 Action Verbs and Linking Verbs (Linking Verbs) • Practice 1

Linking Verbs   A *linking verb* is a verb that connects its subject with a word at or near the end of the sentence.

Forms of *Be* (from *Am* to *Would Have Been*)				Other Linking Verbs	
am	am being	can be	have been	appear	seem
are	are being	could be	has been	become	smell
is	is being	may be	had been	feel	sound
was	was being	might be	could have been	grow	stay
were	were being	must be	may have been	look	taste
		shall be	might have been	remain	turn
		should be	must have been		
		will be	shall have been		
		would be	should have been		
			will have been		
			would have been		

EXAMPLES: Ben should have been happy.   The friends stayed close for years.

Hudson's ship was the *Half Moon*.   The water in the pool became muddy.

> **Exercise 1**   **Recognizing Forms of Linking Verbs.**   Underline the linking verb in each sentence. Then circle the words that each verb links.

EXAMPLE: The (Holts) have been our (neighbors) for years.

1. (Safety) should be your first (concern.)
2. (I) would be (happy) to baby-sit for the Johnsons.
3. (Elaine) is often (late) for appointments.
4. (Andrew) can be an unusually stubborn (child.)
5. (What) could have been the (cause) of the accident?
6. (That) is a sufficient (amount) of sugar.
7. The (setback) was only (temporary.)
8. Surely (Jenny) will be our new class (president.)
9. (Jason) is being exceptionally (polite) today.
10. (Thomas Jefferson) was our third (President.)

> **Exercise 2**   **Identifying Other Linking Verbs.**   Underline the linking verb in each sentence. Then circle the words that each verb links.

EXAMPLE: (Rhoda) became Mary's favorite (friend).

1. (Kevin) appears (taller) on stage.
2. These (sausages) taste (spicier) than the last ones.
3. The (cause) of the accident remained a (mystery.)
4. That (stranger) looks (suspicious.)
5. The (child) stayed (quiet) throughout the doctor's examination.
6. The single white (glove) became the star's (trademark.)
7. (A. A. Milne) remains a popular children's (author.)
8. Sam's (hair) turned (gray) at an early age.
9. These old (books) smell (musty.)
10. (I) felt (queasy) during the boat ride.

16.3 Action Verbs and Linking Verbs (Linking Verbs) • Practice 2

Exercise 1 **Recognizing Forms of *Be* Used as Linking Verbs.** Underline the linking verb in each sentence. Then draw a double-headed arrow to show which words are linked by the verb.

EXAMPLE: We should have been the champions.

1. Poodles can be excellent pets.
2. Albert was being gentle with the newborn kittens.
3. A chef should be creative in the kitchen.
4. The sharp knife is the one on the counter.
5. She should have been an Olympic star.
6. This doughnut is not very fresh.
7. They are being very prompt with their payments.
8. At sunset the sky was a soft pink.
9. We will be the first customers in the door.
10. It had been a long and difficult day.
11. A bear can be a very dangerous animal.
12. The library is a large brick building not far from my house.
13. That peak might be the tallest one in this mountain range.
14. Bananas have been Ryan's favorite fruit for years.
15. The porcupine's quills are very sharp.

Exercise 2 **Identifying Other Linking Verbs.** Underline the linking verb in each sentence. Then draw a double-headed arrow to show which words are linked by the verb.

1. She turned blue from the cold.
2. The foghorn sounded strange in the darkness.
3. Those apples on the ground taste bitter.
4. After years of studying, he finally became a doctor.
5. They remained cheerful in spite of their hardships.
6. Some people stay business partners for years.
7. This rose smells different from that one.
8. They appeared older after their terrifying ordeal.
9. The baby's hair felt sticky from the candy.
10. This coat looks too small for you.

16.3 Action Verbs and Linking Verbs
(Linking Verb or Action Verb?) • Practice 1

Linking Verb or Action Verb?   Some verbs may be used as an action verb in one sentence and as a linking verb in another. If a verb is a linking verb, *am*, *is*, or *are* will make sense when substituted for it in a sentence.

Linking Verb	Action Verb
The child *grew very* sleepy on the way home. (The child *is* very sleepy?) linking	Aunt Polly *grew* a prize-winning lily. (Aunt Polly *is* a prize-winning lily?) action

▶**Exercise 1**   **Distinguishing Between Linking Verbs and Action Verbs.**   On each blank at the right, write whether the sentence contains a *linking* verb or an *action* verb.

EXAMPLE: The milk turned sour.   *linking*

1. The driver turned the corner too quickly.   action
2. The singer appeared slightly nervous.   linking
3. After a half an hour, my date finally appeared.   action
4. I looked the robber directly in the face.   action
5. The table setting looks beautiful.   linking
6. We all felt refreshed after a dip in the pool.   linking
7. Dad finally felt the keys hidden under the car seat.   action
8. Donna's plan sounds excellent.   linking
9. The principal sounded the fire alarm right after lunch.   action
10. Neville remained calm in spite of everything.   linking

▶**Exercise 2**   **Adding Verbs to Sentences.**   Fill in each blank within the sentence with an appropriate verb. On the blank at the right, write *AV* for each action verb and *LV* for each linking verb.

EXAMPLE: Hungry people often   *become*   irritable.   *LV*

1. Litmus paper   turns   blue in an alkaline solution.   LV
2. Allison   turned   the pages quickly, looking for the answer.   AV
3. Johnson Farm   grows   the best corn in the area.   AV
4. The friends have   grown   closer over the years.   LV
5. Ronald Reagan   became   President in 1981.   LV
6. The child's face   looked   flushed.   LV
7.   Look   those facts up in an encyclopedia.   AV
8. Have you ever   tasted   octopus?   AV
9. Chocolate sauce   tastes   delicious on peppermint ice cream.   LV
10. That music   sounds   much too loud.   LV

Name _____ Date _____

16.3 Action Verbs and Linking Verbs
(Linking Verb or Action Verb?) • Practice 2

▶ **Exercise 1** **Distinguishing Between Linking Verbs and Action Verbs.** Complete each sentence, filling in the blank with a form of one of the following verbs: *feel, grow, look, sound,* or *taste.* Then label each verb as *linking* or *action.*

EXAMPLE: The puppy ___looks___ hungry all the time. ___linking___

1. His voice _____ peculiar on the phone. _____

2. In their garden they _____ tomatoes. _____

3. Marion's clam sauce _____ slightly sweet. _____

4. If Jeff _____ sick, he should stay home. _____

5. His face _____ pale when he thinks about his debts. _____

6. Mr. Blake could _____ a bump on his forehead. _____

7. Our furniture _____ new after being reupholstered. _____

8. The boy on horseback _____ the alarm. _____

9. We must _____ for a birthday card after school. _____

10. Craig _____ the lobster stew. _____

11. Wanda _____ on the ground for her lost contact lenses. _____

12. Your idea _____ more than a little intriguing. _____

13. The soup _____ a little bland. _____

14. The shoppers _____ the fabric before making a choice. _____

15. Gloria _____ the gravy before adding a little salt. _____

16. Victor _____ quite handsome in his new suit. _____

17. After the party, Abigail did not _____ very well. _____

18. Tomatoes _____ very well in this climate. _____

19. Sandra _____ out the window. _____

20. The professor _____ fond of his students. _____

▶ **Writing Application** **Writing Sentences with Linking Verbs and Action Verbs.** Use each verb in two sentences, first as a linking verb, then as an action verb.

EXAMPLE: turn _____*He turned purple in anger.*_____
_____*He turned the page and found the answer.*_____

1. appear _____

_____

2. feel _____

_____

3. grow _____

_____

4. look _____

_____

5. smell _____

_____

Name _____   Date _____

 16.4 **Helping Verbs • Practice 1**

Recognizing Helping Verbs *Helping verbs* are verbs that can be added to another verb to make a single verb phrase. Any of the forms of *be* as well as some other common verbs can be used as helping verbs.

HELPING VERBS OTHER THAN *BE*			
do	have	shall	can
does	has	should	could
did	had	will	may
		would	might
			must

Finding Helping Verbs in Sentences Other words may sometimes separate helping verbs from the key verb in a sentence.

Uninterrupted Verb Phrase	Interrupted Verb Phrase
We *will be visiting* you in July.	We *have* not yet *visited* the White House.

▶ **Exercise 1** **Identifying Helping Verbs.** Underline each helping verb in the sentences below. Circle the key verb in the verb phrase.

EXAMPLE: Did anyone (call) for me?

1. Paul has not always (acted) so strangely.
2. Did Helen (tell) you about the party next week?
3. That student does not usually (ride) on this bus.
4. Have you ever (traveled) to Canada?
5. The driver must not have (seen) the stop sign.
6. Jason could have (offered) us his help.
7. Rehearsal should not have (lasted) so long.
8. I have seldom (seen) a more moving performance.
9. Mr. Wills does not always (hear) very well.
10. The plan could not have (succeeded) without your cooperation.

▶ **Exercise 2** **Adding Helping Verbs to Sentences.** Fill in each blank with an appropriate helping verb. Circle each key verb.

EXAMPLE: When ___will___ the show (start)?

1. The woman at the information booth ___can___ (answer) that question.
2. I ___have___ ___been___ (studying) all week for that test.
3. Kyle ___must___ ___have___ (seen) that movie.
4. Someone ___could___ ___have___ ___been___ (hurt).
5. What ___have___ you ___been___ (doing) all week?
6. ___Will___ the art exhibit (open) on Saturday?
7. Some citizens ___have___ (expressed) reservations about the new bill.
8. The caller ___might___ ___have___ (expected) a more favorable response.
9. What time ___did___ the movie (begin)?
10. That construction crew ___had___ ___been___ (working) very hard.

16.4 Helping Verbs • Practice 2

▶ **Exercise 1** **Supplying Helping Verbs.** Complete each sentence, adding one helping verb for each blank.

EXAMPLE: The sun ___will___ ___have___ set by six o'clock.

1. A shark _____ swimming in the water.

2. Todd's car _____ _____ repaired at the gas station on the corner.

3. Our driveway _____ _____ plowed after a snowfall.

4. _____ we _____ studying enough?

5. The woodcutter _____ _____ sawing carefully.

6. Carol _____ not _____ going with us.

7. Poodles _____ be the smartest of the canines.

8. Sandals _____ not considered appropriate for a vacation in Siberia.

9. How many planets _____ we _____ discovered by the year 2050?

10. No species of insect _____ yet become extinct.

▶ **Exercise 2** **Locating Helping Verbs.** Underline the verb phrase or verb phrases in each sentence.

EXAMPLE: Contact lenses <u>are</u> quickly <u>becoming</u> more popular.

(1) Many people are finding contact lenses very convenient. (2) If you are presently considering whether or not you should invest in contacts, you should definitely know this fact. (3) More contacts have been lost down the drain as they were being inserted than while the lenses were actually being worn. (4) Therefore, lenses should be inserted carefully. (5) If you do drop it, you will probably scratch it; then replacement of the lens would be necessary, for a scratch on the lens might seriously damage your eye.

▶ **Writing Application** **Writing Sentences with Helping Verbs.** Use the following instructions to write sentences of your own.

EXAMPLE: Interrupt the verb phrase *have seen* with *never*.

___I have never seen an aardvark.___

1. Use the verb phrase *has been talking* in a question.

_____

2. Interrupt the verb phrase *might know* with *not*.

_____

3. Interrupt the verb phrase *could have sold* with *never*.

_____

4. Use the verb phrase *will have left* in a question.

_____

5. Interrupt the verb phrase *can be seen* with *scarcely*.

_____

17.1 Adjectives (The Process of Modification) • Practice 1

The Process of Modification   An *adjective* is a word used to describe a noun or pronoun or to give a noun or pronoun a more specific meaning. Adjectives answer the question *What kind? Which one? How many?* or *How much?* about the nouns or pronouns they modify.

ADJECTIVE QUESTIONS		
What Kind?	*happy* child	*Small* bird
Which One?	*next* room	*First* place
How Many?	*several* people	*Three* days
How Much?	*little* work	*enough* money

Exercise 1   **Identifying Adjectives.**   Underline each adjective in the following sentences, including the articles *a, an,* and *the.* Then circle the noun or pronoun that each adjective modifies.

EXAMPLE: The tired (horse) pulled the heavy wooden (wagon) over the dirt (road).

1. Several (families) had an outdoor (party) for the new (neighbors.)

2. The quaint and charming old (house) needed several major (repairs.)

3. The wealthy (family) had an extensive (collection) of antique (glass.)

4. The worthy (cause) drew many generous (contributions.)

5. At the (end) of the first (round,) Hawkins held a narrow (lead.)

6. Few people on that (street) have young (children.)

7. Western (movies) were popular for many (years.)

8. A good daily (diet) should include adequate (calcium.)

9. In many (countries) southern (food) is spicier than northern (food.)

10. The entire (kingdom) was under the terrible (spell) of the wicked (sorcerer.)

Exercise 2   **Adding Adjectives to Sentences.**   In each blank write an appropriate adjective that answers the question in parentheses.

EXAMPLE: ___Numerous___   ___younger___   families are moving into ___this___ area.
   (How many?)   (What kind?)   (Which one?)

1. The _____ shopper bought _____ pairs of shoes.
   (What kind?)   (How many?)

2. The _____ workers demanded _____ money.
   (What kind?)   (How much?)

3. _____ girl wore a _____ sweater like mine.
   (Which one?)   (What kind?)

4. The _____ guest at the _____ party wore jeans.
   (Which one?)   (What kind?)

5. _____ _____ _____ dogs howled.
   (How many?)   (What kind?)   (What kind?)

17.1 **Adjectives** (The Process of Modification) • **Practice 2**

▶**Exercise 1** **Recognizing Adjectives.** Underline the adjectives in each sentence.

EXAMPLE: A loud roar greeted the victorious team.

1. The dull walls and dingy carpet give the room a somber atmosphere.
2. The lonesome howl of a coyote came from the woods.
3. With gray faces and hesitant steps, they approached the abandoned house.
4. After a major accident on a highway, there may be few survivors.
5. On the last day of the month, you have an important medical appointment.
6. There wasn't enough money in the wallet to pay the bill.
7. If you add milk to the eggs, a dozen eggs will be enough to make bread.
8. Bluefish give fishermen a good fight.
9. The brilliant diamonds decorated red and callused hands.
10. The railing was silvery in the dim shadows.
11. The athletic young man ran six miles along the scenic coast.
12. The chilly weather suddenly turned pleasant.
13. The large pizza was consumed by the three hungry boys.
14. The newborn baby has tiny, delicate, perfect hands.
15. The latest art exhibit features works by famous photographers.
16. The timid driver was afraid to drive on the icy roads.
17. Marion poured some hot water into the chipped cup.
18. A purple eggplant and a red tomato are in the blue bowl.
19. Chen uses ivory chopsticks on special occasions.
20. The colorful bird in the elaborate cage is a rare parrot.

▶**Exercise 2** **Using Adjectives in Sentences.** Complete the paragraph by writing an appropriate adjective in each blank.

EXAMPLE: The (1) ____tired____ traveler plopped down into the (2) ____uncomfortable____ chair.

The plane would not be leaving for another (1) _____ hours. Jennifer was

(2) _____, but she tried not to become too (3) _____. She went

to the (4) _____ store on the (5) _____ level of the airport. She

looked for (6) _____ items that she could take home to her

(7) _____ nieces and nephews. When she saw the (8) _____

scarf on the (9) _____ shelf, she made a (10) _____ decision.

17.1 # Adjectives (Proper and Compound Adjectives, Nouns Used as Adjectives) • Practice 1

Nouns Used as Adjectives   A *noun used as an adjective* answers the question *What kind?* or *Which one?* about a noun that follows it.

Nouns	Nouns Used as Adjectives
automobile	automobile mechanic (*What kind* of mechanic?)
Consumer	consumer reporter (*Which* reporter?)

Proper and Compound Adjectives   A *compound adjective* is an adjective that is made up of more than one word.

Hyphenated	Combined
upside-down cake	*upright* piano
full-scale rebellion	*keynote* speaker

A *proper adjective* is an adjective formed from a proper noun.

Proper Nouns	Proper Adjectives
Hawaii	*Hawaiian* pineapples
Athens	*Athenian* temple

▶ **Exercise 1**   **Recognizing Nouns Used as Adjectives, Proper Adjectives, and Compound Adjectives.**   Identify the underlined adjectives in the sentences below as *nouns used as adjectives*, *proper adjectives*, or *compound adjectives*.

EXAMPLE: Our family enjoys eating in Chinese restaurants.   *proper adjective*

1. The sitter read the child still another bedtime story. _____

2. The overworked secretary handed in his resignation. _____

3. Our class is visiting the state capital next week. _____

4. The bride wore a mantilla of Spanish lace. _____

5. We always use the good dishes for our holiday meals. _____

6. The concert was held in a downtown park. _____

7. Grandma made a peach cobbler for dessert. _____

8. The town finally rebelled against the back-room politics. _____

9. Edwardian clothing is enjoying a vogue. _____

10. I know the star of that Broadway play. _____

▶ **Exercise 2**   **Using Proper and Compound Adjectives to Modify Nouns.**   Rewrite each word group below, placing a proper adjective or compound adjective before the main noun.

EXAMPLE: tenor from Italy   *Italian tenor*

1. fishing in the deep sea _____

2. sale on a sidewalk _____

3. nation in Asia _____

4. poet from England _____

5. boy from a small town _____

6. villa in Rome _____

7. pool with salt water _____

8. rug from Persia _____

9. coffee from Turkey _____

10. seat in the front row _____

17.1 Adjectives (Proper and Compound Adjectives, Nouns Used as Adjectives) • Practice 2

Exercise 1 **Recognizing Nouns Used as Adjectives.** Underline the noun or nouns used as adjectives in each sentence.

EXAMPLE: Betty put on her red winter coat.

(1) Betty glanced at the storm clouds. (2) She wished she had worn her leather gloves and her fur hat. (3) She waited impatiently at the bus stop. (4) Finally, the school bus arrived, and Betty got on. (5) As the bus stopped at the school door, Betty noticed that tiny snowflakes had begun to fall. (6) If it snowed hard, Betty and her friends could go to the ski slope outside of town on their next vacation day. (7) She wished she had listened to the weather report this morning. (8) Betty thought about the jacket she had seen in a store window yesterday. (9) She remembered the money her aunt had sent her for a birthday present. (10) Perhaps a new ski jacket would be just the thing to spend it on.

Exercise 2 **Recognizing Proper and Compound Adjectives.** Underline the proper and compound adjectives in each sentence.

EXAMPLE: Please pass me the *Swiss* cheese.

1. The red-cheeked girl ate Turkish taffy.
2. The foolishness of their actions was self-evident.
3. She caught a wide-mouthed bass this morning.
4. Well-qualified surgeons do open-heart surgery.
5. In combat, the horse remained steadfast.
6. We bought the Victorian table for the hallway.
7. Phil, who was well-liked, lived in an out-of-the-way place.
8. Although he lived in Utah, Al kept his Bostonian accent.
9. He wore a waterproof Icelandic parka.
10. The hostess served a Scandinavian meal.
11. This group of Russian immigrants includes many sad-looking children.
12. My Irish uncle told many never-to-be-forgotten stories.
13. The best-known song by that German composer was based on a poem.
14. The boy, a good-natured sort, comes from a Spanish background.
15. Her Australian aunt has very old-fashioned attitudes.
16. The light-haired girl has a British accent.
17. The three-bedroom home had African violets on every windowsill.
18. "It is a little-known fact, but I assure you it is true," said the French tourist.
19. The ever-optimistic Wendell ordered Belgian waffles in that run-down café.
20. Our Canadian guest is a quick-witted and entertaining dinner companion.

17.1 Adjectives (Pronouns and Verbs Used as Adjectives)
• Practice 1

Pronouns Used as Adjectives   A pronoun is used as an adjective if it modifies a noun. The chart below summarizes the kinds of pronouns used as adjectives.

Possessive Adjectives		Demonstrative Adjectives	Interrogative Adjectives	Indefinite Adjectives		
				Singular	Plural	Either
my	its	this	which	another	both	all
your	our	that	what	each	few	any other
his	their	these	whose	either	many	more some
her		those		neither	several	most

Verbs Used as Adjectives   Verbs ending in *-ing* and *-ed* may sometimes be used as adjectives.

Verbs Used as Verbs	Verbs Used as Adjectives
Paul *is amusing* the children.	He told them an *amusing* story.
Karen *has broken* her ankle.	Her *broken* ankle is in a cast.

▶ **Exercise 1**   **Adding Pronouns Used as Adjectives.**   Fill in each blank with the kind of pronoun given in parentheses.

EXAMPLE: Anita, ____*your*____ paper was excellent. (possessive)

1. I have been wanting to read _____this_____ book for a long time. (demonstrative)
2. ____Many____ students enjoy doing homework. (indefinite)
3. ____Another____ picture will look good over the mantel. (indefinite)
4. I was uncertain about ____which____ pattern to choose. (interrogative)
5. Mr. Parker always challenges ____his____ students. (possessive)
6. In the summer, the Mannings have many parties beside ____their____ pool. (possessive)
7. ____Each____ contestant hoped to win. (indefinite)
8. ____Most____ homes in that part of town are very old. (indefinite)
9. ____What____ math class will you be in? (interrogative)
10. Are ____those____ chairs the ones we ordered? (demonstrative)

▶ **Exercise 2**   **Recognizing Verbs Used as Adjectives.**   In each sentence, underline the verb used as an adjective. Then circle the noun that it modifies.

EXAMPLE: The damp ground was the only reminder of the melted (snow).

1. Dad replaced the shattered (windowpane.)
2. The screaming (baby) kept us awake all night.
3. In earlier times, a mirror was called a looking (glass.)
4. We moved the fallen (branch) from the driveway.
5. By the time the police apprehended the burglars, the stolen (money) had disappeared.
6. The freezing (rain) was the cause of the hazardous driving.
7. The winning (car) was powered by a large engine.
8. He arrived at the pool just in time to save a drowning (boy.)
9. The answers appear on the following (pages.)
10. The departing (passengers) checked in at the gate.

17.1 Adjectives (Pronouns and Verbs Used as Adjectives) • Practice 2

▶ **Exercise 1** **Supplying Pronouns Used as Adjectives.** Fill in each blank with the kind of adjective given in parenthesis.

EXAMPLE: We picked ___those___ flowers from the garden. (demonstrative)

1. ___Each___ player was cheered by the crowd. (indefinite)
2. ___Our___ bus never came, and we were late for work. (possessive)
3. Harvey will never wear ___those___ ties. (demonstrative)
4. ___What___ human being could endure such a climate? (interrogative)
5. Max told ___his___ son to be quiet. (possessive)
6. I misplaced ___my___ keys, and I can't open the door. (possessive)
7. ___Whose___ mail was placed in our mailbox? (interrogative)
8. ___Some___ children were jumping rope. (indefinite)
9. Sue declared that ___neither___ candidate was qualified. (indefinite)
10. She paid too much for ___that___ coat. (demonstrative)

▶ **Exercise 2** **Recognizing Verbs Used as Adjectives.** Underline each verb used as an adjective.

EXAMPLE: They waited an hour in the <u>pouring</u> rain.

1. The frightened mouse scurried around.
2. The milk was spilled by the hurrying waiter.
3. The meeting room will be available on Tuesday.
4. We handed Mrs. Howard our completed assignments.
5. Are you planning to take swimming lessons?
6. The cheering crowd inspired the team.
7. Did you find the gardening tools?
8. The exhausted baby finally fell asleep.
9. Our grandparents met us in the waiting room.
10. I found the lost keys under my bed.

▶ **Writing Application** **Writing Sentences with Adjectives.** Rewrite each sentence, adding two or more of these adjectives: one noun used as an adjective, one proper adjective, one compound adjective, one pronoun used as an adjective, and one verb used as an adjective.

EXAMPLE: The skater entered the arena.

_____ The *champion* skater entered the *crowded* arena. _____

1. He could not swallow the food. _____
2. Mickey bought a sweater and a pair of pants. _____
3. The seagull's wing trailed on the sand. _____
4. She grew plants with berries. _____
5. Snow covered the branches and ground. _____
6. Donald finally selected a toy for his sister. _____
7. They made posters to announce the carnival. _____
8. A stream flowed past the fence. _____
9. In the evening, fireflies flashed in the darkness. _____
10. At the zoo, they saw seals begging for fish. _____

17.2 Adverbs (Modifying Verbs, Adjectives, and Other Adverbs; Nouns Used as Adverbs) • Practice 1

Adverbs Modifying Verbs, Adjectives, and Other Adverbs An adverb is a word that modifies a verb, an adjective, or another adverb. An adverb answers one of four questions about the word it modifies: *Where? When? In what manner? To what extent?*

Adverbs Modifying Verbs	
drove *off* (Where?)	stayed *late* (When?)
ran *fast* (In what manner?)	*completely* missed (To what extent?)
Adverbs Modifying Adjectives	**Adverbs Modifying Adverbs**
rather special (To what extent?)	*not really* happy (To what extent?)

Nouns used as adverbs answer the question *Where?* or *When?* about a verb.

Nouns	Adverbs
Today is my birthday.	The letter came *today. (Came* when?)
Their home is in Daytona.	David ran *home* (Ran *where?*)

> **Exercise 1** **Recognizing Adverbs.** Underline each adverb in the sentences below. Then, circle the word the adverb modifies.

EXAMPLE: That family just recently moved .

1. The snow melted quite rapidly last spring.
2. Claire has become a surprisingly good pianist.
3. That color suits you very well.
4. Mr. Whitkin seems somewhat dissatisfied with this assignment.
5. The careful attention to details ensured a truly festive party.
6. We completed our chores fairly early.
7. I almost forgot what I wanted to ask you.
8. Our new house is very nearly ready.
9. The storm almost totally destroyed the railroad bridge.
10. That is an exceptionally clever design.

> **Exercise 2** **Identifying Adverbs and Nouns Used as Adverbs.** Circle each noun used as an adverb. Underline all other adverbs.

EXAMPLE: The new play will open tomorrow .

1. The Joneses were not happy with their seat assignments.
2. What time did Danny come home?
3. This position is becoming increasingly uncomfortable.
4. Today will be a truly exciting day.
5. Our team won the big game yesterday.
6. Vinnie often works weekends.
7. The movers will be available Friday.
8. We were pleasantly surprised by their visit.
9. Shall we go to a movie tonight?
10. The silence grew somewhat awkward.

17.2 Adverbs (Modifying Verbs, Adjectives, and Other Adverbs; Nouns Used as Adverbs) • Practice 2

> **Exercise 1**   **Recognizing Adverbs.**   Underline the adverb or adverbs in each sentence.

EXAMPLE: The otter swam <u>very rapidly</u>.

1. We will be leaving for the movie soon.
2. The starving refugees needed much more food.
3. Will you definitely move to Ohio?
4. Everyone thought the movie was too violent.
5. He frowned rather sternly at the boy's antics.
6. Our cat does not like cat food.
7. The multicolored balloons floated away.
8. Some students have nearly completed their papers.
9. Todd accepted the suggestion surprisingly quickly.
10. Sharon was remarkably indifferent.
11. The performance was surprisingly brief.
12. The runner put on a burst of speed at the very last moment.
13. The vet spoke kindly to the frightened cat.
14. In quite recent times, this area enjoyed great prosperity.
15. Although the woman spoke loudly, the child did not seem to hear.

> **Exercise 2**   **Recognizing Nouns Used as Adverbs.**   Underline the two adverbs in each sentence.
> Then circle each noun used as an adverb.

EXAMPLE: (Yesterday) I took a <u>very</u> difficult test.

1. Evenings, my parents and grandparents would loudly discuss politics.
2. I was sent home because I had a very high fever.
3. Tuesday was an extremely bad day, but the things that happened Wednesday were worse.
4. You must definitely see a doctor today.
5. If you decide to visit tomorrow, please come early.
6. Saturdays, I usually babysit for my brother.
7. I did not see her yesterday.
8. I ran approximately two miles Friday.
9. She works days and attends school nights.
10. Winters are always dreadfully cold in that province.
11. Weekends, Todd likes to sleep late.
12. Weekdays, it is usually Jake's job to walk the dog.
13. We saw a remarkably good movie Tuesday.
14. Last winter, we stayed at the lake.
15. Summers, we always went to the beach.

17.2 Adverbs (Adverb or Adjective?) • Practice 1

Adverb or Adjective?   Remember that an *adverb* modifies a verb, an adjective, or another adverb; an *adjective* modifies a noun or pronoun.

Adjectives	Adverbs
That train is *fast*.	A plane goes *fast*.
The *fast* train arrived on time.	An SST travels even *faster*.
Jackie is a *true* friend.	Jackie is *truly* kind.
Our case was *hopeless*.	We were *hopelessly* lost.

▷ **Exercise 1**   **Distinguishing Between Adjectives and Adverbs.**   Write whether the underlined word in each sentence is an *adjective* or an *adverb*.

EXAMPLE: The dancer moved <u>gracefully</u>. ____*adverb*____

1. The child looked <u>longingly</u> through the bakery window. _____
2. Kathy had always been an <u>early</u> riser. _____
3. Why did you come so <u>early</u>? _____
4. Kelly was the <u>only</u> person at home. _____
5. The baby is <u>only</u> six weeks old. _____
6. The accident could have been <u>fatal</u>. _____
7. Happily no one was <u>fatally</u> injured. _____
8. Josh swam <u>farther</u> out than the others. _____
9. The cabin is on the <u>farther</u> shore. _____
10. The neighbors became <u>close</u> friends. _____

▷ **Exercise 2**   **Adding Adverbs and Adjectives to Sentences.**   If an adjective is needed in a sentence below, write the word in parentheses. If an adverb is needed, add *-ly* to the given word.

EXAMPLE: The little girl curtsied ____*gracefully*____. (graceful)

1. Most of my friends exercise _____. (regular)
2. This muscle feels _____ from moving all that furniture. (sore)
3. We made a serious mistake, but an _____ one. (honest)
4. The speaker considered her answer _____. (careful)
5. We _____ go out to a movie on weekends. (frequent)
6. Uncle John is a _____ dinner guest at our house. (regular)
7. You can trust Ms. Franklin to answer your questions _____. (honest)
8. Maria is usually a very _____ driver. (careful)
9. When the trip was canceled, the children were _____ disappointed. (sore)
10. Mr. O'Brien is a _____ visitor at our school. (frequent)

17.2 Adverbs (Adverb or Adjective?) • Practice 2

▶ **Exercise 1** **Distinguishing Between Adverbs and Adjectives.** Identify each underlined word as an *adverb* or *adjective*.

EXAMPLE: His room was very neat. _____*adjective*_____

1. The mounted moose head looked <u>real</u>. _____
2. I <u>really</u> believed the weather forecast. _____
3. Bertram walks to the office <u>daily</u>. _____
4. Our office runs ads in the <u>daily</u> newspaper. _____
5. Matilda spoke <u>darkly</u> of her husband's past. _____
6. No light filtered into the <u>dark</u> cell. _____
7. Immigrants worked <u>hard</u> to build the railroads. _____
8. Sandstone is not a <u>hard</u> rock. _____
9. Zack is an <u>early</u> riser. _____
10. Mildred starts the day <u>early</u> and finishes late. _____
11. I will <u>gladly</u> finish the dishes. _____
12. We are <u>glad</u> to have you as a friend. _____
13. When his aunt died, he was suddenly <u>rich</u>. _____
14. The musketeer was <u>richly</u> dressed in velvet. _____
15. After scrubbing the floor, his hands were <u>rough</u>. _____

▶ **Writing Application** **Writing Sentences with Adverbs.** Rewrite each sentence, adding one or more adverbs. Include at least one noun used as an adverb.

EXAMPLE: Kathleen entered the room.

_____Kathleen *quietly* entered the room._____

1. Tony will go to the grocery store for us.

   _____

2. Barn swallows are helpful because they eat insects.

   _____

3. His poor posture made him seem shorter than he was.

   _____

4. The tired worker yawned and rubbed his eyes.

   _____

5. We were sad about the end of summer.

   _____

6. Many people think snails are delicious.

   _____

7. The boat docked and lowered its sails.

   _____

8. Their enthusiasm faded.

   _____

9. Night fell and the celebration began.

   _____

10. Can a helicopter rescue those men?

    _____

18.1 Prepositions (Words Used as Prepositions, Prepositional Phrases) • Practice 1

Words Used as Prepositions   A *preposition* is a word that relates a noun or pronoun following it to another word in the sentence.

PREPOSITIONS
Jason set the package { on under near next to } the table.

Prepositional Phrases   A *prepositional phrase* is a group of words that begins with a *preposition* and ends with a noun or pronoun called the *object of the preposition.*

PREPOSITIONAL PHRASES	
Prepositions	**Objects of Prepositions**
between	*them*
around	the *museum*
on account of	the severe weather *conditions*

▶ **Exercise 1**   **Supplying Prepositions.**   Fill in each blank with an appropriate preposition.

EXAMPLE: We completed the job _____*in spite of*_____ great difficulty.

1. The guests maintained constant chatter _____ the meal.
2. We found several valuable items _____ the clutter of the attic.
3. Trudy ordered a salad _____ the pizza.
4. The decorator placed the love seat _____ the wing chair.
5. The newscaster filed her report _____ the riots.
6. The guest speaker was delayed _____ heavy traffic.
7. The *Silver Meteor* arrived in New York _____ schedule.
8. You may substitute margarine _____ butter.
9. Everyone _____ Elsa enjoyed the boat ride.
10. _____ the large crowds, we enjoyed the art exhibit.

▶ **Exercise 2**   **Identifying Prepositional Phrases.**   Enclose in parentheses each prepositional phrase in the sentences below. Underline each preposition and circle its object. The number in parentheses tells how many phrases there are.

EXAMPLE: The doctor examined the patient (from (head)) (to (toe)). (2)

1. According to the paper, the concert begins at dusk. (2)
2. I saved a seat for you next to mine. (2)
3. The headlines announced a truce between the two countries. (1)
4. Cut two pounds of apples into quarter-inch slices. (2)
5. A window with a northern exposure is perfect for that plant. (2)
6. The passengers in the back of the boat got wet from the spray. (3)
7. The hotel guests enter through a beautiful courtyard. (1)
8. The house down the street has a weathervane on the top of its garage. (3)
9. We looked into the abandoned house through a crack in the window. (3)
10. Ted found the map underneath the woodpile behind the barn. (2)

18.1 Prepositions (Words Used as Prepositions, Prepositional Phrases) • Practice 2

▶ **Exercise 1** **Supplying Prepositions.** Write an appropriate preposition in each blank. Use at least three compound prepositions.

EXAMPLE: ___Instead of___ apples, we had raisins.

1. Every store _____ this one is having a sale.
2. Water lilies floated _____ the surface of the pond.
3. Some dwarf fruit trees grew _____ the house.
4. _____ the authorities, the alleged robbers were caught.
5. A lantern's gleam could be seen _____ the tunnel.
6. Please buy construction paper _____ scissors and glue.
7. The winning runner leaped _____ the air.
8. He looked _____ the room.
9. _____ the water shortage, we must limit our use.
10. His ancestors left Ireland _____ the potato famine.
11. _____ everything, I don't think we should leave now.
12. Jason asked for peas _____ carrots.
13. _____ those two boxes, Don took nothing from the house.
14. Caroline sat on the bench, _____ her friends Sally and Tina.
15. The courageous man offered to go _____ the others.
16. _____ your special talents, you will get the job.
17. The three friends took a long walk _____ the woods.
18. _____ your support and guidance, I never would have done this.
19. _____ his visit to Vancouver, James had never been in Canada.
20. Stu was invited _____ the fact that he and Cora had argued.

▶ **Exercise 2** **Identifying Prepositional Phrases.** Underline each prepositional phrase. Then, draw another line under each preposition and circle the object.

EXAMPLE: We admire the beauty of animals' tails. of animals' (tails)

(1) The tails of birds and animals can also be useful appendages to their bodies. (2) Because of their tails, beavers can transmit a warning regarding impending danger. (3) With its rattle, a rattlesnake warns those around that they should watch where they are stepping. (4) Apart from protective use, tails also help animals with the more practical side of life. (5) Kangaroos and lizards would not move with such agility without their tails for balance. (6) With their long tails, wagtails, a kind of bird, disturb insects in the grass and thus secure their food. (7) In addition to these uses, tails also help many animals communicate during courtship. (8) A coyote holding his tail high above him is expressing interest in his mate. (9) Similarly, by means of his tail feathers, a male peacock displays his interest in front of the hen. (10) The swordtail, a fish often found in home aquariums, also uses his tail in a courtship dance.

18.1 Prepositions (Preposition or Adverb?) • Practice 1

Preposition or Adverb?   Many words can be either a preposition or an adverb, depending on how they are used. Remember that prepositions always have objects. Adverbs do not.

Prepositions	Adverbs
Sauté the onions *in* butter.	Please let the cat *in*.
Willie ran *through* the town.	These shades let some light *through*.

▶ **Exercise 1**   **Distinguishing Between Prepositions and Adverbs.**   Write whether the underlined word in each sentence is a *preposition* or an *adverb*.

EXAMPLE: The desk has drawers on the bottom and shelves above. ____*adverb*____

1. Once inside, we took our jackets off. ____adverb____
2. Last weekend, my parents moved the living-room furniture around. ____adverb____
3. The splinter is just below the surface of the skin. ____preposition____
4. Just set the package inside the garage. ____preposition____
5. Distribute the raisins evenly throughout, please. ____adverb____
6. The executive's remarks were made off the record. ____preposition____
7. Sign your name in the space below. ____adverb____
8. When the drizzle began, we moved our picnic inside. ____adverb____
9. We planted marigolds around the vegetable garden. ____preposition____
10. The sirens could be heard throughout the town. ____preposition____

▶ **Exercise 2**   **Adding Prepositions and Adverbs to Sentences.**   Add a word that is appropriate to the meaning of both sentences in each pair. In the sentence in which the word is used as a preposition, circle its object.

EXAMPLE:

   a. I had never seen the Statue of Liberty ____*before*____ .

   b. Please set the table ____*before*____ (noon) .

1. a. The cake has two layers with jelly _____.

   b. The Delaware River forms a lengthy boundary _____ two states.

2. a. This sweater was made _____ hand.

   b. When will the parade pass _____ ?

3. a. Did you remember to turn the oven _____ ?

   b. Hannah put a twenty-cent stamp _____ the envelope.

4. a. The owners converted the barn _____ the house into apartments.

   b. The puppy tagged along _____

5. a. Turn right just _____ the library.

   b. The runner had gone _____ before we knew it.

18.1 Prepositions (Preposition or Adverb?) • Practice 2

Exercise 1 **Distinguishing Between Prepositions and Adverbs.** Identify each underlined word as a *preposition* or *adverb*.

EXAMPLE: The spider sat <u>down</u> beside her. _____*adverb*_____

1. Hang <u>on</u> and don't let go! _____*adverb*_____
2. The snoring told him someone slept <u>within</u>. _____*adverb*_____
3. No one can make that horse go <u>over</u> a bridge. _____*prep*_____
4. The snail crept <u>along</u> the bottom of the fish tank. _____*prep.*_____
5. On account of lateness, you have fallen <u>behind</u>. _____*adverb*_____
6. Walk right <u>in</u> if you don't find us at home. _____*adverb*_____
7. She put her work <u>aside</u> and talked with me. _____*adverb*_____
8. The balloon floated <u>up</u>, rising higher and higher. _____*adverb*_____
9. <u>Beneath</u> our house is the cellar of an old cabin. _____*prep*_____
10. We searched <u>around</u> carefully for the lost money. _____*adverb*_____
11. We were warm in the house, but <u>outside</u> there was a blizzard. _____*adverb*_____
12. <u>Since</u> that terrible time, we have not heard a word from Tom. _____*prep*_____
13. Kurt likes the house but wants new carpets <u>throughout</u>. _____*adverb*_____
14. Beatrice has placed a potted palm <u>between</u> the two chairs. _____*prep*_____
15. The feather fluttered gently <u>down</u>. _____*adverb*_____
16. Pierre opened the creaking door and took a look <u>inside</u>. _____*adverb*_____
17. Maria stores boxes of summer clothing <u>under</u> the bed. _____*prep*_____
18. The diver swam <u>toward</u> the surface. _____*prep*_____
19. Dan delivered a speech <u>about</u> the ancient Romans. _____*prep*_____
20. Raoul reached the finish line first, and Sam got there right <u>after</u>. _____*adverb*_____

Writing Application **Writing Sentences with Prepositions.** Use each prepositional phrase in a sentence of your own.

EXAMPLE: across the street

_____We walked across the street to the library._____

1. down the mountain path

_____

2. during English class

_____

3. about six o'clock

_____

4. according to my father

_____

5. by means of hard work

_____

18.2 Conjunctions and Interjections (Different Kinds of Conjunctions) • Practice 1

Different Kinds of Conjunctions A *conjunction* is a word used to connect other words or groups of words. *Coordinating* and *correlative* conjunctions join similar kinds of words or groups or words that are grammatically alike.

COORDINATING CONJUNCTIONS
and   but   for   not   or   so   yet

CORRELATIVE CONJUNCTIONS		
both ... and	neither ... nor	whether ... or
either...or	not only ... but also	

Subordinating conjunctions connect two complete ideas by making one subordinate to, or less important than, the other.

FREQUENTLY USED SUBORDINATING CONJUNCTIONS			
after	because	now that	until
although	before	since	when
as	even if	so that	whenever
as if	even though	than	where
as long as	if	though	wherever
as soon as	in order that	till	while
as though	lest	unless	

▶ **Exercise 1** **Identifying Conjunctions.** Underline the conjunction in each sentence. Then write whether it is *coordinating*, *correlative*, or subordinating.

EXAMPLE: This restaurant is <u>not only</u> elegant <u>but also</u> expensive.   _____correlative_____

1. I had not finished the dishes before the visitors arrived. _____

2. The lines of that dress are simple yet elegant. _____

3. The child was cooperative but wary during the examination. _____

4. The soup needs both salt and pepper. _____

5. I mentally outlined my essay while I waited for the bus. _____

6. The last problem on the test was harder than the others were. _____

7. Neither the hosts nor the guests had a very good time. _____

8. Grandma sat with the baby until he went to sleep. _____

9. Please finish packing your suitcase so that we can load the car. _____

10. Terry jumps up whenever anyone rings the doorbell. _____

▶ **Exercise 2** **Adding Conjunctions in Sentences.** Fill in the blanks with an appropriate conjunction of the kind given in parentheses.

EXAMPLE: Alison offered to help, ___*but*___ the offer came too late. (coordinating)

1. _____While_____ you finish your chores, I will be waiting for you. (subordinating)

2. Voting is ____both____ a right ____and____ a duty. (correlative)

3. Elaine was uncertain ____but____ willing to try the snails. (coordinating)

4. You must hurry, ____or____ we will surely be late. (coordinating)

5. ____Although____ the players were disappointed, they were good sports. (subordinating)

18.2 Conjunctions and Interjections (Different Kinds of Conjunctions) • Practice 2

▶ **Exercise 1** **Identifying Conjunctions.** Underline the conjunction in each sentence. Then label each as *coordinating, correlative,* or *subordinating.*

EXAMPLE: We ran for shelter when the rain started. ___*subordinating*___

1. During his fast, he neither ate food nor drank liquids. _____
2. They promised to return, for everyone had a good time. _____
3. Gordon bit his nails whenever he was nervous. _____
4. The judge listened to the explanation in order that he might decide fairly. _____
5. Evan's joke was not only silly but also too long. _____
6. Already ten inches of rain had fallen, yet the downpour continued. _____
7. Since Ben refuses to vote, he shouldn't complain about our country's leadership. _____
8. Was the opossum actually dead or just pretending? _____
9. Belinda had not succeeded before, and she was not likely to succeed now. _____
10. Buffalo are scarce today because people slaughtered them. _____
11. Miriam's favorite breakfast is cereal and juice. _____
12. It does not really matter whether you want to or not. _____
13. The game will be at noon unless it is raining. _____
14. Wherever Mary went, the puppy was sure to follow. _____
15. Jacob wanted to buy those shoes even though the price was very high. _____
16. The bird's wings have been clipped, so it cannot fly. _____
17. Although he had studied for hours, Emil was not tired. _____
18. Either Marsha wrote the thank you notes, or Elaine did. _____
19. Different foods were served, but Mikey didn't like any of them. _____
20. Both Carla and Jerome visited Auntie Sue in the hospital. _____

▶ **Exercise 2** **Using Conjunctions in Sentences.** Complete each sentence by writing an appropriate conjunction in each blank. Then label the conjunction *coordinating, correlative,* or *subordinating.*

EXAMPLE: He had *neither* a pencil *nor* a pen. ___*correlative*___

1. Ben watered the strawberries daily, ___but___ they did not ripen. ___cordinating___
2. Barbara likes to whistle ___when___ she works. ___subordinating___
3. We saw ___neither___ emus ___nor___ kangaroos on our trip to Australia. ___correlative___
4. ___even if___ you don't enjoy it, you should exercise every day. ___subordinating___
5. I will be here at three o'clock ___unless___ you tell me otherwise. ___subordinating___

18.2 Conjunctions and Interjections (Conjunction, Preposition, or Adverb?) • Practice 1

Conjunction, Preposition, or Adverb?   A few words can be conjunctions, prepositions, or adverbs. Remember that conjunctions always connect words or ideas.

SUBORDINATING CONJUNCTION
Since the Jacksons moved away, the neighborhood has been quieter.
PREPOSITIONS
I haven't seen Paul *since* breakfast.
ADVERB
Jim left town a week ago and hasn't been heard of *since*.

▶ **Exercise 1**   **Identifying Words as Conjunctions, Prepositions, or Adverbs.**   Write whether each word underlined below is a *conjunction*, a *preposition*, or an *adverb*.

EXAMPLE: The game has been postponed until tomorrow. _____*preposition*_____

1. After they returned from the lake, they began to think about dinner. _____conjunction_____

2. I know I have heard that song before. _____adverb_____

3. Alex always does warm-up exercises before he begins jogging. _____conjunction_____

4. After dinner, we played a trivia game. _____preposition_____

5. When will dinner be ready? _____adverb_____

6. Please put the toys away when you are finished with them. _____conjunction_____

7. Until I had seen the show myself, I couldn't understand the jokes. _____conjunction_____

8. Janice will wait for us until noon, and then she will leave. _____preposition_____

9. Look before you leap. _____conjunction_____

10. The team has much work to do before the big game with Central
    High. _____preposition_____

▶ **Exercise 2**   **Adding Conjunctions, Prepositions, or Adverbs to Sentences.**   One word can be used to complete each set of sentences below. Fill in the blanks with the correct word. Then write *conjunction, preposition,* or *adverb* to tell how it is used in each sentence.

EXAMPLE: a. We had almost reached town _____*when*_____ we had a flat tire. _____*conjunction*_____

       b. _____*When*_____ did the alarm go off? _____*adverb*_____

1. a. Have you eaten squid _____? _____

   b. Jerry threw his warm-up pitches _____ the batter came up. _____

   c. Snacks _____ meals can spoil your appetite. _____

2. a. Several guests stayed _____ midnight. _____

   b. You should not give your opinion _____ you have read the book. _____

3. a. The yearbook staff will meet in the cafeteria _____ school. _____

   b. Fran stayed to clean up _____ the party was over. _____

   c. Mrs. Jenkins was grateful to the police ever _____. _____

4. a. _____ Friday, we have been waiting to hear the news. _____

   b. _____ my grandmother came to visit, things have been very quiet. _____

18.2 Conjunctions and Interjections (Conjunction, Preposition, or Adverb?) • Practice 2

> **Exercise 1** **Identifying Words as Conjunctions, Prepositions, or Adverbs.** Identify each underlined word as a *subordinating conjunction, preposition,* or *adverb.*

EXAMPLE: I have not seen him <u>since</u> Thursday. _____*preposition*_____

1. Their house will be vacant <u>till</u> next summer. _____preposition_____
2. The child had never ridden a horse <u>before</u>. _____adverb_____
3. Never stand under a tree <u>when</u> there is lightning. _____conjunction_____
4. Tin is rarely used for foil <u>since</u> aluminum is cheaper. _____conjunction_____
5. <u>Where</u> are you going at this late hour? _____adverb_____
6. The band did not play <u>until</u> it reached the town. _____conjunction_____
7. Don't stop working <u>before</u> noon. _____preposition_____
8. Dolores always brushes her teeth <u>after</u> meals. _____preposition_____
9. Crops grow <u>where</u> once there was only desert. _____conjunction_____
10. They never rise <u>till</u> the rooster crows. _____conjunction_____
11. Jon walked the dog <u>after</u> the storm had ended. _____conjunction_____
12. Do you like to eat your salad before or <u>after</u> dinner? _____preposition_____
13. Dolores wants to wait <u>until</u> spring to buy a new coat. _____preposition_____
14. <u>Before</u> I take another step, I must know where we are going. _____conjunction_____
15. We haven't had any warm weather <u>since</u> September. _____preposition_____
16. Adam took a swim <u>after</u> breakfast. _____preposition_____
17. You said you will come, but I want to know exactly <u>when</u>. _____adverb_____
18. <u>Where</u> did you hide the gifts? _____adverb_____
19. <u>Until</u> I know you are safe, I will worry. _____conjunction_____
20. I would like to finish this chapter <u>before</u> noon. _____preposition_____

> **Exercise 2** **Using Conjunctions, Prepositions, and Adverbs in Sentences.** Write sentences using the underlined word as the part of speech indicated.

EXAMPLE: after
>   conjunction: *We went to the dance after we had our dinner.*
>   preposition: *We went to the dance after dinner.*
>   adverb: *Sally walked out onto the dance floor, and Dave followed after.*

1. <u>before</u>
   conjunction _____
   preposition _____
   adverb _____
2. <u>since</u>
   conjunction _____
   preposition _____
   adverb _____
3. <u>till</u>
   conjunction _____
   preposition _____
4. <u>until</u>
   conjunction _____
   preposition _____

Conjunctions and Interjections (Conjunctive Adverbs, Interjections) • Practice 1

Conjunctive Adverbs   A *conjunctive adverb* is an adverb that acts as a conjunction to connect complete ideas.

FREQUENTLY USED CONJUNCTIVE ADVERBS		
accordingly	finally	nevertheless
again	furthermore	otherwise
also	however	then
besides	indeed	therefore
consequently	moreover	thus

Interjections   An *interjection* is a word that expresses feeling or emotion and functions independently of a sentence.

SOME COMMON INTERJECTIONS		
aha	hey	tsk
alas	hurray	well
darn	oh	whew
goodness	ouch	wow

▶ **Exercise 1**   **Recognizing Conjunctive Adverbs.**   Underline each conjunctive adverb in the sentences below. If a sentence does not have a conjunctive adverb, write *none* in the blank at the right.

EXAMPLE: Please open the door for me; my hands are full. ___*none*___

1. This apartment is quite roomy; besides, the price is right. _____
2. The star was taken ill suddenly; therefore, filming was delayed. _____
3. ‧ The bell rang early; school was dismissed. _____
4. Mr. Zims is a strict marker; indeed, he is strict in every way. _____
5. Grab your sweater; we're leaving right now. _____
6. James does not play tennis well; nevertheless, he is enthusiastic. _____
7. Mom checked the mouse traps; again, they were empty. _____
8. The crowd stood for the National Anthem; then, the game began. _____
9. These trees are deciduous; those are evergreens. _____
10. The river flooded many roads; consequently, traffic was rerouted. _____

▶ **Exercise 2**   **Adding Interjections to Sentences.**   Fill in each blank with an interjection that shows the feeling or emotion given in parentheses.

EXAMPLE: ___*Darn*___ ! I was afraid that might happen. (annoyance)

1. _____! I burned my finger! (pain)
2. _____, my favorite sweater shrank. (regret)
3. _____! Look at that rainbow! (delight)
4. _____! I never knew that. (surprise)
5. _____! This is some race. (excitement)
6. _____! I'm going to fall! (fear)
7. _____! I lost my keys again. (annoyance)
8. _____! It's another rainy day. (disappointment)
9. _____! The Bombers won! (enthusiasm)
10. _____! I'm ready for a break. (exhaustion)

18.2 Conjunctions and Interjections (Conjunctive Adverbs, Interjections) • Practice 2

> **Exercise 1** **Supplying Conjunctive Adverbs.** Write a conjunctive adverb that could be used to tie together the ideas in each pair of sentences.

EXAMPLE: Snow fell steadily. We trudged onward. _____nevertheless_____

1. His plane was delayed in Dallas. It arrived two hours late. _____

2. I have listened long enough to your excuses. I am tired of your lack of originality. _____

3. Some materials are more expensive than others. Wool and linen are often quite costly. _____

4. Fewer people bought new cars this year. There was less profit for the automotive industry. _____

5. First Frank smiled. He laughed heartily. _____

6. Raymond can be demanding and impatient. He is sometimes very helpful and understanding. _____

7. Please bring paper cups and napkins. Bring something to drink. _____

8. The general instructed the soldiers to move ahead. They advanced several paces. _____

9. Blanche has a beautiful voice. She is often asked to sing at weddings. _____ .

10. Rosemary has many trophies over the fireplace. I assumed she had won them. _____

11. Most Americans eat far more than people in other countries. Our population has a higher percentage of overweight people. _____

12. Education costs have been rising over the past few decades. They are likely to continue to rise. _____

13. Snow fell for three days in a row. The principal had to shut down the school. _____

14. Our team was favored to win the game. Our quarterback was injured and we lost. _____

15. Andrew practices his piano playing for two hours every day. He is not very good at it. _____

16. Fire damaged the hall. The party had to be canceled. _____

17. Your dog needs a bath. He needs a flea collar. _____

18. This is a very beautiful orchid. It is the most spectacular in your entire collection. _____

19. My appointment is at four o'clock. I will leave the house at three. _____

20. You do not have enough money to buy those boots. You will have to wait until they go on sale. _____

19.1 Subjects and Verbs (Complete Subjects and Predicates) • Practice 1

Complete Subjects and Predicates   A *sentence* is a group of words with two main parts: a complete subject and a complete predicate. Together these parts express a complete thought.

Complete Subjects	Complete Predicates
Everyone on the team	tried hard.
The opposing players	did their best, too.
We	lost.

Exercise 1   **Recognizing Complete Subjects and Predicates.**   Draw a vertical line between each complete subject and predicate.

EXAMPLE: The runner in the green shirt | won.

1. Wild zebras | roamed through the game preserve.
2. Elena | did not allow enough time for the last essay question.
3. That game | requires recalling a lot of trivial information.
4. That huge package in the hallway | makes me curious.
5. The owners | arranged a private tour for us.
6. The first zoo in the United States | was in Philadelphia.
7. It | continues to operate even today.
8. Children | enjoy it immensely.
9. Rides on camels or elephants | are available.
10. I | accepted the invitation promptly.

Exercise 2   **More Work with Complete Subjects and Predicates.**   Follow the instructions in Exercise 1.

EXAMPLE: The pilgrims on the *Mayflower* | first landed at Provincetown.

1. That grapefruit tree in the corner | grew from a seed ten years ago.
2. The stranger's behavior | aroused the security guard's suspicion.
3. Male and female crocodiles | carry their young in their mouths.
4. Hieroglyphics | were the picture writings of the ancient Egyptians.
5. Spectators | applauded with great enthusiasm.
6. A small ferry boat | takes passengers on cruises around the islands.
7. Thanksgiving Day | is always on the fourth Thursday in November.
8. Pumpkin pie | is my favorite dessert.
9. Automobile safety belts | save thousands of lives every year.
10. Jeremy | phoned home after school.

19.1 Subjects and Verbs (Complete Subjects and Predicates) • Practice 2

▶ **Exercise 1** **Recognizing Complete Subjects and Predicates.** For each sentence, write the complete subject in the first column and the complete predicate in the second column.

EXAMPLE: The fluffy squirrel chattered at us.

Complete Subject   Complete Predicate

_____*The fluffy squirrel*_____   _____*chattered at us.*_____

1. The new puppy won't leave the older dog alone.
2. An old-fashioned spinning wheel sat in the corner of the room.
3. Seasonal winds in India are called monsoons.
4. New skin was grafted onto his burned leg.
5. We should have been on the road before now.
6. Anyone could have made a mistake like that.
7. My umbrella handle is carved from wood.
8. The Sons of Liberty was a secret society.
9. Mink oil is excellent for conditioning leather shoes, boots, and baseball mitts.
10. Her stationery is always simple but elegant.
11. Fourteen squealing children played in the sprinklers.
12. One of the best exercises you can do is swim.
13. My aunt's best friend knit this sweater for me.
14. The two volumes of the series will be published later this year.
15. The ancient Egyptians stained their fingernails with henna.

Complete Subject	Complete Predicate
1. _____	_____
2. _____	_____
3. _____	_____
4. _____	_____
5. _____	_____
6. _____	_____
7. _____	_____
8. _____	_____
9. _____	_____
10. _____	_____
11. _____	_____
12. _____	_____
_____	_____
_____	_____

…e Workbook

19.1 Subjects and Verbs (Sentence or Fragment?)
• Practice 1

Sentence or Fragment?   A *fragment* is a group of words that does not express a complete thought but is punctuated as if it were a sentence.

Fragments	Complete Sentences
Over the weekend.	What did you do over the weekend?
Each of the judges.	Each of the judges had a different opinion.
Made its home under the woodpile.	A small brown toad made its home under the woodpile.

▶**Exercise 1**   **Distinguishing Between Sentences and Fragments.**   In the blanks below, write *S* for each sentence and *F* for each fragment.

EXAMPLE: Within minutes after the call. ___*F*___

1. In spite of Susanna's objections. ___F___
2. Hot dogs and hamburgers were on the grill. ___S___
3. Amanda helped. ___S___
4. Throughout the summer. ___F___
5. Inspector Snootch followed his hunch. ___S___
6. Visitors from near and far. ___F___
7. The player with the highest batting average in the league. ___F___
8. Spends several hours a week on her hobby. ___F___
9. The whale appeared. ___S___
10. A bat does not have true wings. ___S___

▶**Exercise 2**   **Writing Sentences from Fragments.**   Rewrite five of the items labeled *F* above as complete sentences.

EXAMPLE: ___The emergency crew arrived within minutes after the call.___

1. _____

   _____

2. _____

   _____

3. _____

   _____

4. _____

   _____

5. _____

   _____

19.1 Subjects and Verbs (Sentence or Fragment?)
• Practice 2

▶ Exercise 1 **Distinguishing Between Sentences and Fragments.** Decide whether each item is a sentence or fragment. If it is a sentence, write S. If it is a fragment, rewrite it to make it a sentence.

EXAMPLE: By the swimming pool.

_____ _They met by the swimming pool._

1. A sewing machine with all the frills. F

_____

2. Stories about creatures in the ocean's depths. F

_____

3. Jan did not finish her breakfast. S

_____

4. Jumped higher and higher on the trampoline. F

_____

5. Few, if any. F

_____

6. Basketball, the most popular spectator sport. F

_____

7. Wearing a white, heavy knit sweater. F

_____

8. A stitch in time saves nine. S

_____

9. Trembled and shook with fear. F

_____

10. Beside the pool, soaking up the sunshine. F

_____

▶ Exercise 2 **Converting Fragments to Sentences.** Write a sentence using each given fragment.

EXAMPLE: Closed the door behind him.

_____ _Samuel closed the door behind him._

1. a sudden streak of light in the night sky

_____

2. during the eclipse, the moon

_____

3. wondering how far she had to walk

_____

4. knocked on the door for a full minute

_____

5. kicked the ball around for hours

_____

19.1 Subjects and Verbs (Simple Subjects and Predicates) • Practice 1

Simple Subjects and Predicates The *simple subject* is the essential noun, pronoun, or group of words acting as a noun that cannot be left out of the complete subject. The *simple predicate* is the essential verb or verb phrase that cannot be left out of the complete predicate. A word that interrupts the verb phrase is not part of the simple predicate. In the chart below, the simple subjects are underlined once and the simple predicates are underlined twice.

Complete Subjects	Complete Predicates
Looking worried, Tom	tried the phone call again.
Most of us	thought the movie was boring.
Many citizens in this country	do not vote.
Sherry	called.

▶ **Exercise 1** **Recognizing Simple Subjects and Predicates.** Draw a line between the complete subject and complete predicate in each sentence. Then, underline each simple subject once and predicate twice.

EXAMPLE: Each of my friends | has an entirely different personality.

1. Many of the photographs had become brittle with age.
2. We enjoyed the picnic in spite of the showers.
3. The organizers of the event were unhappy with the turnout.
4. The sound of emergency vehicles pierced the night.
5. All of the members of that group wear outrageous clothing.
6. You promised me another chance.
7. A few of the committee members did not attend.
8. A number of beachfront properties were destroyed by the hurricane.
9. Who volunteered for the clean-up committee?
10. Mom had not ordered the curtains yet.

▶ **Exercise 2** **Adding Sentence Parts.** Each word group below is missing either a complete subject or a complete predicate. Write the missing part to create a complete sentence. Then circle the simple subject and underline the simple predicate.

EXAMPLE: ___The guest (speaker) at the banquet___ ___was___ the governor.

1. _____ reads several books a week.

2. _____ receives a friendly welcome.

3. No one in my homeroom _____.

4. _____ bats left-handed.

5. The chef in that restaurant _____.

6. _____ arrived in record time.

7. _____ are elected to six-year terms.

8. Every member of the club _____.

9. The nickname of our state _____.

10. Most of the animals in the circus _____.

19.1 Subjects and Verbs (Simple Subjects and Predicates) • Practice 2

▶**Exercise 1** **Recognizing Subjects and Verbs.** In the following paragraph, underline each simple subject once and each simple predicate twice.

EXAMPLE: Ancient legends continue to be fascinating.

(1) Greek literature contains many stories about Amazons. (2) Supposedly living near the Black Sea, the Amazons were a nation of women warriors noted for their strength. (3) Not enjoying the presence of men, the Amazons lived apart in their own cities. (4) Ares, the god of war, was worshipped in their temples. (5) They fought against the Greeks during the Trojan War. (6) They were also fearless hunters. (7) Their bravery made them famous. (8) Many Greek statues of Amazons with bows and arrows can be seen today in museums. (9) These women never really existed, however, according to some scholars. (10) They are merely the product of the Greeks' imagination.

▶**Exercise 2** **Using Simple Subjects and Simple Predicates in Sentences.** Write a sentence for each given simple subject or simple predicate. Then underline each *simple subject* once and each *simple predicate* twice.

EXAMPLE: horses (simple subject): *The horses trotted past the judges.*

1. had flown (simple predicate)

   _____

2. pilot (simple subject)

   _____

3. conquered (simple predicate)

   _____

4. garden (simple subject)

   _____

5. were wondering (simple predicate)

   _____

6. dentist (simple subject)

   _____

7. have ordered (simple predicate)

   _____

8. basketball (simple subject)

   _____

9. might have been (simple predicate)

   _____

10. candles (simple subject)

    _____

19.1 # Subjects and Verbs (Compound Subjects and Verbs) • Practice 1

Compound Subjects and Verbs   A *compound subject* is two or more subjects that have the same verb and are joined by a conjunction such as *and* or *or*. A *compound verb* is two or more verbs that have the same subject and are joined by a conjunction such as *and* or *or*.

COMPOUND SUBJECT
Henry, Florence, and the Broudys spent their vacation together.
COMPOUND VERB
The storm continued and worsened throughout the night.

> **Exercise 1**   **Recognizing Compound Subjects.**   Underline the nouns or pronouns in each compound subject.

EXAMPLE: The pitcher and the catcher must have good communication.

1. Neither Jake nor I understood the problem.
2. The President and the Vice President rode in separate cars.
3. The Senate, the House of Representatives, and the Supreme Court assemble for the State of the Union Address.
4. Not only the guests but also the hosts enjoyed the party.
5. Both lilacs and roses are highly scented flowers.
6. Shrimp and other shellfish are good sources of iodine.
7. Oranges, lemons, limes, and grapefruits are citrus fruits.
8. Paul and I loved our new bunk beds.
9. The museum guide or one of the guards should be able to direct you.
10. Measles and mumps have been nearly eliminated by vaccines.

> **Exercise 2**   **Recognizing Compound Verbs.**   Underline the verbs in each compound verb.

EXAMPLE: The sales representative opened her bag and began her talk.

1. The plane touched the ground and rolled to a stop.
2. Amanda did not give up, but practiced her music even harder.
3. Joe writes with his right hand but bats with his left.
4. Ginny often writes or calls home from college.
5. Kelly added the vegetables, adjusted the seasoning, and turned the soup down to a simmer.
6. The audience clapped, cheered, and called for an encore.
7. Jessica put down her book and yawned.
8. Pam checked the card catalog but found few books on her topic.
9. The clematis overgrew the trellis and began climbing the chimney.
10. The troops neither retreated nor surrendered.

19.1 Subjects and Verbs (Compound Subjects and Verbs) • Practice 2

▶ **Exercise 1** **Recognizing Compound Subjects and Verbs.** Draw one line under the words that make up each subject and two lines under each verb.

EXAMPLE: A hummingbird can hover and then fly straight up.

1. A hat, gloves, and warm coat should be worn in this weather.
2. Our aunt and uncle visit us every year and bring many gifts.
3. Both salt and pepper are used as seasonings.
4. In the summer, my friends and I swim and ride our bicycles on country roads.
5. Moles have very poor eyesight and, therefore, burrow in dark tunnels underground.
6. The team not only had a perfect season but also won the tournament.
7. Hair dyes and lipsticks come in almost every shade.
8. The mother cat and her kittens mewed pitifully and rubbed against our legs.
9. A small airplane was gliding and spiraling above us.
10. Moths cluster on the screen and beat their wings.

▶ **Exercise 2** **Finding Simple and Compound Subjects and Verbs.** Write the subject and verb in each sentence in the correct columns.

EXAMPLE: After school the band met and practiced.

Subject	Verb
band	met, practiced

1. The nozzle of the garden hose was clogged with dirt.
2. Many people have trouble with the high note of "The Star Spangled Banner."
3. Rats and mice eat huge amounts of valuable grains.
4. Today, Aunt Jennie and Uncle Nick will fly in from Hawaii and bring us crates of pineapples.
5. Miners and their families do not lead easy lives.
6. Max can hear a tune once and whistle it perfectly.
7. Remedies for colds usually do not help much.
8. During the dry season, campfires and carelessly tossed matches can cause raging forest fires.
9. Phoebe's hard work and honesty won our respect.
10. Hilary, Miranda, and their cousin could dance, sing, and play musical instruments.

	Subject	Verb
1.		
2.		
3.		
4.		
5.		
6.		
7.		
8.		
9.		
10.		

19.2 # Hard-to-Find Subjects • Practice 1

Subjects in Orders and Directions   In sentences that give orders or directions, the subject is understood to be *you*. Notice that this is true even when a person is addressed by name.

Orders or Directions	With Subjects Added
After dinner, please wash the dishes.	After dinner, (you) please wash the dishes.
Just put the box over there.	(You) just put the box over there.
Andy, pass in your paper.	Andy, (you) pass in your paper.

Subjects in Inverted Sentences   In questions, the subject often follows the verb. To find the subject, mentally rephrase the question.

Question	Rephrased as Statement
Did the bus leave?	The bus did leave.

The subject of a sentence is never *there* or *here*. Like inverted questions, such sentences can usually be rephrased as statements to find the subject.

Sentence Beginning with *There* or *Here*	Rephrased with Subject First
There is the lost puppy.	The lost puppy is there.

In some sentences the subject is placed after the verb in order to receive greater emphasis. Such sentences can be mentally rephrased in normal subject-verb order to find the subject.

Inverted Word Order	Rephrased in Subject-Verb Order
Outside the door was a package.	A package was outside the door.

▶ **Exercise 1**   **Finding Subjects in Orders or Directions.**   Write the subject of each sentence in the blank at the right. Put a caret (^) where the subject belongs in the sentence.

EXAMPLE: Simon,^ take this note to the office. ____*(you)*____

1. After the third traffic light, turn right. ____(you)____
2. Erica, let me see your needlepoint. ____(you)____
3. Remember to feed the cat. ____(you)____
4. Tonight, read the first two chapters of *Moby Dick*. ____(you)____
5. Jodi, remind me to bring my camera. ____(you)____

▶ **Exercise 2**   **Finding Subjects in Inverted Sentences.**   Underline the subject in each sentence.

EXAMPLE: Here is your essay.

1. Into the burning building rushed the firefighters.
2. How can we ever find our way out of here?
3. Somewhere between the two extremes lies the best solution.
4. There are two errors in this report.
5. Beyond the stream bloomed a multitude of wildflowers.

19.2 Hard-to-Find Subjects • Practice 2

> **Exercise 1** **Creating Sentences with Understood Subjects.** Use each verb in a sentence that gives an order or direction. Add the understood subject in parentheses in each sentence.

EXAMPLE: lend

<u>Joe, (you) lend me your pencil.</u>

1. give	3. speak	5. step	7. clean	9. rake
2. wipe	4. wash	6. drive	8. brush	10. mix

1. _____

2. _____

3. _____

4. _____

5. _____

6. _____

7. _____

8. _____

9. _____

10. _____

> **Exercise 2** **Finding Subjects in Questions.** In each sentence, underline the subject once and the verb twice.

EXAMPLE: Who knocked on the door?

1. Is a tomato a fruit or a vegetable?
2. Where did you put the buttered rolls?
3. Which shade of blue looks best?
4. Should a murderer ever be released from prison?
5. Who won the prize for the silliest costume?
6. May we have a little peace and quiet?
7. Was the key under the mat?
8. How long will you take to decide?
9. Whose honor was at stake?
10. Can we climb these mountains safely?

> **Exercise 3** **Finding Subjects in Sentences Beginning with *There* or *Here*.** In each sentence, underline the subject once and the verb twice.

1. Here are your gloves.
2. There was the leaky pipe.
3. There he was, with no bus fare.
4. Here are some suggestions for your composition.
5. There are two possible answers to that question.
6. There were the lost documents.
7. Here is a new slant on that topic.
8. Here comes Megan.
9. Here is your change from the dollar bill.
10. There are no mistakes in this needlepoint sampler.

19.3 Direct Objects, Indirect Objects, and Objective Complements (Direct Objects)

• Practice 1

Direct Objects A *direct object* is a noun or pronoun that receives the action of a transitive action verb. A direct object is one type of complement, which is a word or group of words that completes the meaning of a sentence.

DIRECT OBJECTS
DO   DO
The nurse awoke the ⌷patient⌷. (awoke *whom?* patient)
DO   DO   DO
I ordered ⌷ham⌷ and ⌷eggs⌷. (ordered *what?* ham and eggs)

▶ **Exercise 1**   **Identifying Direct Objects.**   Draw a box around each direct object.

EXAMPLE: We planted ⌷peas⌷, ⌷beans⌷, and ⌷carrots⌷ in our garden.

1. We usually change the ⌷sheets⌷ on Monday.
2. That author has published a ⌷novel⌷ and several magazine ⌷articles⌷.
3. The three students took a ⌷bus⌷ to the museum.
4. You could ask the ⌷doorkeeper⌷ for directions.
5. Carol asked the ⌷teacher⌷ for an extension on her term paper.
6. You can follow either ⌷State Street⌷ or ⌷High Road⌷ to the fair grounds.
7. The florist used ⌷daffodils⌷ and other spring ⌷flowers⌷ in the arrangement.
8. We need an interesting ⌷fabric⌷ for the pillows.
9. Paula borrowed my ⌷notes⌷ before the test.
10. They sell only three different ⌷kinds⌷ of ice cream.

▶ **Exercise 2**   **More Work with Direct Objects.**   Each sentence below contains an action verb. Draw a box around each direct object after a transitive action verb. Draw a line under each intransitive action verb.

EXAMPLE: The train <u>screeched</u> to a stop.

1. The children played board ⌷games⌷ for hours.
2. The cat <u>played</u> with a ball of yarn.
3. Everyone enjoyed the ⌷party⌷.
4. Queen Anne's lace <u>grew</u> by the side of the road.
5. That restaurant serves only ⌷steaks⌷ and ⌷seafood⌷.
6. The chef prepares ⌷everything⌷ with great care.
7. The actor <u>moved</u> in front of the camera.
8. The driver moved the ⌷car⌷ to a shadier spot.
9. Hillary has never ridden a ⌷horse⌷ before.
10. The cowboy has <u>ridden</u> out of town.

19.3 Direct Objects, Indirect Objects, and Objective Complements (Direct Objects)
• Practice 2

▶ **Exercise 1** **Recognizing Direct Objects.** Underline the direct object in each sentence, including any compound direct objects.

EXAMPLE: You can save energy and money through conservation of electricity.

(1) You should never use unnecessary lights. (2) In daylight hours, the sun can often provide enough light. (3) You can also use bulbs of lower wattage in some areas of a home or business. (4) These use less energy. (5) Some areas, however, require lots of light. (6) You should usually use one larger bulb there. (7) You can also install dimmer switches and three-way bulbs in your home. (8) These will control the amount of light from your lighting fixtures. (9) Fluorescent fixtures in contrast to incandescent bulbs give more light at less cost. (10) Everyone should regularly practice these methods of energy conservation in their homes and places of business.

▶ **Exercise 2** **Writing Sentences with Direct Objects.** Write a sentence using each given direct object in the kind of sentence indicated in parentheses.

EXAMPLE: apples and pears (question): *Did you buy apples and pears today?*

1. accident (statement)

   _____

2. walruses and sea lions (question)

   _____

3. fans (statement)

   _____

4. dogs or cats (question)

   _____

5. muffins, toast, and bagels (statement)

   _____

6. lotion (question)

   _____

7. dancers and singers (statement)

   _____

8. manicure (question)

   _____

9. elephants and giraffes (statement)

   _____

10. raisins (question)

   _____

19.3 Direct Objects, Indirect Objects, and Objective Complements (Indirect Objects, The Objective Complement) • Practice 1

Indirect Objects   An *indirect object* is a noun or pronoun that receives a direct object.

INDIRECT OBJECTS
IO   DO Aunt Ella made │Stephen│ a Halloween │costume│. (Made for *whom?* Stephen)
IO   IO   DO I read my │brother│ and │sister│ a │story│ . (read to *whom?* brother and sister)
IO   DO We should give the │wall│ another │coat│ of paint. (give *to what?* wall)

The Objective Complement   An *objective complement* is an adjective or noun that follows a direct object and describes or renames it.

OBJECTIVE COMPLEMENTS
DO   OC The committee appointed │Tim│ │fact-finder│. (appointed Tim *what?* fact-finder)
DO   OC   OC All that exercise made the │children│ │tired│ and │hungry│. (made the children *what?* tired and hungry)

▶ **Exercise 1**   **Identifying Indirect Objects.**   Underline each indirect object in the sentences below.

EXAMPLE: Sue showed Tom and me the pictures from her trip.

1. Grandma brought Michelle and Joe new bathing suits.
2. The prisoner finally told his lawyer the whole story.
3. Ellis offered each guest a tour of the mansion.
4. Has Jenkins shown the police the evidence?
5. The judges awarded Kelly a blue ribbon for her prize heifer.
6. Tess passed Helen and Kim a message in code.
7. The chess master showed Boris a new opening move.
8. Did you leave Mom and Dad a note?
9. Danny wrote Aunt Helen a warm thank-you note.
10. Uncle Dave taught me the breast stroke.

▶ **Exercise 2**   **Recognizing Objective Complements.**   Underline each objective complement.

EXAMPLE: The last scene left the audience frightened.

1. The dessert made the meal very satisfying.
2. The club elected Susan treasurer.
3. The judge declared the complaint invalid.
4. The new game kept everyone busy for hours.
5. The family called the new puppy Toby.

19.3 Direct Objects, Indirect Objects, and Objective Complements (Indirect Objects, The Objective Complement) • Practice 2

Exercise 1 **Recognizing Indirect Objects.**   Write each indirect object, including any compound indirect objects. If a sentence has no indirect object, write *none*.

EXAMPLE: They gave Mark and Elizabeth a puppy.   _Mark   Elizabeth_

1. Trading vessels brought people exotic spices. _____

2. Our committee distributed fliers to our neighbors. _____

3. Mr. Hinkle taught Harriet and Alberta a good lesson. _____

4. Please bring the children and me some ice cream. _____

5. The Constitution guarantees freedom to all. _____

6. She sold her home for very little profit. _____

7. When will Lena tell him the truth? _____

8. Education gives men and women more opportunities. _____

9. Lucille made herself some hot chocolate. _____

10. The article had a warning for cigarette smokers. _____

11. Albert sent his sister a postcard from Greece. _____

12. Virginia gave music lessons to several clients. _____

13. Frank's dad tossed him the baseball, and Frank tossed it back. _____

14. The tailor altered the suit to fit Martin. _____

15. Sidney paid the man fifty dollars. _____

Exercise 2 **Recognizing Objective Complements.**   Underline the objective complement in each sentence, including any compound objective complements.

EXAMPLE: Mr. Montes made his reply very short.

1. The neighborhood bully considered Martin a sissy.

2. A card for Father's Day makes my dad very happy.

3. That pleasant woman called me kind and helpful.

4. A stubborn man, Mr. Fenston thinks other people obstinate.

5. John's uncle makes everyone welcome.

6. Her friends nominated Jane president.

7. The ointment made the wound less red and sore.

8. Impulsively, she painted the doors to the dining room pink.

9. The boss appointed Ms. Brady chairwoman.

10. Such experiences make life worthwhile.

11. The critics declared the play a winner.

12. The doctor pronounced the patient cured.

13. The delighted mother called her daughter an angel.

14. The ambitious workers imagined themselves successful and wealthy.

15. The shy girl thought herself unattractive.

19.4 Subject Complements • Practice 1

Predicate Nominatives There are two different kinds of *subject complements*: predicate nominatives and predicate adjectives. A *predicate nominative* is a noun or pronoun that follows a linking verb and renames, identifies, or explains the subject of the sentence.

PREDICATE NOMINATIVES
PN
Watson is Sherlock Holmes's assistant.
PN   PN
My favorite desserts are lemon cake and ice cream.

Predicate Adjectives A *predicate adjective* is an adjective that follows a linking verb and describes the subject of the sentence.

PREDICATE ADJECTIVES
PA
Adam remained loyal to his friends.
PA   PA
Jenny s idea sounds interesting and practical.

▷ **Exercise 1** **Recognizing Predicate Nominatives and Predicate Adjectives.** Underline each subject complement in the sentences below. Then identify each as either a *PA* (predicate adjective) or a *PN* (predicate nominative).

EXAMPLE: The baby's best friends are his blanket and his teddy bear. ___PN___

1. After the race, the runners felt tired but exhilarated. __PA__
2. Janet became tan and muscular during her month at camp. __PA__
3. That novel became an overnight bestseller. __PN__
4. The singer's albums are as popular now as ever. __PA__
5. A straight line is the shortest distance between two points. __PN__
6. The retired officer remained a consultant on special projects. __PN__
7. Paula, Pam, and Patty are triplets. __PN__
8. Barbara will become either a surgeon or an internist. __PN__
9. The police search was extremely thorough. __PA__
10. Jim's suggestion was neither constructive nor workable. __PA__

▷ **Exercise 2** **Writing Sentences with Compound Subject Complements.** Each sentence below contains a subject complement. On the first line, add a second subject complement. Then identify the added subject complement as a *PA* (predicate adjective) or a *PN* (predicate nominative).

EXAMPLE: That sentence is unclear and ___uninteresting___. ___PA___

1. Anita's suggestion was tactful and _____. _____
2. Some sauces are both rich and _____. _____
3. Not all writers become famous and _____. _____
4. The teams in the finals will be the Majors and the _____. _____
5. The co-captains are Sandy and _____. _____

19.4 Subject Complements • Practice 2

Exercise 1 **Recognizing Predicate Nominatives.** Underline the predicate nominative in each sentence, including any compound predicate nominatives.

EXAMPLE: Gwendolyn was a lawyer and a mother.

1. The girl in the green sweater is she.
2. Bill's favorite sports were hockey and football.
3. Good sources of protein are eggs, meat, or beans.
4. Agatha remained an athlete in spite of her illness.
5. The winning essay will be the one with the most originality.
6. Audubon was an American naturalist and artist.
7. Gold and silver are valuable metals.
8. Peace of mind and a clear conscience are everything.
9. Bob's idea for the assembly seems the best.
10. My best friends are you and he.
11. The price of the hat was seventy-five dollars.
12. The nucleus of an atom is its central core.
13. Jupiter is the largest planet in our solar system.
14. Cherise and Frannie will remain friends forever.
15. Benicia was once the capital of California.

Exercise 2 **Recognizing Predicate Adjectives.** Underline the predicate adjective in each sentence, including any compound predicate adjectives.

EXAMPLE: That soup smells delicious.

1. Her voice on the telephone sounded muffled.
2. After work Eugene's muscles felt stiff and sore.
3. The mayor's policy is important to our city.
4. My sandwich at the beach was gritty and inedible.
5. Joan grew kinder and more understanding.
6. A crossword puzzle should be fairly difficult.
7. This item on the list appears unnecessary.
8. The sergeant's criticism was harsh yet impersonal.
9. Because of fright Ted's face looked drawn and pale.
10. Janice became successful overnight.
11. Heather became more skilled at tennis this year.
12. The earthquake was quite destructive.
13. The polar bear exhibit at the zoo seems very popular with the visitors.
14. The dog has been slightly nervous all morning.
15. The substitute teacher appears prepared for anything.

20.1 # Prepositional Phrases (Adjective and Adverb)
• Practice 1

Adjective Phrases   A *phrase* is a group of words that functions in a sentence as one part of speech. An *adjective phrase* is a prepositional phrase that modifies a noun or pronoun by telling what kind or which one.

Adjectives	Adjective Phrases
These dessert plates are antiques.	These plates *for dessert* are antiques.
We defeated the *Boston* team.	We defeated the team *from Boston*.

Adverb Phrases   An *adverb phrase* is a prepositional phrase that modifies a verb, adjective, or adverb by pointing out where, when, in what manner, or to what extent.

Adverbs	Adverb Phrases
I packed *hastily*.	I packed *with great haste*.
The child was *irrationally* upset.	The child was upset *beyond reason*.
The band played *somewhat* louder.	The band played louder *to some extent*.

▶ **Exercise 1**   **Identifying Adjective Phrases.**   Underline each adjective phrase in the sentences below. Circle the noun or pronoun it modifies.

EXAMPLE: The maple (tree) in the back yard is (one) of my favorite trees.

1. Everyone in the lab completed the experiment on page 30.
2. The new house at the end of the street is nearly finished.
3. The gate in the fence around the estate was padlocked.
4. Tomorrow, the mayor will announce her plans for the new committee.
5. Exchange students from France are visiting a family in our neighborhood.

▶ **Exercise 2**   **Identifying Adverb Phrases.**   Underline each adverb phrase in the sentence below. Circle the verb, adjective, or adverb it modifies.

EXAMPLE: Without a word to anyone, John (walked) out of the house.

1. The nervous applicant shifted from one foot to the other.
2. Without any hesitation, Frank stepped to the microphone.
3. No unauthorized personnel were permitted close to the launch pad.
4. After the game, we stopped at the diner on Hudson Street.
5. Hundreds of fans were eager for a glimpse of the star.

20.1 Prepositional Phrases (Adjective and Adverb)
• Practice 2

Exercise 1 **Identifying Adjective Phrases.** Underline the adjective phrase or adjective phrases in each sentence. Then draw an arrow from each phrase to the word it modifies.

EXAMPLE: Tom's mother wrote a note for her son's absence.

1. Agatha Christie was a widely read writer of mysteries.

2. The article about Native American folklore is fascinating.

3. My uncle designed the props for the play by Ibsen.

4. Her masterpiece is a book with three parts.

5. A trellis near the door supported the climbing vines.

Exercise 2 **Identifying Adverb Phrases.** Underline the adverb phrase or adverb phrases in each sentence. Then draw an arrow from each phrase to the word it modifies.

EXAMPLE: He quietly rapped upon the door.

1. The Pied Piper lured the children from the village.

2. Calcium is essential for strong bones and teeth.

3. The crab was fairly safe inside its skeleton.

4. After the ceremony, the bride left with the groom.

5. The whale died in silent agony on the beach.

Writing Application **Writing Sentences with Adjective and Adverb Phrases.** Use each prepositional phrase in two sentences, first as an adjective phrase, then as an adverb phrase.

EXAMPLE: about trout fishing

_____ *I read an article about trout fishing.* _____

_____ *I have been thinking about trout fishing all day.* _____

1. on the train   2. before school   3. in the attic   4. in front of the store   5. during the night

1. _____

_____

2. _____

_____

3. _____

_____

4. _____

_____

5. _____

_____

20.1 Appositives and Appositive Phrases
• Practice 1

Appositives   An *appositive* is a noun or pronoun placed next to another noun or pronoun to identify or explain it.

```
┌─────────────────────────────────────────────────────┐
│                   APPOSITIVES                        │
├─────────────────────────────────────────────────────┤
│                                                      │
│   Mistletoe, a parasite, has poisonous berries.      │
│                                                      │
│   The poet Keats studied to become a doctor.         │
│                                                      │
└─────────────────────────────────────────────────────┘
```

Appositive Phrases   An *appositive phrase* is a noun or pronoun with modifiers, placed next to a noun or pronoun to add information and details.

```
┌─────────────────────────────────────────────────────┐
│               APPOSITIVE PHRASES                     │
├─────────────────────────────────────────────────────┤
│                                                      │
│   Her hat, a pillbox covered with feathers, was      │
│   quite sensational.                                 │
│                                                      │
│   Aunt Mary loves both her pets, a full-sized        │
│   poodle and an alley cat.                           │
│                                                      │
└─────────────────────────────────────────────────────┘
```

▷ **Exercise 1**   **Identifying Appositives and Appositive Phrases.**   Underline each appositive or appositive phrase in these sentences. Circle the noun or pronoun it renames.

EXAMPLE: Captain Ahab pursued ⟨Moby Dick⟩ , the great white whale.

1. Bastille Day, July 14, is French Independence Day.
2. Only one person, either Juan or Linda, will get the job.
3. Kory had his standard lunch: tuna fish with lettuce and cheese.
4. The safari stopped at an oasis, a moist, fertile spot in the desert.
5. The attorney handed Jenkins, her faithful clerk, a pile of briefs to file.
6. We all enjoyed ourselves.
7. The class agreed on two captains: Phyllis and Len.
8. Our new neighbors, a young couple from Paris, are quite friendly.
9. The class play will be the comedy Arsenic and Old Lace.
10. All of them, Pete, Sue, and Judy, tried out for parts.

▷ **Exercise 2**   **Writing Sentences with Appositives and Appositive Phrases.**   Turn each pair of sentences into a single sentence by adding one or more appositives or appositive phrases.

EXAMPLE: We served a traditional St. Patrick's Day dinner. It was corned beef and steamed cabbage.
>   *We served a traditional St. Patrick's Day dinner: corned beef and steamed cabbage.*

1. The explorers opened the Northwest Territory. They were Lewis and Clark.

_____

2. Delaware has only three counties. They are Kent, Sussex, and New Castle.

_____

3. My cousin lives in Austin. It is the capital of Texas.

_____

4. A local reporter broke the story. She is Annette Jackson.

_____

5. Both finalists are fine competitors. They are Logan and Bruce.

_____

20.1 Appositives and Appositive Phrases
• Practice 2

▶ **Exercise 1** **Identifying Appositives.** Underline the appositive in each sentence. Then circle the word each appositive renames.

EXAMPLE: The (view), a sunset, was spectacular.

1. Edna discussed her favorite (topic,) food.
2. My (cousin), Phyllis, will spend this summer with us.
3. We thought he would give Cara, a girlfriend, something for Valentine's Day.
4. *Moby Dick* was written by the American (writer) Herman Melville.
5. Our (cat,) a Manx, has free run of the house.
6. The (poem) "Snow Fall" is my favorite.
7. Douglas looks good in his favorite (color,) blue.
8. We remembered one important (item,) a flashlight.
9. She played a woodwind instrument, the clarinet.
10. The (inventor) Frankenstein created a monster.

▶ **Exercise 2** **Identifying Appositive Phrases.** Underline the appositive phrase in each sentence, including any compound appositive phrases. Then circle the word each appositive phrase renames.

EXAMPLE: The (dogs), an old hound and a tiny poodle, were very friendly.

1. Tammy learned a new safety measure, a technique for saving people from choking.
2. The bobcat, an endangered species, has been hunted as a pest in the East.
3. At the circus, the clown rode a dromedary, a one-humped camel, rapidly around the ring.
4. He was proud of owning his first car, an old jalopy.
5. She named Don Jones chairman, a well-deserved title.
6. I will tell you, my good friend, an intriguing story.
7. Herb will read anything: old matchbooks, junk mail, or the backs of cereal boxes.
8. Marsha gave the baby two stuffed animals: a white, woolly lamb and a huggable teddy bear.
9. My family took our guests to a French restaurant, one of the best places in the city.
10. Bill excelled in two outdoor sports, cross-country skiing and ice hockey.

▶ **Writing Application** **Using Appositives and Appositive Phrases.** On another piece of paper, write each pair of sentences as a single sentence with an appositive or appositive phrase.

EXAMPLE: They lived in India. India is a huge country.
 _____ They lived in India, a huge country. _____

1. The ostrich is a native of Africa and parts of Asia. The ostrich is the largest of all birds.
2. Mrs. Gordon had a piano in her parlor. Her parlor was a room for special guests.
3. The restaurant serves lobster in a delicious Newburg sauce. Newburg sauce is a creamy sauce made with butter and wine.
4. Marjorie is one of the most interesting people I know. She is a gourmet, an expert ventriloquist, and a very good poet.
5. Donny's father is a neurologist. He is a specialist on the nervous system.

20.1 Participles and Participial Phrases
(Participles, Verb or Participle?) • Practice 1

Participles   A *participle* is a form of a verb that can act as an adjective.

Present Participles	Past Participles
The runner, *panting*, waved to the *cheering* spectators.	The *broken* vase can be repaired by an *experienced* potter.

Verb or Participle?   A *verb form* shows an action or condition. A *participle* acting as an adjective modifies a noun or a pronoun.

Verbs	Participles
The barometer is *falling*.	The *falling* barometer indicated a change.
Gunther *trained* the lion.	The *trained* lion went through the hoop.

▶ **Exercise 1**   **Identifying Participles.**   Underline the participle in each sentence and circle the word it modifies. On the line at the right, write *present* or *past* to tell which kind it is.

EXAMPLE: Jessica is a spoiled (child) .   *past*

1. Bob had a splint on his broken (finger)   *past*
2. The sitter finally quieted the crying (baby.)   *present*
3. The crowd applauded the governor's stirring (speech)   *present*
4. We put the injured (bird) in a shoe box.   *past*
5. I have never tried that frozen (dessert.)   *past*
6. Please send a copy to the acting (chairman.)   *present*
7. The lifeguard tried to save the drowning (man.)   *present*
8. Have you already applied for a building (permit?)   *present*
9. Louise regretted her broken (promise.)   *past*
10. The committee approved the revised (proposal.)   *past*

▶ **Exercise 2**   **Distinguishing Between Verbs and Participles.**   On the line at the right, write whether each underlined word is a *verb* or a *participle*.

EXAMPLE: My favorite act was the <u>dancing</u> bear.   *participle*

1. That noise is <u>disturbing</u> the neighbors.   *verb*
2. I had a <u>disturbing</u> dream last night.   *participle*
3. Can you repair this <u>torn</u> page?   *participle*
4. Someone has <u>torn</u> all the coupons out of this magazine.   *verb*
5. The <u>opening</u> chapter got off to a slow start.   *participle*
6. Ron's play will be <u>opening</u> next week.   *verb*
7. Are you <u>laughing</u> at me?   *verb*
8. The <u>laughing</u> child got hiccups.   *participle*
9. Please put these <u>cut</u> flowers in some water.   *participle*
10. I <u>cut</u> my finger on a jagged rock along the path.   *verb*

20.1 Participles and Participial Phrases
(Participles, Verb or Participle?) • Practice 2

▶ **Exercise 1** **Identifying Present and Past Participles.** Underline the participle in each sentence. Then label each as *present* or *past*.

EXAMPLE: The <u>returning</u> players had a story to tell. _____*present*_____

1. Mrs. Jefferson's fractured hip is very painful. _____*past*_____
2. A fluttering white flag appeared in the distance. _____*present*_____
3. Water surged over the banks of the swollen river. _____*past*_____
4. This arsonist has an established pattern for fires. _____*past*_____
5. Drizzling rain kept us all in the house. _____*present*_____
6. We sat and listened to the pounding waves and the cry of seagulls. _____*present*_____
7. The handyman left splattered paint all over the floor. _____*past*_____
8. Lisping, the child told us about the Tooth Fairy. _____*present*_____
9. During the storm a broken branch fell onto the roof of our house. _____*past*_____
10. Disgusted, his mother glowered at the mess. _____*past*_____
11. At closing time, all the customers were asked to leave. _____*present*_____
12. With a worried look, Sid watched Celeste start the car. _____*past*_____
13. Corinne greeted her cousin with a welcoming smile. _____*present*_____
14. The doctor wrapped Joan's broken arm in plaster. _____*past*_____
15. Paul's speaking voice is louder than that of most people. _____*present*_____
16. The job applicant's tattered clothes did not make a good impression. _____*past*_____
17. The acting president stepped down when Herman was elected. _____*present*_____
18. Amy enjoyed listening to the singing birds outside her window. _____*present*_____
19. The teacher returned the corrected papers to the students. _____*past*_____
20. The clerk filed the signed documents in a safe place. _____*past*_____

▶ **Exercise 2** **Distinguishing Between Verbs and Participles.** Identify each underlined word as a *verb* or *participle*. If the word is a participle, write the word it modifies.

EXAMPLE: The 1984 Olympics added an <u>exciting</u> new event.

_____*participle   event*_____

(1) In the Los Angeles Memorial Coliseum, 77,000 people <u>waited</u>. (2) Through the streets, <u>tired</u> runners raced toward the Coliseum. (3) The <u>cheering</u> crowd rose as Joan Benoit, a member of the United States Olympic team, entered. (4) She ran around the track easily and <u>crossed</u> the finish line. (5) <u>Smiling</u>, Joan waved to the spectators as they cheered her. (6) About four months before the race, Joan <u>underwent</u> surgery on her right knee. (7) <u>Training</u>, she had wondered whether or not she would be able to <u>compete</u>. (8) When the race was over, Joan <u>learned</u> that she had run the third-fastest marathon ever run by a woman. (9) She ran the 26 miles and 385 yards of the <u>exhausting</u> race in 2 hours, 24 minutes, and 52 seconds. (10) <u>Pleased</u>, Joan accepted her gold medal as the winner of the first women's marathon in Olympic history.

1. _____V_____   6. _____✓_____
2. __P – runners__   7. __P – she__
3. __P – crowd__   8. _____
4. _____V_____   9. __P – race__
5. __P – Joan__   10. __P – Joan__

20.1 Participles and Participial Phrases
(Participial Phrases) • Practice 1

Participial Phrases A *participial phrase* is a participle modified by an adverb or adverb phrase or accompanied by a complement. The entire phrase acts as an adjective.

PARTICIPIAL PHRASES
The woman *playing the harp* is my aunt.
Feeling calmer, the driver explained what had happened.
The clerk *standing behind the counter* was helpful.
The person *coming out now* will do a solo.
Shaking hands warmly, the two candidates had made up their differences.

▶ **Exercise 1** **Recognizing Participial Phrases.** Underline the participial phrase in each sentence. Then circle the word it modifies.

EXAMPLE: This (bread), made without preservatives, is delicious.

1. The family visiting the Jacksons once lived on this street.
2. A letter signed by Napoleon was found among the papers.
3. Feeling uneasy, the baby sitter checked all the locks.
4. Every pie sold at the farm store is baked on the premises.
5. Bought by an eccentric millionaire, the antique car will never run again.
6. Sylvia saw Mike standing outside the library.
7. Anyone having a pet is welcome to enter it in the show.
8. Confused by the directions, the contestant failed to answer.
9. That large plant hanging from the ceiling is a Boston fern.
10. The child, lost in the department store, became panicky.

▶ **Exercise 2** **Writing Sentences with Participial Phrases.** Turn each pair of sentences into a single sentence with a participial phrase.

EXAMPLE: The enlargement was made from the negative. It was clearer than the original.

The enlargement made from the negative was clearer than the original.

1. The person is looking in the window. It is our neighbor.
   The person looking in the window is our neighbor

2. The storm is coming from the west. It is bringing precipitation.
   The storm coming from the west is bringing prec.

3. Early sketches were made by that painter. They have become valuable.
   Early sketches made by that painter have become valuable

4. The wallet was found on the street. It had no identification in it.
   The wallet found on the street had no ident. in it

5. Food was served at the party. We all enjoyed the food.
   We enjoyed all the food served at the party

20.1 Participles and Participial Phrases
(Participial Phrases, Essential or Nonessential?)
• Practice 2

Essentials and Nonessential Phrases Participial phrases that can be removed without altering the basic meaning of the sentence are *nonessential*. Participial phrases that cannot be removed without altering the sentence meaning are *essential*.

▶ **Exercise 1** **Recognizing Participial Phrases.** Underline the participial phrase in each sentence. Then, circle the word the participial phrase modifies. Label the phrase as *nonessential* or *essential*.

EXAMPLE: The (box) wrapped in orange is for you. _____*essential*_____

1. Andrea, waking from a dream, cried fearfully. _____
2. Slumped over a chair, I could think only of sleep. _____
3. The boat, making large waves, overturned our canoe. _____
4. She picked up debris thrown by a careless motorist. _____
5. Feeling jaunty in his borrowed tuxedo, Barney sauntered into the room. _____
6. We stared at the horizon, broken only by sails. _____
7. As Zack fell, he grabbed a branch jutting out from the cliff. _____
8. Shivering in anticipation, I could hardly wait for the conclusion to Poe's "The Pit and the Pendulum." _____
9. She ordered a plate piled high with flapjacks. _____
10. She saw in the mirror a face streaked with tears. _____
11. The woman standing at the end of the line is my cousin Sylvie. _____
12. Tyler, disappointed by Dana's refusal, felt abandoned. _____
13. Ignored by the fans, the singer decided to give up on her career. _____
14. The people fleeing the area are trying to escape a fire. _____
15. The path, worn smooth by millions of feet, leads to a spectacular view. _____
16. Exhausted by her effort, Myra slept for twelve hours. _____
17. The man working at that desk rarely takes a break. _____
18. Barry, eating at the counter, looked up to see Susan. _____
19. Grace, being interviewed for a job, wore a blue suit. _____
20. The bird singing loudly on that branch is a song sparrow. _____

▶ **Exercise 2** **Using Participial Phrases to Combine Sentences.** Turn each pair of sentences into a single sentence with a participial phrase.

EXAMPLE: The orange grove stretches to the horizon. It produces thousands of oranges.
_____*The orange grove stretching to the horizon produces thousands of oranges.*_____

1. The girls on the stage are Laurel, Hillary, and Jamie. They are practicing some new dance steps.

   _____

2. The boy is headed toward the park. He is walking his dog.

   _____

3. The artist is my cousin. He is sketching scenes of children at play.

   _____

4. The Komodo dragon's skin is marked with the scars of many battles. It is wrinkled with age.

   _____

5. The radio station is located in Sacramento. It transmits this entertaining program.

   _____

20.1 Participles and Participial Phrases
(Nominative Absolutes) • Practice 1

Nominative Absolutes   A *nominative absolute* is a noun or pronoun followed by a participle or participial phrase that functions independently of the rest of the sentence.

NOMINATIVE ABSOLUTES
Two weeks having gone by, our vacation was over. (time)
My grandmother being ill, we changed our plans. (reason)
The tide having just gone out, we got plenty of clams. (circumstance)
The power [being] off, we read by candlelight. (elliptical)

Exercise 1   **Recognizing Nominative Absolutes.**   Underline the nominative absolute in each sentence.

EXAMPLE: The players headed for the locker room, <u>the game over</u>.

1. The band continuing to play, diners stayed on to dance.
2. Hours having passed without any word, the family began to worry.
3. The patient recovering nicely, the doctor removed the "no visitors" order.
4. Janet took the exam orally, her right hand broken.
5. The team has lost three straight games, their best players injured.
6. Their chores completed, the children ran outside to play.
7. The train having broken down, commuters were bused to the next stop.
8. The buffet table looking so tempting, Sam went back for thirds.
9. Their argument resolved, the two friends went off arm in arm.
10. The air conditioning not working, the office closed at noon.

Exercise 2   **Writing Sentences with Nominative Absolutes.**   Rewrite each sentence below, adding a nominative absolute that gives the time, reason, or circumstance for the main statement.

EXAMPLE: The committee postponed the street fair.

    <u>*The steady rain continuing, the committee postponed the street fair.*</u>

1. The police put up no-parking signs along the main street.

_____

2. The room looked very festive.

_____

3. Lucy was chilly at the picnic.

_____

4. We were able to borrow a bike for Kenny.

_____

5. The speaker was finally able to begin.

_____

20.1 Participles and Participial Phrases
(Nominative Absolutes) • Practice 2

▶ **Exercise 1** **Recognizing Nominative Absolutes.**   Underline the nominative absolute in each sentence.

EXAMPLE: The play having ended, we left.

1. Her smile vanishing from her face, Julia listened in stunned silence.
2. Six huskies pulled the sled, its runners skimming over the ice.
3. The furnace broken, we huddled under blankets throughout the cold night.
4. Several minutes having gone by, the bank teller finally pushed the alarm button.
5. Roger carefully whittled a stick, his dog Briar lying at his feet.
6. A bonnet tied around her head, Lisa resembled a Puritan woman.
7. Candles and flowers on every table, the room looked inviting.
8. Several delays being unavoidable, our guests finally departed.
9. Midnight striking, she hurried down the steps toward her carriage.
10. His glasses at home, Mr. Owens squinted at the paper with bleary eyes.
11. Night having fallen, the rangers ordered everyone out of the park.
12. Doris received the highest scores, her performance having been flawless.
13. My homework completed, I played some board games with Frances.
14. Her ankle having been sprained, Katie had to forfeit the race.
15. Hector headed to the locker room, his exercise routine over.
16. Her veil arranged beautifully, the bride made her entrance.
17. Its head caught in the pet door, the cat whined loudly.
18. We all retreated to the house, our arms covered with mosquito bites.
19. The air conditioner broken, we decided to go to a movie that hot afternoon.
20. Spring coming nearer, the air smelled fresh.

▶ **Writing Application**   **Writing Sentences with Participial Phrases.**   Use the following instructions to write sentences with participial phrases.

1. Use *tell* as a present participle.

   _____

2. Use *cook* as a past participle.

   _____

3. Use *toss* as a past participle.

   _____

4. Use *work* as a present participle.

   _____

5. Use *having left* in a nominative absolute.

   _____

Name _____ Date _____

20.1 Gerunds and Gerund Phrases (Gerunds; Verb, Participle, or Gerund?) • Practice 1

Gerunds A *gerund* is a form of a verb that acts as a noun.

GERUNDS
Subject: *Jogging* is a popular exercise.
Direct Object: That device makes *driving* safer.
Indirect Object: Ellen gives *studying* her undivided attention.
Predicate Nominative: Quentin's first love is *swimming*.
Object of a Preposition: The guests grew tired of *waiting*.
Appositive: Kathy is dedicated to her profession, *teaching*.

Verb, Participle or Gerund? Words ending in *-ing* that act as nouns are gerunds. They do not show an action, nor do they act as adjectives.

Verb	Participle	Gerund
Dad is *cooking* fish.	He took *cooking* lessons.	He enjoys *cooking*.

Exercise 1 **Recognizing Gerunds.** Underline the gerund in each sentence. Then identify the use of each gerund, using one of these labels: *S* (subject), *DO* (direct object), *IO* (indirect object), *PN* (predicate nominative), *OP* (object of a preposition), or *APP* (appositive).

EXAMPLE: Mrs. Hill thanked us for helping. ___OP___

1. Fishing can be a relaxing pastime. ___S___
2. On rainy days, Andrew enjoys coloring. ___DO___
3. Erica is afraid of flying. ___OP___
4. Losing is never a happy experience. ___S___
5. The teacher accused Gail of cheating. ___OP___
6. We looked forward to the main event, bowling. ___APP___
7. Pruning is important to the health of trees and shrubs. ___S___
8. Les's favorite sport, skiing, is an expensive interest. ___APP___
9. Marge gave volunteering an important role in her life. ___IO___
10. Hank has shown no aptitude for drawing. ___OP___

Exercise 2 **Recognizing Verbs, Participles, and Gerunds.** Write *V*, *P*, or *G* to indicate whether the underlined word in each sentence is a *verb*, a *participle*, or a *gerund*.

EXAMPLE: The team is hoping for a win. ___V___

1. Ed never stopped hoping. ___G___
2. The gravy needs stirring. ___G___
3. Cal gave a stirring speech. ___P___
4. I was stirring the stew. ___V___
5. I have been shopping for new shoes. ___V___
6. Bruno hates shopping. ___G___
7. The shopping trip lasted all day. ___P___
8. Everyone was singing daily. ___V___
9. Jo practices singing daily. ___G___
10. Her singing teacher gives her great encouragement. ___P___

© Prentice-Hall, Inc.

20.1 Gerunds and Gerund Phrases (Gerunds; Verb, Participle, or Gerund?) • Practice 2

▶ **Exercise 1** **Identifying Gerunds.** Underline the gerund in each sentence. Label each one as a *subject, direct object, indirect object, predicate nominative, object of a preposition,* or *appositive.*

EXAMPLE: She gave skiing her best effort. _____*indirect object*_____

1. Gardening can be enjoyable and profitable. _____ S _____
2. The school offered classes in weaving. _____ OP _____
3. To arrive on time for his appointment, Fred started running. _____ DO _____
4. The man's crime was counterfeiting. _____ PN _____
5. Milking was one of Wilbur's chores. _____ S _____
6. Denise's hobby, sky diving, is a thrilling one. _____ APP _____
7. Esther's favorite occupation, eavesdropping, can be most unpleasant. _____ APP _____
8. My father enjoys the art of fencing. _____ OP _____
9. Jogging can be very satisfying. _____ S _____
10. With this machine, vacuuming seems easy. _____ S _____
11. Moving can be an enjoyable experience. _____ S _____
12. Maurice took his pogo stick outside and started hopping. _____ DO _____
13. Lunch for Wesley meant eating an entire sub sandwich. _____ PN _____
14. The last thing on Gene's mind was quitting. _____ PN _____
15. Winning is not the only goal of an athlete. _____ S _____
16. Jackie really enjoys exercising. _____ DO _____
17. Her new skill, walking, seemed to give the baby great pleasure. _____ APP. _____
18. Chris never gave practicing a moment of his time. _____ IO _____
19. The thought of leaving made Melissa feel sad. _____ OP _____
20. The cat's favorite activity, napping, took up most of the day. _____ APP _____

▶ **Exercise 2** **Distinguishing Between Verbs, Participles, and Gerunds.** Identify each underlined word as a *verb, participle,* or *gerund.*

EXAMPLE: They are quitting early today. _____*verb*_____

1. Do we have any wrapping paper left? _____ P _____
2. The detective was wrapping up the case. _____ V _____
3. Wrapping the gifts took longer than expected. _____ G _____
4. Ann must have been dreaming about her future. _____ V _____
5. The dreaming boy stared absently out the window. _____ P _____
6. Rarely do I remember dreaming. _____ G _____
7. Many athletes use running as a means of exercise. _____ G _____
8. Our summer cabin has running water in the kitchen. _____ P _____
9. Shopping can become tiresome after a few hours. _____ G _____
10. Lou is shopping for a new trenchcoat. _____ V _____

20.1 Gerunds and Gerund Phrases (Gerund Phrases) • Practice 1

Gerund Phrases   A *gerund phrase* is a gerund with modifiers or a complement, all acting together as a noun. In the chart, notice the words before the gerunds in the second and third examples. Remember that the possessive form of a noun or pronoun is used before a gerund.

GERUND PHRASES

S
Sleeping late is a luxury to many people.
 	
                                                                 PN
By far the biggest inconvenience was *the store's closing early.*
                                DO
Ann encouraged *our staying so long.*
                                OP
The guide helped by *giving us directions.*

▶ **Exercise 1**   **Recognizing Gerund Phrases.**   Underline the gerund phrase in each sentence. Then tell whether each phrase is acting as a subject, predicate nominative, direct object, or object of a preposition.

EXAMPLE: The runner started for home without tagging third base. ___*OP*___

1. At the age of five, Pam began learning French. _____

2. My little brother's latest skill is counting to ten. _____

3. Training long hours is not unusual for an athlete. _____

4. Wilma kept changing her mind about the color for the walls. _____

5. Working for the mayor's reelection has been a learning experience. _____

6. Mom appreciated our working so hard. _____

7. The guard prevented us from entering the house. _____

8. The hardest part was choosing a good topic. _____

9. We still have hope of finding the buried treasure. _____

10. Marci became a superb pianist by practicing hard. _____

▶ **Exercise 2**   **Writing Nouns and Pronouns Before Gerunds.**   Fill in each blank with the correct word form from the parentheses at the right.

EXAMPLE: ___*Your*___ helping us out made the job easier. (You, Your)

1. The team celebrated _____ winning the championship. (they, their, them)

2. _____ playing of that piece was excellent. (Suzi, Suzi's)

3. The audience applauded _____ singing of the duet. (we, our, us)

4. _____ crying so long became annoying. (He, His, Him)

5. _____ rising so early surprised my roommates. (I, My, Me)

6. _____ becoming a dentist was a goal for years. (She, Her)

7. _____ decorating the gym was a bad idea. (They, Their, Them)

8. We were amazed at _____ diving off the high board. (he, his, him)

9. The guests impatiently awaited _____ carving of the turkey. (Ken, Ken's)

10. _____ buying the same outfit is a strange coincidence. (You, Your)

20.1 Gerunds and Gerund Phrases (Gerund Phrases) • Practice 2

▶ **Exercise 1** **Identifying Gerund Phrases.** Underline the gerund phrase or gerund phrases in each sentence. Label each one as a *subject, direct object, predicate nominative, object of a preposition,* or *appositive.*

EXAMPLE: Swimming before dawn was forbidden. ____*subject*____

1. She is good at remembering trivia. _____

2. The most amusing event, catching a greased pig, was the highlight of the fair. _____

3. As a child, his household tasks were setting the table before dinner and washing the dishes afterwards. _____

4. Caring for pets is a good way of earning money. _____

5. During the summer, Hal taught deep-sea diving and horseback riding. _____

6. Drying fruits and vegetables for winter use is good for cutting down expenses. _____

7. Morris's worst habits are complaining about everyone's faults and worrying unceasingly. _____

8. After the football game was over, we enjoyed trading stories. _____

9. To me, summer, fall, and winter are just times for mowing grass, raking leaves, and shoveling snow. _____

10. Hoarding money under the mattress is not the best way to beat inflation. _____

11. Betty is very good at baking cakes. _____

12. Our most important job, passing this class, will take some effort. _____

13. Talking your problems over with your friends can be therapeutic. _____

14. Her method of choosing vegetables was squeezing them first. _____

15. The librarian forbids talking in the study areas. _____

▶ **Writing Application** **Writing Sentences with Gerund Phrases.** Use the following instructions to write sentences with gerund phrases. Then, underline the gerund phrase in each.

1. Use *cooking* as a direct object.

   _____

2. Use *preparing* as a predicate nominative.

   _____

3. Use *explaining* as the object of a preposition.

   _____

4. Use *traveling* as a subject.

   _____

5. Use *directing* as a predicate nominative.

   _____

20.1 Infinitives and Infinitive Phrases (Infinitives, Prepositional Phrase or Infinitive?) • Practice 1

Infinitives An *infinitive* is a form of a verb that generally appears with the word *to* and acts as a noun, adjective, or adverb.

INFINITIVES
Subject: To forgive takes understanding and generosity.
Direct Object: Warren offered *to help.*
Predicate Nominative: The team's desire was *to win.*
Object of a Preposition: We had no choice but *to follow.*
Appositive: Nina has one great desire, *to travel.*
Adjective: I am looking for something *to read.*
Adverb: This tool is easy *to use.*

Prepositional Phrase or Infinitive? A prepositional phrase always ends with a noun or pronoun. An infinitive always ends with a verb.

Prepositional Phrase	Infinitive
We went *to Mexico* for vacation.	Is this a good place *to stand?*

> **Exercise 1** **Identifying Infinitives.** Underline the infinitive in each sentence. Then tell whether it is being used as a *noun*, an *adjective*, or an *adverb*.

EXAMPLE: From here, the speaker is hard to hear. _____adverb_____

1. Mrs. Link's advice was hard to accept. _____adverb_____
2. Tom's willingness to work impressed his employer. _____adjective_____
3. Is the Chinese language difficult to learn? _____adverb_____
4. That plan is not likely to succeed. _____adverb_____
5. New foods are often interesting to try. _____noun adverb_____
6. Daedalus's great dream was to fly. _____adjective noun_____
7. Hockey is an exciting sport to watch. _____adjective_____
8. Hal's desire to rule has become an obsession. _____adjective_____
9. In spite of the noise and confusion, we tried to listen. _____noun_____
10. The band finally began to play. _____noun_____

> **Exercise 2** **Distinguishing Between Prepositional Phrases and Infinitives.** Write *PP* (prepositional phrase) or *INF* (infinitive) to describe each underlined group of words.

EXAMPLE: Dad went to the market. _____PP_____

1. Is this the road to take? ___INF___
2. Is this the road to town? ___PP___
3. Fran walks to school. ___PP___
4. Mom walks to exercise. ___INF___
5. Just listen to this. ___PP___

6. Pam is willing to learn. ___INF___
7. Who is the one to select? ___INF___
8. Hand this to Kerry. ___PP___
9. This is important to me. ___PP___
10. This is important to know. ___INF___

20.1 Infinitives and Infinitive Phrases (Infinitives, Prepositional Phrase or Infinitive?) • Practice 2

> **Exercise 1** **Identifying Infinitives.** Underline the infinitive in each sentence. Then, label each as a *subject, direct object, predicate nominative, object of a preposition, appositive, adjective,* or *adverb.*

EXAMPLE: Her goal is to sing. ___*predicate nominative*___

1. To fantasize was his only way out of a dreary life. _____
2. We were reluctant to leave. _____
3. Worried by my decision, I decided to reconsider. _____
4. Seth had only one alternative—to flee. _____
5. The teacher assigned us too many pages to read. _____
6. Our best tactic is to watch. _____
7. To build was the architect's fondest dream. _____
8. To escape, the cat clawed at the top of the box. _____
9. Hated by the people, the king was about to abdicate. _____
10. They produced one of the first airplanes to fly. _____
11. To teach was Alicia's goal in life. _____
12. Nobody wanted to participate. _____
13. Hoping for first prize, Donald began to paint. _____
14. Laura had one great ambition, to dance. _____
15. Before graduating, Emma has three more classes to take. _____

> **Exercise 2** **Distinguishing Between Prepositional Phrases and Infinitives.** Underline the infinitive or the prepositional phrase beginning with *to* in each sentence. Then label each as a *prepositional phrase* or *infinitive.*

EXAMPLE: When I am in New York, I like to shop. ___*infinitive*___

1. At the outdoor market, my grandmother likes to bargain. _____
2. Would you try to explain? _____
3. Give an explanation to Glenn. _____
4. To believe took considerable faith. _____
5. Lindsey wrote letters to friends. _____
6. After working so hard, he wanted to rest. _____
7. Our trip to China was filled with surprises. _____
8. Baxter's gift to me was too extravagant. _____
9. When do you plan to graduate? _____
10. On Vicky's way to town, she had a flat tire. _____
11. Although he may fail, James wants to try. _____
12. Jessie went to the mountains this weekend. _____
13. To understand, you must read the book. _____
14. While Margie was writing to her sister, the computer crashed. _____
15. It is not easy to learn this difficult song. _____

20.1 Infinitives and Infinitive Phrases (Infinitive Phrases) • Practice 1

Infinitive Phrases An *infinitive phrase* is an infinitive with modifiers, complements, or a subject, all acting together as a single part of speech.

INFINITIVE PHRASES
DO
We offered *to give them a hand.*
DO
Have June *tell them the news.*
DO
No one dared *speak above a whisper.*
S
To sit still was hard for the child.

Notice that the infinitives in the second and third examples do not include the word *to.* When an infinitive or infinitive phrase is used as the direct object of certain verbs, *to* is often omitted.

▶ Exercise 1 **Recognizing Infinitive Phrases.** Underline the infinitive phrase in each sentence below. Then write the part of speech as it is used: *noun, adjective,* or *adverb.*

EXAMPLE: The candidate's promise, to lower taxes, won her the election. _____*noun*_____

1. The coach's example is one to take seriously. ____adjective____
2. We all made an effort to work harder. ____~~adverb~~ adjective____
3. The contest requires all entries to be mailed by Thursday. ____~~noun~~ adjective____
4. The players were eager to try on their new uniforms. ____~~noun~~ adverb____
5. The director asked Mindy to audition for the part. ____noun____
6. The children did not want to wait till dinnertime. ____~~adjective~~ noun____
7. The innkeeper provided us with a place to spend the night. ____~~noun~~ adjective____
8. This is the best place to find that game. ____~~noun~~ adjective____
9. All of us will have to sell some of these tickets. ____noun____
10. Vera's parents encouraged her to apply for the job. ____noun____

▶ Exercise 2 **More Work with Infinitive Phrases.** Underline the infinitive phrase in each sentence. On the line at the right, write the infinitive itself. If *to* has been omitted, write it in parentheses.

EXAMPLE: Let someone else have a turn. _____(to) have_____

1. We saw that team win the World Series. ____to win____
2. The guide offered to show us an alternate route. ____to show____
3. I have never heard him play that concerto before. ____to play____
4. We watched the pitcher practice before the game. ____to practice____
5. We invited our cousins to come for the weekend. ____to come____
6. No one would dare disagree with the President in public. ____to disagree____
7. Can't we make you stay for dinner? ____to stay____
8. Please bring an inexpensive, humorous gift. ____to bring____
9. The candidate's family encouraged her to run again. ____to encourage____
10. Let's take a break from raking these leaves. ____to take____

20.1 Infinitives and Infinitive Phrases (Infinitive Phrases) • Practice 2

▶ **Exercise 1** **Identifying Infinitive Phrases.** Underline the infinitive phrase or infinitive phrases in each sentence. Label each one as a *subject, direct object, predicate nominative, object of a preposition, appositive, adjective,* or *adverb.*

EXAMPLE: I have an assignment to finish before tomorrow. ___*adjective*___

1. To describe the hockey game in an understandable manner required gestures. _____
2. The birdwatcher's ambition was to see one hundred different species during one weekend. _____
3. My friends and I went to see the exhibit on Indian art and to gather material for our reports. _____
4. Huck and Tom swore to keep the secret about Injun Joe. _____
5. To inhale these fumes is to die instantly. _____
6. With no money to pay our bill, we had no choice except to wash dishes. _____
7. To heed his warning was to be prepared for anything. _____
8. Ray hopes to become a veterinarian. _____
9. They made plans to meet on Friday night. _____
10. Since we were about to sink in the leaky boat, the only answer was to bail it out. _____
11. To visit every state was the purpose of the trip. _____
12. The gift Tony wanted was to go snowboarding for two days straight. _____
13. Don and Marsha decided to shop at the farmer's market and to create a fresh meal for their friends. _____
14. Joe asked Marilyn to attend the winter dance with him. _____
15. To see the waterfall is to be overwhelmed by its beauty. _____
16. Darlene wants to improve her relationship with her sister. _____
17. We have a date to have brunch on Sunday. _____
18. Inez tried to be kind to the stray dog, but it ran away. _____
19. After the quarterback was injured, the coach decided to give Al a chance. _____
20. After the move, Sally had fifty boxes of books to unpack immediately. _____

▶ **Writing Application** **Writing Sentences with Infinitive Phrases.** Use the following instructions to write sentences with infinitive phrases. Then underline each infinitive phrase.

1. Use *to erase* as a subject.

_____

2. Use *to draw* as a predicate nominative.

_____

3. Use *to read* as an adjective.

_____

4. Use *to show* as a direct object.

_____

5. Use *to begin* as the object of a preposition.

_____

20.2 Adjective Clauses • Practice 1

A *clause* is a group of words with its own subject and verb. An *independent clause* can stand by itself as a complete sentence. A *subordinate clause* can only be part of a sentence.

The Adjective Clause   An *adjective clause* is a subordinate clause that modifies a noun or pronoun by telling what kind or which one. Adjective clauses begin with relative pronouns or relative adverbs.

ADJECTIVE CLAUSES
The woman who made the speech is not, herself, a candidate.
He is a performer whose work I always enjoy.

Introductory Words   Relative pronouns connect adjective clauses to the words they modify. They also play a role within their own clauses, as shown in the chart. Relative adverbs connect adjective clauses to the words they modify and act as adverbs within the clauses. Note in the second example that an introductory word may be understood.

USES OF INTRODUCTORY WORDS
The movie *that* is playing now is a comedy. (subject)
The movie *(that)* we saw last night was a documentary. (direct object)
The movie *in* which *Tony appeared* was a hit. (object of a preposition)
He is an actor whose *work I admire.* (adjective)
I remember the day when *they began filming.* (adverb)

▶ **Exercise 1**   **Recognizing Adjective Clauses.**   Underline the adjective clause in each sentence. Circle the word it modifies.

EXAMPLE: Grace is the (person) I met at Reggie's party. _____

1. The house where John F. Kennedy was born is now a museum. _____

2. This soup has a spice that I can't identify. _____

3. Mom is the one for whom I left the message. _____

4. Len is the one whose mother is the district attorney. _____

5. Ohio is a state that cherishes football. _____

6. Mr. Paulson is the teacher who inspired me to study chemistry. _____

7. Wendy is someone I have known since kindergarten. _____

8. Emily Dickinson is a poet whose work was once ignored. _____

9. A calculator is something Dad will surely like. _____

10. Where is the box in which I keep my change? _____

▶ **Exercise 2**   **Recognizing the Use of Introductory Words.**   On the line at the right of each sentence in Exercise 1, write the introductory word and its use in the clause.

EXAMPLE: Grace is the (person) I met at Reggie's party. ___*(that) direct object*___

20.2 Adjective Clauses • Practice 2

▶ Exercise 1 **Identifying Adjective Clauses and the Words They Modify.** Underline the adjective clause in each sentence. Then, circle the word the adjective clause modifies. Finally, label the clause as *nonessential* or *essential*. Remember that an *essential clause* cannot be removed without altering sentence meaning.

EXAMPLE: (James), who plays the flute, joined our band. ____nonessential____

1. The student whom Mr. Stein chose was first in her class. _____

2. Is this the year when the planets will align? _____

3. Henry VIII was a king whose many wives fared badly. _____

4. Those were the years that I remember best. _____

5. Our school play, which lasted two hours, was enjoyed by everyone. _____

6. Books that deal with current events in an exciting way often become
   bestsellers. _____

7. My father works in an office where everyone helps each other. _____

8. People still remember June's last letter, which arrived twenty years
   ago. _____

9. The position that Jackie wanted was already filled. _____

10. The man whose playing you admired is an internationally recognized chess
    champion. _____

▶ Exercise 2 **Recognizing the Uses of Relative Pronouns and Relative Adverbs.** Underline the adjective clause in each sentence and circle the relative pronoun or relative adverb. Then label the use of the circled word as *subject, direct object, object of a preposition, adjective,* or *adverb.*

EXAMPLE: Gina, (who) likes to travel, is a flight attendant. ____subject____

1. We look forward to a weekend when we can rest. _____

2. A sales representative whose approach is too insistent may anger potential
   customers. _____

3. The person with whom you spoke is my father. _____

4. In the time since Maria returned, she has talked only about her
   trip. _____

5. My friend whom you admired liked you also. _____

6. The play featured too many actors who had not learned their lines. _____

7. In the centuries before the car was invented, people relied on horses for
   transportation. _____

8. A historian who knows the facts can compare the past with the probable
   future. _____

9. Physics is a subject about which I know nothing. _____

10. The first person on the moon walked on land where no one had ever walked
    before. _____

20.2 Adverb Clauses • Practice 1

The Adverb Clause Subordinate adverb clauses modify verbs, adjectives, adverbs, or verbals by telling *where, when, in what manner, to what extent, under what condition,* or *why.* All adverb clauses begin with subordinating conjunctions.

SUBORDINATING CONJUNCTIONS		
after	even	unless
although	though	until
as	if	when
as if	in order	whenever
as long	that	where
as	since	wherever
because	so that	while
before	than	
	though	

ADVERB CLAUSES
When friends sleep over, we don't usually sleep very much.
Anita looks better *than I have ever seen her look before.*
Moving *wherever there was work,* the migrant family had no permanent home.

Elliptical Adverb Clauses An elliptical clause is one in which the verb or subject and verb are understood, but not actually stated.

ELLIPTICAL ADVERB CLAUSES
Verb Understood: Peter was in a bigger hurry *than I [was].*
Subject and Verb Understood: I like apple pie better *than [I like] peach.*

▶ **Exercise 1** **Identifying Adverb Clauses.** Underline the adverb clause in each sentence. Then circle the subordinating conjunction.

EXAMPLE: We enjoyed the picnic (until) the storm began.

1. My parents will be happy if we are home by eleven.
2. We planted the garden where it would get the most sun.
3. Dad volunteers at the hospital whenever he has time.
4. After the butter has melted, add the chopped vegetables.
5. Sally will help if you ask her.

▶ **Exercise 2** **Identifying Elliptical Clauses.** Underline the adverb clause in each sentence. If the clause is elliptical, write *elliptical* in the space provided. If it is not elliptical, leave the space blank.

EXAMPLE: Is everyone as excited as you? ____*elliptical*____

1. While sick, Fran read several books a day. _____
2. Each applicant was better qualified than the one before. _____
3. Dan is the same age as Ben. _____
4. The couch was delivered today, as the clerk had promised. _____
5. I like swimming better than jogging. _____

20.2 Adverb Clauses • Practice 2

Exercise 1 **Identifying Adverb Clauses and the Words They Modify.** Underline the adverb clause in each sentence. Then circle the word or words each adverb clause modifies.

EXAMPLE: While you were out, someone (telephoned) you.

1. Before she gave the assignment, Miss Martin explained the method for review.
2. Mark looks gloomy whenever that topic is discussed.
3. After the sun goes down, the temperature drops several degrees.
4. We wanted to stop so that we could enjoy the scenery.
5. The Petersons have lived in Seattle since I was young.

Exercise 2 **Recognizing Elliptical Adverb Clauses.** Write each sentence, adding the missing words in any elliptical clause. Then underline the complete adverb clause in each sentence and circle any words you have added.

EXAMPLE: I am as angry as you.

    I am as angry as you (are).

1. We think our cheerleaders are better than theirs.

_____

2. Blake is happier working with people than working by himself.

_____

3. My younger brother is as tall as I.

_____

4. Small children sometimes appreciate classical music more than nursery jingles.

_____

5. In Riley's backyard you can find junk heaped wherever there is an inch of space.

_____

Writing Application **Using Adverb Clauses to Combine Sentences.** Turn each pair of sentences into a single sentence with an adverb clause. Then underline each adverb clause.

EXAMPLE: Livia is unhappy. Her parakeet died.

    Livia is unhappy because her parakeet died.

1. The mother called the doctor in the middle of the night. Her child's temperature was abnormally high.

_____

2. The crowd looked up in wonder. Another brilliant display of fireworks went off.

_____

3. We toasted marshmallows over the dying embers. We silently shared a feeling of closeness.

_____

4. Randolph will never learn to study. He will learn to concentrate.

_____

5. Give me some more ideas. I can think of a topic.

_____

20.2 **Noun Clauses • Practice 1**

The Noun Clause   A *noun clause* is a subordinate clause that acts as a noun. In a sentence, a noun clause may have any function of a single-word noun.

NOUN CLAUSES
Subject: How the accident happened remains a mystery.
Direct Object: We couldn't decide *what the best plan would be.*
Indirect Object: Now you can tell *whomever you want* the plan.
Predicate Nominative: More shelf space is *what you need.*
Object of a Preposition: The committee disagreed about *what its role should be.*
Appositive: His idea, *that all people are equal,* is central to American democracy.

Introductory Words   Introductory words may act as subjects, direct objects, objects of prepositions, adjectives, or adverbs in noun clauses; or they may simply introduce the clauses without any internal function.

USES OF INTRODUCTORY WORDS IN NOUN CLAUSES
Subject: We will nominate |*whoever*| *can win.*
Direct Object: |*Whomever*| *you hire* must have excellent references.
Adjective: I don't know |*which*| *path is the right one.*
Adverb: The usher showed us |*where*| *we should sit.*
No Function: I wonder |*if*| *you can help me.*

▶ **Exercise 1**   **Identifying Noun Clauses.**   Underline the noun clause in each sentence. In the first space at the right, tell the function of the clause: *S* (subject), *DO* (direct object), *IO* (indirect object), *PN* (predicate nominative), *OP* (object of a preposition), or *APP* (appositive).

EXAMPLE: We all agreed <u>that you would do a good job</u>.   *DO* _____

1. That we arrived just then was lucky. _____ _____
2. Do you know when the last bus leaves? _____ _____
3. The committee will give whoever wins a savings bond. _____ _____
4. That she was sick was obvious to all. _____ _____
5. One consideration was which house has more space. _____ _____
6. I suggest that you enter the contest again. _____ _____
7. We wondered about whatever became of Jane. _____ _____
8. Please tell whomever you see the time of the party. _____ _____
9. What Carol reported surprised all of us. _____ _____
10. Tom's dilemma was whether he should work or go fishing. _____ _____

▶ **Exercise 2**   **Recognizing the Use of Introductory Words.**   On the second line in each sentence in Exercise 1, write the introductory word from each noun clause above. Then, using the key above plus *ADJ* (adjective), *ADV* (adverb), or *NONE*, write the function of the introductory word within the clause.

EXAMPLE: We all agreed <u>that you would do a good job</u>.   *DO*   *that   NONE*

20.2 Noun Clauses • Practice 2

Exercise 1 **Identifying Noun Clauses.** Underline the noun clause in each sentence. Then label the clause as a *subject, direct object, indirect object, predicate nominative, object of a preposition,* or *appositive.*

EXAMPLE: I made whoever was hungry a sandwich. _____*indirect object*_____

1. Whoever is interested in the past will like the book *Foxfire.* _____

2. The governor's dilemma, how it would be possible to please both factions, required hard thinking. _____

3. Everyone wants to hear about what you wore to the party. _____

4. That the play is a financial success is the result of the critics' reviews. _____

5. Leon discusses politics with whoever is unfortunate enough to sit next to him. _____

6. The planning committee needed more suggestions, whatever ideas people thought would be workable. _____

7. The brochure describes what a tourist can see in Kenya. _____

8. Tell Ms. Cato when she should expect you to arrive. _____

9. Carmella's selection of fabrics will be whichever ones she orders from the retailer. _____

10. Mr. James gave whoever came into his store a warm greeting. _____

Exercise 2 **Recognizing the Uses of Introductory Words.** Write the introductory word from each noun clause in Exercise 1. Then label the use of each within the clause as a *subject, direct object, object of a preposition, adjective, adverb,* or a word with *no function.*

EXAMPLE: I made whoever was hungry a sandwich.

_____*whoever* (subject)_____

1. _____
2. _____
3. _____
4. _____
5. _____

6. _____
7. _____
8. _____
9. _____
10. _____

Writing Application **Writing Sentences with Noun Clauses.** Use the following instructions to write sentences with noun clauses.

1. Use *whoever* as an introductory word; the clause should function as the subject of the sentence.

_____

2. Use *how* as an introductory word; the clause should function as the subject of the sentence.

_____

3. Use *what* as an introductory word; the clause should function as a direct object in the sentence.

_____

4. Use *whether* as an introductory word; the clause should function as a predicate nominative in the sentence.

_____

5. Use *whatever* as an introductory word; the clause should function as an object of a preposition in the sentence.

_____

21.1 Sentences Classified by Structure and Function (The Four Structures of Sentences)

• Practice 1

The Four Structures of Sentences Sentences can be classified by their *structure*, or the number and kind of clauses they contain.

Kind of Sentence	Number and Kind of Clauses	Examples (subjects underlined once, verbs twice)
Simple	One independent clause (subject or verb or both may be compound)	Tom played well. Tom and Ali played well. Tom and Ali played well and won.
Compound	Two or more independent clauses	The train arrived on time, but no one got on or off.
Complex	One independent clause and one or more subordinate clauses	SUBORD. CLAUSE IND. CLAUSE Though no one got off, we still waited.
Compound-complex	Two or more independent clauses and one or more subordinate clauses	IND. CLAUSE SUBORD. CLAUSE I saw someone who looked familiar, IND CLAUSE but it was someone else.

> **Exercise 1** **Distinguishing Between Simple and Compound Sentences.** Identify each sentence as simple or compound. The simple sentences may have compound parts.

EXAMPLE: Kenny swung at the ball and missed. ____*simple*____

1. We had hoped for a break in the weather, but the forecast is bleak. _____
2. Friends and strangers alike worked side by side piling sandbags. _____
3. Jan poised on the end of the board, took a deep breath, and dived. _____
4. The children may have been pleased, but their parents were not. _____
5. Paul finished his chores early, so he was free to go with us. _____
6. The aide denied ever having made that statement. _____
7. The task seemed impossible; nevertheless, we agreed to try. _____
8. We stood inside the clubhouse, waiting for the rain to stop. _____
9. Some people offered to help; some agreed reluctantly; others refused. _____
10. Jody made a wish and blew out the candles. _____

> **Exercise 2** **Identifying the Structure of Sentences.** Identify each sentence as (1) simple, (2) compound, (3) complex, or (4) compound-complex by writing the proper number in the blank.

EXAMPLE: Jeremy ordered more than he could eat. ____3____

1. The group is trying to decide how they will raise the money. _____
2. The inspector warned the investigators to use extreme caution. _____
3. The horses approached the finish line, and the spectators roared. _____
4. We should hurry, or the train will leave without us. _____
5. The Bombers and the Torpedoes will play in the championship. _____
6. Amy would be a better choice, for she speaks better than I. _____
7. The President smiled and shook hands with each guest. _____
8. Although I like math and science, I do better in languages. _____
9. The baby picked up the spoon and threw it across the room. _____
10. Can you fix the dessert Hal likes, or shall I have him bring it? _____

21.1 Sentences Classified by Structure and Function (The Four Structures of Sentences)
• Practice 2

▶ **Exercise 1** **Identifying the Structure of Sentences.** In the blanks, identify each sentence as *simple, compound, complex,* or *compound-complex.*

EXAMPLE: Before Matthew went to school, he fed the puppy. _____*complex*_____

(1) Matthew had always wanted a dog of his own. (2) One day he went to an animal shelter that offered all kinds of dogs for adoption. (3) As he entered, Matthew remembered his parents' asking if he was sure that he had time in his busy schedule for a dog. (4) Matthew put the question out of his mind; he was intent on picking out his dog. (5) Matthew finally chose a small brown bundle of fluff with sparkling eyes and a wagging tail. (6) In the weeks that followed, Matthew sometimes felt that days were too short to do all that had to be done, but somehow he managed. (7) He found that he needed to organize his time carefully. (8) He kept his grades up, played soccer, and wrote articles for the school newspaper. (9) Giving the puppy plenty of water, food, exercise, and attention took time, but every minute was well spent. (10) As Matthew worked at his desk every evening, a small brown chin often rested on his foot, and two floppy ears perked up whenever he spoke.

1. _____   6. _____
2. _____   7. _____
3. _____   8. _____
4. _____   9. _____
5. _____   10. _____

▶ **Exercise 2** **Writing Sentences with Different Structures.** Write a sentence, of the type listed in parentheses, that uses the given independent clause. Supply your own independent clause for each simple sentence.

EXAMPLE: The train sped over the bridge. (compound sentence)

_____*The train sped over the bridge, and the passengers looked out at the river.*_____

1. (simple sentence)

_____

2. I wanted to learn how to do the tango. (compound sentence)

_____

3. Carol introduced Norma to Carl. (complex sentence)

_____

4. I hid the key under the greenish rock. (compound-complex sentence)

_____

5. (simple sentence)

_____

6. The artist paints with oil on canvas. (compound sentence)

_____

7. Mr. Johnson brought his puppets to school today. (complex sentence)

_____

8. Salads taste better with seasoning. (compound-complex sentence)

_____

9. (simple sentence)

_____

10. Maria will visit her grandmother. (compound-complex sentence)

_____

21.1 Sentences Classified by Structure and Function (The Four Functions of Sentences)

• Practice 1

The Four Functions of Sentences   Sentences can also be classified by their *function*.

Kind of Sentence	Function	Example	End Mark
Declarative	States an idea	Those flowers are dandelions.	Period (.)
Interrogative	Asks a question	Where have I seen that face before?	Question mark (?)
Imperative	Gives an order or direction	Stand still! Fold your paper in half.	period or exclamation mark (. or !)
Exclamatory	Conveys a strong emotion	What an odd creature that is! How hard we worked!	Exclamation mark (!)

▶ **Exercise 1**   **Identifying the Function of Sentences.**   Identify each sentence as *declarative, interrogative, imperative,* or *exclamatory.*

EXAMPLE: Leave a message if no one is at home.   ____*imperative*____

1. Print clearly or type all information needed. _____
2. Have you found the book you were looking for? _____
3. Which of the candidates do you plan to support? _____
4. Trivia games are becoming increasingly popular. _____
5. Be sure the two surfaces are securely glued together. _____
6. What an unkind thing that was to say! _____
7. Follow Main Street for two miles. _____
8. Seashells were an early form of money. _____
9. Smoke curled from the chimney of the little cabin. _____
10. Have you spoken to Megan this week? _____

▶ **Exercise 2**   **Choosing the Correct End Mark by Function.**   Supply the correct end mark for each sentence.

EXAMPLE: Chameleons have protective coloration ___.___

1. Stop that car_____
2. Did you take a message_____
3. What an unusual shade of red that is_____
4. Please stop talking_____
5. Tomorrow's forecast sounds promising_____
6. Who directed that movie_____
7. Now that's what I call a car_____
8. Deciduous trees shed their leaves in the fall_____
9. Be sure to tell Sandy I stopped by_____
10. Interest on those accounts is compounded daily_____

21.1 Sentences Classified by Structure and Function (The Four Functions of Sentences)
• Practice 2

▶ **Exercise 1** Writing Sentences with Different Structures and Functions. Identify each sentence as *declarative, interrogative, imperative,* or *exclamatory.* Write the end mark for each sentence.

EXAMPLE: I must return this overdue book to the library _____*declarative*_____ .

1. Look carefully in both directions before crossing the street _____

2. When the alarm sounds, it summons firefighters _____

3. Your dress is absolutely ruined _____

4. All of my tires are new _____

5. Is there any way to tell when the corn is ripe _____

6. Will you please turn off the light before you leave _____

7. Should we whitewash this wall or leave it as it is _____

8. The toast is burning _____

9. Oil the hinges, and this door will no longer squeak _____

10. If you look in that tree, you will see a bird's nest _____

11. Have you ever been to the Grand Canyon _____

12. Don't touch those flowers _____

13. Melanie planted corn by the fence in the backyard _____

14. The two-year-old tried to climb up on the counter _____

15. What an ugly painting _____

16. Why do you have to be there at six o'clock _____

17. The movie is over at two-forty _____

18. How lucky you are _____

19. Come over here this instant _____

20. What would you like to do for a living _____

▶ **Writing Application** Writing Sentences with Different Structures and Functions. Use the following instructions to write sentences of your own.

1. Write a simple exclamatory sentence.

2. Write a simple imperative sentence.

3. Write a compound declarative sentence.

4. Write a simple interrogative sentence.

5. Write a compound interrogative sentence.

1. _____

2. _____

3. _____

4. _____

5. _____

21.2 Sentence Combining • Practice 1

Combining Ideas   Join two or more short sentences by using compound subjects or verbs, by using phrases, or by writing compound, complex, or compound-complex sentences.

Separate Sentences	Combined Sentences
Westfield won its game last night. Branford also won.	*Westfield and Branford* won their games last night.
The boy screamed for his mother. He realized that he was lost.	*Realizing that he was lost*, the boy screamed for his mother.
The firemen battled to control the fire. It continued to spread. The wind had shifted directions.	The firemen battled to control the fire, *but* it continued to spread *because* the wind had shifted directions.

> **Exercise 1**   **Combining Sentences.**   Combine the sentences in each item into a single sentence.

EXAMPLE: Al refused to go to the top of the Empire State Building. He is terrified of high places.

> *Because he is terrified of high places, Al refused to go to the top of the Empire State Building.*

1. Broadway musicals are often difficult for amateurs. They have large casts and elaborate production numbers.

    _____

    _____

2. My favorite breakfast is pancakes. I like to have bacon with my pancakes.

    _____

3. It is a quality magazine. It is intended for people interested in science.

    _____

4. Timmy made the birdhouse himself. He just followed the directions.

    _____

5. Today's editorial was quite alarming. It was about toxic waste.

    _____

6. He is a very gifted athlete. He works hard in practice. He is the best player on the team.

    _____

7. The band members wanted to leave the stage. The crowd implored them to continue. They played another song.

    _____

    _____

8. Gerri's children were grown. She went back to school. She became a physical therapist.

    _____

9. Sean never does well on standardized tests. He gets good grades in school. He works very hard.

    _____

10. The ice storm lasted for two days. The roads were treacherous. School was canceled for the week.

    _____

    _____

21.2 **Sentence Combining • Practice 2**

▶ **Exercise 1**   **Combining Sentences.**   Rewrite each of the following items, combining sentences.

EXAMPLE: A tan car sped along the highway. It attempted to turn sharply. It nearly flipped.

Speeding along the highway, a tan car attempted to turn sharply and nearly flipped.

1. Snow fell steadily upon the Acadian Forest. It fell for seven days.

   _____

   _____

2. Jason lost his grip on the rope tow. He slid all the way to the bottom of the hill.

   _____

   _____

3. Eating balanced meals is essential for good health. Exercising regularly is necessary too.

   _____

   _____

4. Thomas Jefferson was the third President of the United States. He was a key writer of the Declaration of Independence.

   _____

   _____

5. Horses communicate with each other. They snort and make sounds of different pitch.

   _____

   _____

6. Reading magazines is a good way to stay informed. They usually give several different viewpoints on a subject.

   _____

   _____

7. A walrus looks clumsy. It appears sluggish. It is quite agile when it swims.

   _____

   _____

8. The temperature rose. The snowbanks glistened in the sun. Tiny beads of water trickled down the hill.

   _____

   _____

9. We were miles away. We could hear Alan. He was practicing his trumpet.

   _____

   _____

10. The Tower of London was built about nine hundred years ago. It was originally a prison. Today it houses the crown jewels.

    _____

    _____

21.3 Varying Your Sentences (Expanding Short Sentences, Shortening Long Sentences) • Practice 1

Expanding Short Sentences   Expand short sentences by adding details.

Short Sentences	Expanded Sentences
The boy swam across the lake. The girl studied all night.	The *young* boy swam *easily* across the *large* lake. The girl, *Wendy Baker, an excellent student*, studied all night.

Shortening Long Sentences   Break up lengthy, complicated sentences into shorter, more direct sentences.

Long, Complicated Sentence	Shorter, Clearer Sentences
The essay contest, which was announced last week by the Chamber of Commerce, appealed to many of us in the Scribblers Club, particularly because of the cash prize, but many of us were reluctant to enter because of the early deadline, which would conflict with studying for final exams.	The Chamber of Commerce essay contest announced last week appealed to many of us in the Scribblers Club. The cash prize was particularly appealing. However, the conflict between studying for final exams and meeting the early deadline made many of us reluctant to enter.

▶ **Exercise 1**   **Adding Details to Short Sentences.**   Improve each of the following sentences by adding the item or items in parentheses.

EXAMPLE: The player won the tournament. (two adjectives)

　　　　　　　The best player won the tennis tournament.

1. Jody speaks French fluently. (appositive phrase)_____

_____

2. The guitarist broke a string. (prepositional phrase)_____

_____

3. Jane skied to the bottom of the hill. (two adverbs)_____

_____

4. Senator Williams came to our school. (verbal phrase)_____

_____

5. The soldiers marched across the field. (two adjectives)_____

_____

▶ **Exercise 2**   **Shortening Long Sentences.**   Divide the sentence below into two or more sentences.

　　Although the doctors had not held out much hope for the surgery, the family remained optimistic throughout the long hours of the operation, thinking that if they wanted it badly enough surely things would work out, and they were ecstatic when the surgeon appeared and reported that the operation had indeed been a success.

_____

_____

_____

_____

_____

21.3 Varying Your Sentences (Expanding Short Sentences, Shortening Long Sentences) • Practice 2

▶ **Exercise 1**   **Adding Details.**   Rewrite each short simple sentence by adding the item or items in parentheses.

EXAMPLE: Science boasts a staggering amount of published information. (appositive phrase)

_____*Science, the last and probably endless frontier, boasts a staggering amount of published*_____
information.

1. Some of the local residents use the service road. (prepositional phrase) _____

_____

2. The treasure aroused people's curiosity. (two adjectives and an adverb) _____

_____

3. A coat of paint brightened my room. (two adjectives) _____

_____

4. Mrs. Hamilton did her best to influence the town council. (appositive) _____

_____

5. The mechanic pried the flat tire from the wheel rim. (verbal phrase) _____

_____

▶ **Exercise 2**   **Shortening Long Sentences.**   Divide these long sentences into short, clear sentences.

EXAMPLE: Denver, which is the capital of Colorado and sits on the Great Plains of America, began as a mining camp in 1858 and quickly became a boomtown.

_____*Denver, the capital of Colorado, sits on the Great Plains of America. The city began as a*_____
*mining camp in 1858 and quickly became a boomtown.*_____

1. Many people laughed at Adam when he first set out to find an old Spanish galleon that had sunk in 1622, but within a year he had converted many a disbeliever, because in that short time he had found millions of dollars of submerged treasure. _____

_____

_____

2. The art of wood carving was perfected so early in history that few records have been preserved, except relics, such as a recently excavated set of wood carver's tools, which prove that even before metal was used, people cut and decorated wood with tools of shell, bone, and flint. _____

_____

_____

3. I finally saw the movie, and I am glad that I read the book first because important plot details and even some characters that made the story understandable were left out of the movie version. _____

_____

_____

4. She clutched the letter tightly, refusing to talk about it and refusing to show it to us, yet tears streamed down her face and small sobs shook her, and we did want to help her, but she was unreachable. _____

_____

_____

5. In the first few hours of torrential rain, flood waters began to rise, and many people left their homes in search of higher ground, but most of these people got stuck in traffic jams and had to wait out the crisis in their stalled automobiles. _____

_____

Name _____ Date _____

21.3 Varying Your Sentences (Using Different Sentence Openers and Structures) • Practice 1

Using Different Sentence Openers and Structures   Use a variety of sentence openers and structures.

VARIED SENTENCE OPENERS	
Modifier First	*Carefully*, the detective put the evidence into the bag.
Phrase First	*Looking down from the mountain*, we saw the winding river.
Clause First	*Whenever Grandma visits us*, she bakes an applesauce cake.

Monotonous Sentence	Varied Sentence
My sister is a doctor. She went to college for four years. She spent four years in medical school. She has spent three years in residency. She will finish this summer. She will go into private practice. She specialized in internal medicine.	My sister, who is a doctor, spent four years in medical school after her four years of college. When she finishes her three-year residency this summer, she will go into private practice in internal medicine.

> **Exercise 1**   **Using Different Sentence Openers.**   Rewrite each sentence to make it begin with a one-word modifier, a phrase, or a clause.

EXAMPLE: Alison sometimes baby-sits for her cousins.

       Sometimes, Alison baby-sits for her cousins.

1.   Phone the box office for further information.

   _____

2.   The youngsters were especially excited about their trip because they had never been camping before.

   _____

3.   Can you join us for a pizza after the game?

   _____

4.   Uncle John frequently dozes off after dinner.

   _____

5.   The band members will have a bake sale to raise money for their trip.

   _____

> **Exercise 2**   **Varying Sentence Structures.**   Rewrite the following paragraph, using a variety of sentence structures.

   (1) Jeremy wants to be a veterinarian. (2) He has loved animals all his life. (3) He had a whole menagerie of pets as a child. (4) He took excellent care of them. (5) He never could bear to see an animal suffer. (6) He nursed several injured chipmunks and other small animals back to health. (7) He has always been a good student. (8) He has done especially well in math and science. (9) He will graduate from high school this June. (10) He plans to take pre-med courses at college this fall.

_____

_____

_____

21.3 Varying Your Sentences (Using Different Sentence Openers and Structures) • Practice 2

▶ **Exercise 1** **Using Different Sentence Openers.** Rewrite each of the following sentences, rearranging the words to make the sentence begin differently.

EXAMPLE: I tossed and turned constantly during the night.

During the night I tossed and turned constantly.

1. Oceanographers have worked endlessly to study the habits of undersea animals.

   _____

2. I lost my concentration when the phone began to ring.

   _____

3. The confused tourists stared at the timetable in the train station.

   _____

4. Lucky contestants have won hundreds of thousands of dollars on television game shows.

   _____

5. Burning coals and boiling lava erupted from the mouth of Mount Etna.

   _____

6. Clarissa, running to answer the phone, slipped on a magazine and twisted her ankle.

   _____

7. You must fulfill basic requirements to be a good student and earn high grades.

   _____

8. The mountain, jagged and menacing, loomed above us.

   _____

9. A building can be condemned if it does not meet safety standards.

   _____

10. My uncle, however, would not play golf again.

   _____

11. There was an audience of nearly ten thousand at the concert.

   _____

12. After skiing all day, Kurt was tired and hungry.

   _____

13. Cindy used many colors because she wanted the house to look cheerful.

   _____

14. Albert has to work overtime, so he will be late for dinner.

   _____

15. Generously, Maggie donates four hours a week tutoring poor readers.

   _____

▶ **Exercise 2** **Varying Sentence Structure.** On another piece of paper, rewrite the following passage using a variety of sentence structures.

(1) Aunt Helen's heirs were an eager group. (2) Eight men and nine women sat around the giant parlor table. (3) They waited anxiously for the lawyer's arrival. (4) Enthusiastically, they exchanged talk of "our dear, departed Helen." (5) Most of the heirs had never met before this evening. (6) Each pair of eyes glanced regularly toward the parlor doorway. (7) The attorney finally appeared. (8) He was carrying an impressive looking document. (9) Suddenly, the heirs fell silent. (10) The atmosphere became tense.

21.3 Varying Your Sentences (Using Special Sentence Patterns) • Practice 1

Using Special Sentence Patterns   Use parallelism to underscore ideas. Use a new structure after a series of similar structures to underscore an idea.

SPECIAL SENTENCE PATTERNS	
Parallel Structures	In store windows, in the buildings on the town green and in private homes, a single candle burned in each window. Jackson would tax the rich and the corporations; Hillyer would tax the poor and the small businesses.
Breaking a Pattern	I have studied the manual; I have assembled the materials; I have set up a work space. Now wish me luck!

▶ **Exercise 1**   **Using Parallelism.**   Each sentence below contains an element that is not parallel to others. Rewrite each one using parallel structures.

EXAMPLE: We were hungry and cold but not feeling tired.

_____*We were hungry and cold but not tired.*_____

1. Sewing, painting, and to cook gourmet meals are Alice's hobbies.

   _____

2. Hank explained his idea clearly, completely, and with patience.

   _____

3. Jamie agreed to work at night and on weekends but not holidays.

   _____

4. Clapping hands, stamping feet, and with loud whistles, the audience demanded an encore.

   _____

5. Fran likes to swim and to sail but not playing baseball.

   _____

▶ **Exercise 2**   **Using Special Sentence Patterns.**   Follow the instructions to write sentences that make good use of parallel structures.

EXAMPLE: Write two parallel clauses that emphasize a contrast.

_____*Ramon is reflective and deliberate; Jed is impulsive and spontaneous.*_____

1. Write a sentence with three parallel prepositional phrases that emphasize thoroughness.

   _____

2. Write two parallel clauses that emphasize similarity.

   _____

3. Write two parallel clauses that emphasize a contrast.

   _____

4. Set up a pattern with three similar sentences. Then break the pattern to emphasize a final point in the fourth sentence.

   _____

   _____

   _____

   _____

21.3 Varying Your Sentences (Using Special Sentence Patterns) • Practice 2

▶ **Exercise 1**   **Using Patterns for Emphasis.**   Tell whether the strength of each of the following passages is achieved purely through *parallelism* or through *breaking a pattern*.

EXAMPLE: Spittle physically nauseated Dickens; slavery morally sickened him. —Jeanne and Norman MacKenzie   *parallelism*

1. Education makes a people easy to lead, but difficult to drive; easy to govern, but impossible to enslave. —Lord Brougham _____

2. The past is only the present become invisible and mute; and because it is invisible and mute, its memorized glance and its murmurs are infinitely precious. We are tomorrow's past. —Mary Webb _____

3. Feast, and your halls are crowded; fast, and the world goes by. —Ella Wilcox

   _____

4. The country needs, and, unless I mistake its temper, the country demands bold, persistent experimentation. It is common sense to take a method and try it: If it fails, admit it frankly and try another. But above all, try something. —Franklin Delano Roosevelt

   _____

5. Better by far you should forget and smile than that you should remember and be sad. —Christina Rossetti _____

▶ **Writing Application**   **Writing Varied Sentences.**   Rewrite the following composition, varying the lengths, beginnings, structures, and possibly the patterns of the sentences.

(1) Millions of people are injured yearly in their own homes. (2) Any area of your home can possess a safety hazard. (3) No one can afford to overlook possible hazards. (4) You should inspect all rooms of your house. (5) You should then eliminate all of the dangers you recognize.

(6) Too many home accidents happen in kitchens so you must take special care to ensure safety by making sure that electrical appliances are away from the sink and by preventing their cords from slipping into the water, and you should keep a fire extinguisher in the kitchen because fires can occur all too quickly and they can spread rapidly.

(7) You can also help prevent accidents in bathrooms. (8) Inspect them for potential hazards, keep pills and medicines out of the reach of children, and label all medicines to avoid dangerous mix-ups, and cover a slippery floor with a carpet or bath rug that cannot slip, and never place a telephone near the tub or sink. (9) The phone cord can become wet. (10) It can cause an electrical shock.

_____

_____

_____

_____

_____

_____

_____

_____

_____

_____

21.4 **Fragments • Practice 1**

Fragments   A *fragment* is a group of words that does not express a complete thought but is punctuated as if it were a sentence. It is part of a sentence and may have a subject or a verb.

Fragments	Sentences
Without even knocking.	I opened the door without even knocking.
A woman of strong convictions.	We chose Marian, a woman of strong convictions.
Thought long and hard.	Ken thought long and hard before deciding.
A dog, two cats, and a gerbil.	I have a dog, two cats, and a gerbil.
That everyone wants.	The game that everyone wants is on sale.
Where the weather is warmer.	I want to go where the weather is warmer.

▶ **Exercise 1**   **Identifying Sentence Fragments.**   Write whether each group of words is a *sentence* or a *fragment*.

EXAMPLE: Following her own instincts. _____*fragment*_____

1. To believe everything you hear. _____

2. A person who has everything. _____

3. Who got the right answer? _____

4. The woman on the speaker's platform. _____

5. Plays with enthusiasm and energy. _____

6. Remember the Alamo! _____

7. Heaping platters and bowls of delicacies. _____

8. One of the most exciting performances I have ever seen. _____

9. Driving along the Pacific Coast. _____

10. Andrew lost his first tooth. _____

▶ **Exercise 2**   **Correcting Sentence Fragments.**   Use five of the fragments you identified in Exercise 1 in complete sentences.

EXAMPLE: ____*Following her own instincts often got Clara into trouble.*____

1. _____

   _____

2. _____

   _____

3. _____

   _____

4. _____

   _____

5. _____

   _____

21.4 Fragments • Practice 2

Exercise 1 **Correcting Fragments.** Identify each item as a *phrase fragment*, *clause fragment*, or *series fragment*. Then use each fragment in a complete sentence.

EXAMPLE: a terrible case of poison ivy ____*phrase fragment*____

____*I had a terrible case of poison ivy*____

1. laughed, shouted, and romped _____

_____

2. while she was running after the bus _____

_____

3. frequent loud interruptions _____

_____

4. petrified dinosaur bones _____

_____

5. where cattails and reeds grew high _____

_____

6. sometimes downcast, depressed, or just unhappy _____

_____

7. watching, stalking, and pouncing _____

_____

8. which recalled a time of carefree days _____

_____

9. must have been abandoned by someone _____

_____

10. whomever he invites _____

_____

11. writing letters, reading poetry, and listening to music _____

_____

12. after he took the dog to the vet _____

_____

13. colorful and fragrant bouquets _____

_____

14. a gallon of lavender paint _____

_____

15. when dinosaurs ruled the earth _____

_____

21.4 Run-ons • Practice 1

Run-ons   Use punctuation, conjunctions, or other means to join or separate the parts of a run-on sentence.

Run-on Sentences	Corrected Sentences
The dog ran away no one ever found it.	The dog ran away; no one ever found it. The dog ran away, and no one ever found it. The dog ran away and was never found.
Ella found the treasure, she never told anyone.	Ella found the treasure. She never told anyone. Ella found the treasure but never told anyone. Although Ella found the treasure, she never told anyone.

▶ **Exercise 1**   **Identifying Run-ons.**   Label each item below as a *run-on* or a *sentence.*

EXAMPLE: The fans were eager for a win the odds were against it. _____*run-on*_____

1. Gloria offered to make baked Alaska, which is her specialty. _____

2. The beach is pleasant during the week, it is crowded on weekends. _____

3. The play was excellent, the cast was only mediocre. _____

4. Jason wants to become a teacher, he is my brother. _____

5. Wringing her hands nervously, Alicia paced back and forth in her dressing room. _____

6. You'll love that book it's a mystery. _____

7. Ben applied for a variety of jobs, everyone said he was overqualified. _____

8. In general I hate exercise swimming is one thing I do enjoy. _____

9. Juliette fell off the swing, she broke her wrist. _____

10. Whenever we visit our cousins, we either take a picnic lunch to the park or spend the day at the beach. _____

▶ **Exercise 2**   **Correcting Run-ons.**   Correct five of the run-ons you identified in Exercise 1, using a variety of methods.

EXAMPLE: _____*Although the fans were eager for a win, the odds were against it.*_____

1. _____
   _____

2. _____
   _____

3. _____
   _____

4. _____
   _____

5. _____
   _____

21.4 Run-ons • Practice 2

> **Exercise 1** **Correcting Run-ons.** Use an end mark, a comma and a coordinating conjunction, or a semicolon to correct each of the first five run-ons. Form a simple or complex sentence to correct each of the last five run-ons.

EXAMPLE: Davy Crockett was a frontiersman, he was also a congressman.

_____*Davy Crockett was a frontiersman. He was also a congressman.*_____

1. Every year at this time the snow melts and the creek flows, in six months, however, it will be dry.

   _____

2. They bought an old mill, eventually they were able to make it into a unique and beautiful home.

   _____

3. Jody dropped out of school in her junior year, she received a diploma years later.

   _____

4. Days turned into years, the years seemed endless.

   _____

5. Will he leave his job and its security to try his luck at farming it seems unlikely.

   _____

6. Sir Winston Churchill was a brilliant man he was the English Prime Minister during World War II.

   _____

7. Catherine II was a Russian empress, she was called Catherine the Great.

   _____

8. Marty was afraid of bees, he had a severe allergic reaction to their stings.

   _____

9. In the spring cardinals come to our bird feeder, an occasional blue jay also makes an appearance.

   _____

10. Rapunzel let her long hair fall to the ground, her name means "lettuce."

    _____

> **Writing Application** **Correcting Fragments and Run-ons.** On another piece of paper, rewrite the following paragraphs, correcting all fragments and run-ons.

(1) The storm had suddenly come upon them. (2) Surprising the two boys. (3) Their jackets offered little protection from the rain. (4) Jack led the way to the cabin, it was almost hidden by the trees. (5) Within minutes they stood on the porch. (6) The door opened, they entered, throwing their backpacks onto the floor. (7) They shivered. (8) The room was cold, it was damp.

(9) They could not see in the darkness, Jack felt for the lantern. (10) Which he knew was on the table. (11) If they had started out earlier, they would not have been caught in the rain. (12) Unable to reach the cabin before night. (13) A warm fire and supper would certainly help.

(14) When the lantern was lit, Jack gasped, the doors to the cupboard which his father had filled were opened, revealing empty shelves. (15) Walking back onto the porch. (16) He stared at the empty place where wood had been stacked. (17) Obviously, someone had been warm and well-fed at their expense. (18) Phil, he knew, would accept his apology, that was a small consolation for the uncomfortable night they would have. (19) At least a lesson had been learned, next time he would prepare for any emergency. (20) That might occur.

21.4 Misplaced and Dangling Modifiers
(Recognizing Misplaced and Dangling Modifiers)
• Practice 1

Recognizing Misplaced and Dangling Modifiers   A *modifier* should be placed as close as possible to the word it modifies. A *misplaced modifier* appears to modify the wrong word in a sentence. A *dangling modifier* appears to modify the wrong word or no word at all because the word it should logically modify is missing.

Misplaced Modifier	Dangling Modifier
Jack got a watch from his uncle *with fluorescent hands.*	*Sniffing the carton cautiously,* the milk didn't smell sour.

> **Exercise 1**   **Recognizing Misplaced Modifiers.**   Underline each misplaced modifier. If a sentence contains no misplaced modifier, leave it unmarked.

EXAMPLE: Dr. Sweet showed pictures of rare birds he had photographed <u>at the Rotary Club</u>.

  1. Nancy discovered that Bowser had eaten the tea sandwiches with a cry of dismay.

  2. His mother had asked Charles to have his hair cut a dozen times.

  3. Stepping off the curb, Aunt Clare was nearly hit by a delivery truck.

  4. Merriwell vowed to set a new freestyle record with deep emotion in his voice.

  5. Erin was reading limericks written by Edward Lear with squeals of delight.

  6. Written in Portuguese, the message made no sense to Arthur.

  7. Dad called to me to finish mowing the lawn from the upstairs window.

  8. Maggie found a sweater that had never been worn in the thrift shop.

  9. John was reprimanded for his classroom behavior in the principal's office.

10. Dad bought a desk from an antique dealer with a secret compartment.

> **Exercise 2**   **Recognizing Dangling Modifiers.**   Underline each dangling modifier. If a sentence contains no dangling modifier, leave it unmarked.

EXAMPLE: <u>Before handing in your paper</u>, each answer should be carefully checked.

  1. Flying low over the treetops, a herd of elephants charged into our view.

  2. Shucking oysters at Caro's Clam Bar, a huge pearl was discovered.

  3. Marking the way with string, Theseus was able to find his way back out of the maze.

  4. Clearing the bar at seventeen feet, a new record was set.

  5. The ball was lost practicing last week.

  6. How beautiful the autumn foliage looked motoring through Vermont!

  7. Cheered by a taste of success, his next play had a happy ending.

  8. Checking through her calculation, Mary found her error and corrected it.

  9. Peering through the keyhole, nothing in the room seemed out of order.

10. Arriving at the theater an hour late, the seats were taken.

21.4 Misplaced and Dangling Modifiers
(Recognizing Misplaced and Dangling Modifiers)
• Practice 2

▶ **Exercise 1** **Identifying Misplaced and Dangling Modifiers.** Identify each underlined phrase or clause as *misplaced*, *dangling*, or *correct*.

EXAMPLE: He ran to the car <u>with arms full of boxes</u>. *misplaced*

1. <u>Grinning happily</u>, the prize for first place was accepted. _____
2. Wait for the bus <u>that stops at the corner</u>. _____
3. They planned to win <u>before the game started</u>. _____
4. <u>Hoping to succeed in the interview</u>, long hours were spent in preparation. _____
5. She flew in a small aircraft <u>trembling with fear</u>. _____
6. <u>Jumping out of his seat</u>, Milton shouted with surprise. _____
7. <u>Reading the directions carefully</u>, the test was quite easy. _____
8. This letter, <u>which I found behind a drawer</u>, was written over a century ago. _____
9. She fearfully pointed to the spider over her head <u>that hung from a transparent web</u>. _____
10. We joined the crowd in cheering the winner <u>with enthusiasm</u>. _____
11. She served dessert to the children <u>on blue paper plates</u>. _____
12. <u>Complaining loudly</u>, the broken toy was returned to the store. _____
13. The mayor was able to cut the ribbon <u>because someone found scissors</u>. _____
14. Phil opened the book given to her on her birthday <u>by Charles Dickens</u>. _____
15. The bell is an antique <u>that you hear chiming</u>. _____
16. Bill built the bookcase of oak <u>that you see in the corner</u>. _____
17. <u>Nodding politely</u>, Aaron acknowledged the older man. _____
18. <u>Quacking loudly</u>, Heather fed the ducks in the park. _____
19. Tom fed the kitten in the kitchen <u>that his aunt had given him</u>. _____
20. <u>Diving into the pool</u>, Marion did not even make a splash. _____

▶ **Exercise 2** **Identifying Misplaced and Dangling Modifiers in Paragraphs.** Underline each misplaced or dangling modifier in the following paragraph. Then, in each blank, identify the modifier as either misplaced or dangling.

EXAMPLE: <u>Waving good-bye to their friends on the dock</u>, the ship pulled away. *dangling*

(1) Whistling cheerfully, the bikes were fixed in no time. (2) Then Bob and Marie rode their bikes to the movies that they had just repaired. (3) Waiting in line to get their tickets, it started to rain. (4) Marie waited near the entrance while Bob got the tickets under someone else's big umbrella. (5) Paying with a twenty-dollar bill, the ticket seller handed the tickets to Bob.
(6) Getting into the lobby, the line for popcorn was very long. (7) Skipping the popcorn, the seats they found were good ones. (8) A tall man sat right in front of them coming in late. (9) Twisting into an uncomfortable position, the screen was visible. (10) Getting on their bikes after the movie, the ride home was pleasant and invigorating.

1. _____   6. _____
2. _____   7. _____
3. _____   8. _____
4. _____   9. _____
5. _____   10. _____

21.4 # Misplaced and Dangling Modifiers
(Correcting Misplaced Modifiers) • Practice 1

Correcting Misplaced Modifiers   Correct a misplaced modifier by moving the phrase or clause closer to the word it should logically modify.

Misplaced Modifiers	Corrected Sentences
Clara saw the tornado approaching *through the bedroom window.*	Through the bedroom window, Clara saw the tornado approaching.
Hugo wore a hat on his head *that was several sizes too small.*	Hugo wore a hat that was several sizes too small on his head. On his head, Hugo wore a hat that was several sizes too small.

▶ **Exercise 1**   **Recognizing Misplaced Modifiers.**   Underline each misplaced modifier.

EXAMPLE: I was happy to find the cookies in my lunchbox <u>that my mother had made.</u>

1. Tonight, WCTV presents a special program for viewers interested in changing to new careers at 8:00 P.M.

2. The retriever swam to his master on shore with a duck in his mouth.

3. Dad took a picture of a hummingbird using his high-speed camera.

4. The customer demanded an explanation in an angry voice.

5. Cheering wildly, the home team was greeted by their fans.

6. Mom remembered she had not turned the oven off in the middle of our trip.

7. Please don't give scraps to the dogs with small bones in them.

8. We saw many fine old houses strolling around the village green.

9. David waited patiently for a bee to come along with a jelly jar.

10. Let us know if you plan to make the trip on the enclosed postcard.

▶ **Exercise 2**   **Correcting Misplaced Modifiers.**   Rewrite five sentences in Exercise 1, correcting the misplaced modifiers.

EXAMPLE: *I was happy to find in my lunchbox the cookies that my mother had made.*

1. _____

_____

2. _____

_____

3. _____

_____

4. _____

_____

5. _____

_____

21.4 Misplaced and Dangling Modifiers
(Correcting Misplaced Modifiers) • Practice 2

▶ **Exercise 1** **Recognizing and Correcting Misplaced Modifiers.** Rewrite each sentence, correcting the misplaced modifier. Then underline the corrected modifier and draw an arrow from it to the word it modifies.

EXAMPLE: He ran to the car with arms full of boxes.

With arms full of boxes, he ran to the car.

1. The watch was his favorite gift that broke.

_____

2. Lionel sold his bicycle to a friend with four speeds.

_____

3. The zookeeper captured the escaped iguana brandishing a net in his upraised hand.

_____

4. The boys ran from the abandoned house noticeably trembling.

_____

5. Brenda put oranges into the punch that came from Florida.

_____

6. The deer bounded into the woods shaking in panic.

_____

7. Jed ordered a steak and a salad cooked rare.

_____

8. The fish were photographed at the pier that we caught.

_____

9. Perched on top of the counter in a red dress, the child sat.

_____

10. Leaving the party after midnight, we waved farewell to our happy guests.

_____

11. Jill sewed buttons on the jacket using red thread.

_____

12. The man served hot dogs wearing a green beret.

_____

13. We saw the graffiti passing the building.

_____

14. Grazing peacefully, we saw a herd of cattle.

_____

15. Crumbling with decay, the women posed by the old building.

_____

21.4 Misplaced and Dangling Modifiers
(Correcting Dangling Modifiers) • Practice 1

Correcting Dangling Modifiers Correct a dangling modifier by rewriting the sentence to include the missing word.

Dangling Modifier	Corrected Sentences
Reaching the top of the hill, the camp was a welcome sight.	Reaching the top of the hill, we found the camp a welcome sight. When we reached the top of the hill, the camp was a welcome sight.

▶ **Exercise 1** **Recognizing Dangling Modifiers.**   Underline each dangling modifier.

EXAMPLE: Waiting in the wings, stage fright gripped her heart.

1. Strolling through the narrow streets, the native quarter was picturesque.

2. Searching for the missing contract, the whole house was turned upside down.

3. Doing my homework, the radio next door was distracting.

4. Before parking in that lot, a sticker must be purchased.

5. His wallet was stolen while watching the fireworks display.

6. Having sent the suspect to jail, the case seemed to be closed.

7. Vegetation became sparse approaching the summit of the mountain.

8. While farming in Texas, oil was discovered.

9. Entering the dining room, the roast turkey looked appetizing.

10. Born into an immigrant family, the White House seemed an impossible goal.

▶ **Exercise 2** **Correcting Dangling Modifiers.**   Rewrite five sentences in Exercise 1, correcting the dangling modifiers.

EXAMPLE: *Waiting in the wings, the actress felt stage fright grip her heart.*

1. _____
   _____

2. _____
   _____

3. _____
   _____

4. _____
   _____

5. _____
   _____

21.4 Misplaced and Dangling Modifiers
(Correcting Dangling Modifiers) • Practice 2

Exercise 1 **Recognizing and Correcting Dangling Modifiers.** Write each sentence, correcting the dangling modifier. Then underline the corrected modifier and draw an arrow from it to the word it modifies.

EXAMPLE: Folding laundry, the phone rang.

Folding laundry, we heard the phone ring.

1. Researching that topic, three new ideas were found.

   _____

2. Picketing for improved working conditions, the strike continued.

   _____

3. Searching for the missing diamond ring, every possible nook and cranny was explored.

   _____

4. Swallowing the bitter medicine, a cold was avoided.

   _____

5. Lost in a daydream, my words went unheard.

   _____

6. When he was nine months old, Jeremy's father decided that the family should move to Alaska.

   _____

7. Driving into Santa Fe, the desert looked like the moon.

   _____

8. Winning the race, the losers applauded loudly.

   _____

9. When they misbehaved, the boys' parents complained.

   _____

10. Returning the wallet, the owner gave a reward.

    _____

Writing Application **Correcting Misplaced and Dangling Modifiers.** Rewrite the following paragraph, correcting all misplaced or dangling modifiers.

(1) Sue is a successful architect and interior designer whose custom-built homes stagger the imagination. (2) Priced beyond what the average person can afford, you can see her houses in many expensive neighborhoods. (3) The front of one house is made entirely of glass. (4) Extending outward from the second floor, potted flowers grow on an elaborate balcony. (5) Within the center of the house, a huge tropical aquarium rests on a marble floor with exotic fish. (6) A wrought iron staircase winds its way around the aquarium connecting the first and second stories. (7) Recessed in the ceilings, each room is softly lit by fluorescent lights. (8) Turning a dial in any room, your favorite kind of music can be heard. (9) In the winter, fireplaces provide warmth; in the summer, cool air is circulated by fans. (10) With enough money, the house can become yours.

_____

_____

_____

_____

_____

● 21.4 Faulty Parallelism (Recognizing Faulty Parallelism)
• Practice 1

Recognizing Faulty Parallelism   *Parallelism* is the placement of equal ideas in words, phrases, or clauses of similar type.

SOME COMMON PARALLEL STRUCTURES
Parallel Words: The camp has excellent facilities for *riding, hiking,* and *swimming.* *Parallel Phrases:* Jennings had gone to the country *to rest, to think,* and *to catch a few fish.* *Parallel Clauses:* A news story should tell *what happened, when it happened,* and *who was involved.*

▶ **Exercise 1**   **Recognizing Parallel Ideas.**   Underline the parallel ideas in each sentence.

EXAMPLE: Ms. Downing has already gained considerable fame on stage, on television, and in the movies.

1. The summer program includes courses in cooking, sewing, and painting.
2. The safest way to lose weight is by eating less and by exercising more.
3. Entries will be judged for originality and for aptness of expression.
4. The history of the Pony Express was brief but colorful.
5. Polonius advised his son to be true to himself, to value his friends, and to keep his own counsel.
6. The increase in the sales tax will not affect the prices of groceries, children's clothing, or prescription drugs.
7. Management hopes to improve profits by cutting costs, increasing productivity, and improving distribution.
8. Ms. Collins stressed the importance of taking careful notes and reviewing the material daily.
9. As yet the inspector has no idea who could have committed so bizarre a crime or what the motive might have been.
10. A good adviser should be imaginative, patient, and sympathetic.

▶ **Exercise 2**   **Distinguishing Between Correct and Faulty Parallelism.**   In the blank at the right, indicate whether each sentence is correct as written (*C*) or contains faulty parallelism (*F*).

EXAMPLE: The guidance counselor recommended studying harder and to turn off the television set at homework time. ___*F*___

1. You can apply the stain with a cloth or by brushing it on. ___F___
2. The witness testified calmly, clearly, and convincingly. ___C___
3. A successful ballerina needs skill, stamina, and to have good coordination. ___F___
4. Skateboarding, roller skating, and bicycle riding are not permitted. ___C___
5. The inspector reported the situation and that something should be done. ___F___
6. The morning was hot, muggy, and with a cloudy sky. ___F___
7. The Ferret Sedan is roomy, inexpensive, and operates efficiently. ___F___
8. Carol likes browsing through encyclopedias and to learn odd facts. ___F___
9. The company's annual report showed an increase in sales but that profits had dropped. ___F___
10. Disease-causing agents may be present in air, food, or water. ___C___

21.4 Faulty Parallelism (Recognizing Faulty Parallelism)
• Practice 2

▶ **Exercise 1** **Recognizing Parallel Ideas.** Underline the two or more parallel ideas in each sentence. Then label each sentence as *correct parallelism* or *faulty parallelism.*

EXAMPLE: In her lecture the professor discussed migration, courtship, and how birds establish nesting territories. _*faulty parallelism*_

1. Good speech must be audible, logical, and have clarity. _____
2. My paper received a high grade for originality and for neatness. _____
3. Claire likes hiking for great distances and to climb mountains. _____
4. You can adjust the swing by lengthening one rope or you can shorten the other rope. _____
5. The insurance agent sold my parents a homeowners' policy and a life insurance policy. _____
6. The clock is compact, silent, and runs accurately. _____
7. The dolls were Russian, Italian, and one from England. _____
8. We interviewed the principal, a teacher, and with the nurse. _____
9. The football sailed across the yard, over the fence, and into our neighbor's prize dahlias. _____
10. In India we saw neither the Ganges nor went to Calcutta. _____
11. Riding a bike is not only good for your health but it is also fun. _____
12. My choices were either to do a dance or singing. _____
13. After waiting for hours, pacing the floor, and biting her nails, Sandy was frantic with worry. _____
14. Judy wanted an after-school job rather than to ask for a raise in her allowance. _____
15. Chuck sorted the books neatly and with great efficiency into piles. _____
16. To make a good stew, marinate the meat, add plenty of vegetables, and simmer slowly. _____
17. Joan took classes in history, science, and how to use computers. _____
18. The garden includes irises, roses, and it also has lilies. _____
19. Barbara is well liked because she is friendly, helpful, and she has a lot of confidence. _____
20. You can learn to dance if you sign up for a class, if you attend the class, and if you practice faithfully. _____

21.4 Faulty Parallelism (Correcting Faulty Parallelism)
• Practice 1

Correcting Faulty Parallelism   Correct a sentence containing faulty parallelism by rewriting it so that each parallel idea is expressed in the same grammatical structure.

Nonparallel Structures	Parallel Structures
The manager protested *loudly* and *with emotion*.	The manager protested *loudly* and *emotionally*.
A guard dog must be *tough, obedient,* and *without fear*.	A guard dog must be *tough, obedient,* and *fearless*.
Mr. Darling liked *weeding his garden, mowing his lawn,* and *to putter around his house*.	Mr. Darling liked *weeding his garden, mowing his lawn,* and *puttering around his house*.
The twins were identical *in appearance* and *how they behaved*.	The twins were identical in *appearance* and *behavior*.
The Dolphins were elated *over defeating the Seals* and *because they had won the championship*.	The Dolphins were elated over *defeating the Seals* and *winning the championship*.

▶ **Exercise 1**   **Identifying Faulty Parallelism.**   Underline the nonparallel structures in each sentence below.

EXAMPLE: The children loved playing in the surf and to build sand castles on the beach.

1. The candidate was criticized for being colorless and that he was overly cautious.
2. Paul likes cooking but dislikes to clean up afterward.
3. Mr. Asforis needs someone who will help in the stockroom and to make deliveries.
4. Reading the book was fun but to write a report on it was hard.
5. The pianist played with great feeling but occasionally hitting some sour notes.
6. The scouts especially liked hiking and to camp out.
7. The company can become profitable by cutting costs or sell more widgets.
8. Nick enjoyed receiving letters but not to write them.
9. The main duties of the job are typing, filing, and to do simple bookkeeping.
10. If you plan on flying or to take a train this weekend, you can expect crowds.

▶ **Exercise 2**   **Correcting Faulty Parallelism.**   Rewrite five sentences in Exercise 1, correcting the faulty parallelism.

EXAMPLE: *The children loved to play in the surf and to build sand castles on the beach.*

1. The candidate was critisized for being colorless & overly cautious.
2. Paul likes cooking but dislikes cleaning up afterwards
3. The scouts especially liked camping & hiking
4. Nick enjoyed receiving letters but not writing them.
5. Reading the book was fun but writing a report on it was hard

21.4 Faulty Parallelism (Correcting Faulty Parallelism) • Practice 2

Exercise 1 Correcting Faulty Parallelism of Words, Phrases, and Clauses. Write each sentence, correcting the faulty parallelism.

EXAMPLE: Joel likes imitating people and to tell jokes.

Joel likes imitating people and telling jokes.

1. We were happy to hear the good news and for being the first to congratulate them.

_____

2. The florist arranged the flowers, placing a few ferns here and there and then added a ribbon.

_____

3. Searching for buried treasure was fun, but to find real pirate booty was astounding.

_____

4. We talked to one another, not talking about one another.

_____

5. By thinking clearly and with being patient, you can unscramble an anagram.

_____

6. The man and his wife were served soup that offended them, a main course that sickened them, and the dessert made them nauseated.

_____

_____

7. My desires were to visit the museum and seeing everything in the displays.

_____

8. These plants need water and looking after.

_____

9. In the pond small beetles darted to and fro, pollywogs wriggling, and snails climbing up stems.

_____

10. He agreed to participate in the talent show but refused singing without a microphone.

_____

Writing Application Writing Sentences with Parallel Structures. Use the following instructions to write sentences of your own.

1. Use *and* to join two parallel prepositional phrases.

_____

2. Use *and* to join two parallel gerund phrases.

_____

3. Use *either* and *or* to join parallel infinitive phrases.

_____

4. Use *and* to join two parallel subordinate clauses.

_____

5. Write a comparison beginning "Listening to the radio is often more interesting than . . ."

_____

22.1 Verb Tenses (The Six Tenses of Verbs, The Four Principal Parts of Verbs) • Practice 1

The Six Tenses of Verbs A *tense* is a form of a verb that shows the time of action or state of being. Each tense has a basic and a progressive form. The progressive form of a verb ends in *ing*.

Tenses	Basic Forms	Progressive Forms
Present	He *obeys.*	He *is obeying.*
Past	He *obeyed.*	He *was obeying.*
Future	He *will obey.*	He *will be obeying.*
Present Perfect	He *has obeyed.*	He *has been obeying.*
Past Perfect	He *had obeyed.*	He *had been obeying.*
Future Perfect	He *will have obeyed.*	He *will have been obeying.*

on going / continuing action

The Four Principal Parts of Verbs A verb has four principal parts: the *present*, the *present participle*, the *past*, and the *past participle*.

THE FOUR PRINICPAL PARTS			
Present	**Present Participle**	**Past**	**Past Participle**
arrive	arriving	arrived	(have) arrived
begin	beginning	began	(have) begun
buy	buying	bought	(have) bought

▷ **Exercise 1** **Recognizing Tenses and Forms of Verbs.** Underline the verb or verb phrase in each sentence below. Then write the tense on each line to the right. If the form is progressive, write the word *progressive* after the tense.

EXAMPLE: We have been hearing rumors about Jake. _____*present perfect progressive*_____

1. I followed the recipe carefully. _____
2. The state police were pulling over many drivers. _____
3. I have tried several times to lose weight. _____
4. Tomorrow Grandma will have been visiting here a month. _____
5. That shop carries beautiful fabrics. _____
6. Soon that group will release a new video. _____
7. Dad and I will be waiting for you at the station. _____
8. Columbus had planned to reach the Orient. _____
9. Detectives had been investigating for months. _____
10. The workers will have finished by now. _____

▷ **Exercise 2** **Identifying Principal Parts.** On the lines below, write the principal part used to form the verb in each sentence above. Then write the name of that principal part.

EXAMPLE: _____*hearing   present participle*_____

1. _____   6. _____
2. _____   7. _____
3. _____   8. _____
4. _____   9. _____
5. _____   10. _____

22.1 Verb Tenses (The Six Tenses of Verbs, The Four Principal Parts of Verbs) • Practice 2

▶ Exercise 1 **Recognizing Basic and Progressive Forms.** Identify the form of each verb as *basic* or *progressive*.

EXAMPLE: She had been exercising. _____*progressive*_____

1. He is trying. _____
2. I had forgotten. _____
3. It will sink. _____
4. She was relaxing. _____
5. They had been dancing. _____
6. He promises. _____
7. She will understand. _____
8. They had finished. _____
9. We lost. _____
10. I will have been waiting. _____

11. You wish. _____
12. I had been reading. _____
13. They will be visiting. _____
14. I have finished. _____
15. They have been arguing. _____
16. She is working. _____
17. He sang. _____
18. You are joking. _____
19. It will be late. _____
20. We shopped. _____

▶ Exercise 2 **Recognizing the Six Tenses.** Write the tense of each verb in Exercise 1. If the form is not basic, add the name of the form.

EXAMPLE: She had been exercising. _____*past perfect progressive*_____

1. _____
2. _____
3. _____
4. _____
5. _____
6. _____
7. _____
8. _____
9. _____
10. _____

11. _____
12. _____
13. _____
14. _____
15. _____
16. _____
17. _____
18. _____
19. _____
20. _____

▶ Exercise 3 **Recognizing Principal Parts.** Identify the principal part used to form each verb in Exercise 1.

EXAMPLE: She had been exercising. _____*present participle*_____

1. _____
2. _____
3. _____
4. _____
5. _____
6. _____
7. _____
8. _____
9. _____
10. _____

11. _____
12. _____
13. _____
14. _____
15. _____
16. _____
17. _____
18. _____
19. _____
20. _____

22.1 Verb Tenses (Regular and Irregular Verbs)
• Practice 1

Regular and Irregular Verbs A *regular verb* forms the past and past participle by adding *-ed* or *-d* to the present form. The final consonant is sometimes doubled.

PRINCIPAL PARTS OF REGULAR VERBS			
Present	**Present Participle**	**Past**	**Past Participle**
cry	crying	cried	(have) cried
drop	dropping	dropped	(have) dropped
deprive	depriving	deprived	(have) deprived
grant	granting	granted	(have) granted

An *irregular verb* forms the past and past participle by changing spelling of the present form, not by adding *-ed* or *-d* to the present form.

PRINCIPAL PARTS OF IRREGULAR VERBS			
Present	**Present Participle**	**Past**	**Past Participle**
hurt	hurting	hurt	(have) hurt
shut	shutting	shut	(have) shut
find	finding	found	(have) found
teach	teaching	taught	(have) taught
fly	flying	flew	(have) flown
sing	singing	sang	(have) sung
write	writing	wrote	(have) written

▷ **Exercise 1** **Writing the Principal Parts of Irregular Verbs.** Add the missing principal parts.

EXAMPLE: rise ___*rising*___ ___*rose*___ ___*(have) risen*___

	Present	Present Participle	Past	Past Participle
1.	_____	beginning	_____	_____
2.	_____	_____	drew	_____
3.	freeze	_____	_____	_____
4.	_____	_____	_____	(have) run
5.	_____	_____	put	_____
6.	_____	thinking	_____	_____
7.	_____	_____	_____	(have) fallen
8.	catch	_____	_____	_____
9.	_____	_____	bound	_____
10.	_____	speaking	_____	_____

▷ **Exercise 2** **Recognizing Principal Parts of Verbs.** Fill in each blank with the correct verb form from those given in parentheses.

EXAMPLE: The final bell hasn't ___*rung*___ yet. (rang, rung)

1. Our water pipes _____ during the January freeze. (burst, busted)

2. We _____ the blanket on the sand. (spread, spreaded)

3. Paula _____ her foil at her opponent's vest. (thrust, thrusted)

4. Brenda has _____ in competitions for years. (dived, dove)

5. Someone has _____ into the computer file. (broke, broken)

22.1 Verb Tenses (Regular and Irregular Verbs)
• Practice 2

Exercise 1 **Learning the Principal Parts of Irregular Verbs.** Write the *present participle*, the *past*, and the *past participle* of each verb.

EXAMPLE: ride _____*riding rode ridden*_____

1. fight _____
2. let _____
3. split _____
4. shrink _____
5. arise _____
6. catch _____
7. sell _____
8. slay _____
9. cost _____
10. hang _____

11. sit _____
12. freeze _____
13. swim _____
14. draw _____
15. stick _____
16. teach _____
17. sing _____
18. win _____
19. tear _____
20. lay _____

Exercise 2 **Recognizing Principal Parts in Sentences.** Underline the correct form of the verb in parentheses.

EXAMPLE: She (throwed, threw) the ball over the fence.

1. The child (knowed, knew) the answer.
2. The customers (payed, paid) the bill promptly.
3. Grandfather (taught, teached) us how to whittle.
4. The high winds (blew, blowed) all night on the open sea.
5. The audience thought the judges (choosed, chose) the wrong contestant as the winner.
6. Jennifer (layed, laid) the package on the table.
7. Alice (wore, weared) a different blouse every day last week.
8. The bellboy (leaded, led) us to our rooms.
9. On Christmas morning, the eager child (tore, teared) the wrapping paper to pieces.
10. No one knew who had (stealed, stolen) the money.

Exercise 3 **Choosing Between the Past and Past Participle.** Underline the correct form of the verb in parentheses. Remember that the past participle is used with a helping verb.

(1) As early as 3000 B.C., the Egyptians had already (began, begun) keeping cats as pets. (2) Over the years cats (grew, grown) very valuable. (3) In particular, the Egyptians (gave, given) cats the job of keeping rats out of their grain supplies. (4) Egyptians (saw, seen) cats as so important that they embalmed them along with Pharaohs! (5) Archaeologists have found cat mummies in tombs where they have (lay, lain) for centuries. (6) Eventually, the Egyptians (came, come) to worship a cat-god called Bast. (7) According to legend, the defeat of the Egyptian army in 525 B.C. (arose, arisen) because of Bast. (8) The Persian enemy (knew, known) of Egyptian cat worship. (9) Therefore, the Persian general had (came, come) to battle with a row of cats in front of his troops. (10) Because Egyptian archers refused to shoot toward the sacred animals, victory (gone, went) to the Persians.

22.1 Verb Tenses (Conjugating the Tenses) • Practice 1

Conjugating the Tenses   A *conjugation* is a complete list of the singular and plural forms of a verb. A short conjugation lists just the forms that are used with a single pronoun. As you study the following short conjugations, note that the verbs used with *you* are also used with *we* and *they*. The verbs used with *she*, likewise, are also used with *he* and *it*.

SHORT CONJUGATIONS			
Basic, Progressive, and Emphatic Forms	**go (with I)**	**go (with you)**	**go (with she)**
Present	I go	You go	She goes
Past	I went	You went	She went
Future	I will go	You will go	She will go
Present Perfect	I have gone	You have gone	She has gone
Past Perfect	I had gone	You had gone	She had gone
Future Perfect	I will have gone	You will have gone	She will have gone
Present Progressive	I am going	You are going	She is going
Past Progressive	I was going	You were going	She was going
Future Progressive	I will be going	You will be going	She will be going
Present Perfect Progressive	I have been going	You have been going	She has been going
Past Perfect Progressive	I had been going	You had been going	She had been going
Future Perfect Progressive	I will have been going	You will have been going	She will have been going
Present Emphatic	I do go	You do go	She does go
Past Emphatic	I did go	You did go	She did go

▶ **Exercise 1**   **Conjugating Verbs.**   Complete each of the following short conjugations, giving all six basic forms and the first three progressive forms.

1. try (with *I*)   2. find (with *he*)   3. speak (with *we*)   4. run (with *they*)

_____   _____   _____   _____

_____   _____   _____   _____

_____   _____   _____   _____

_____   _____   _____   _____

_____   _____   _____   _____

_____   _____   _____   _____

_____   _____   _____   _____

_____   _____   _____   _____

_____   _____   _____   _____

▶ **Exercise 2**   **Supplying the Correct Verb Form.**   Fill in each blank with the form of each verb given in parentheses.

EXAMPLE: I _____*will be studying*_____ French next year. (study, *future progressive*)

1. We _____ our theory in the lab. (test, *future perfect*)

2. The lake _____ during the first week in January. (freeze, *past*)

3. Dad _____ the mantel clock already. (wind, *present perfect*)

4. Uncle Ed _____ dinner on Friday. (prepare, *past emphatic*)

5. The candidate _____ lower taxes. (promise, *past perfect*)

22.1 Verb Tenses (Conjugating the Tenses) • Practice 2

▶ **Exercise 1**   **Conjugating the Basic Forms of Verbs.**   Conjugate the basic forms of the two verbs below in the manner shown in the example.

EXAMPLE: choose (conjugated with *I*)

Present: ___*I choose*___

Past: ___*I chose*___

Future: ___*I will choose*___

Present Perfect: ___*I have chosen*___

Past Perfect: ___*I had chosen*___

Future Perfect: ___*I will have chosen*___

1. climb (conjugated with *we*)

_____

_____

_____

_____

_____

_____

2. say (conjugated with *they*)

_____

_____

_____

_____

_____

_____

▶ **Exercise 2**   **Conjugating the Progressive Forms of Verbs.**   Conjugate the progressive forms of the two verbs below in the manner shown in the example.

EXAMPLE: choose (conjugated with *I*)

Present Progressive: ___*I am choosing*___

Past Progressive: ___*I was choosing*___

Future Progressive: ___*I will be choosing*___

Present Perfect Progressive: ___*I have been choosing*___

Past Perfect Progressive: ___*I had been choosing*___

Future Perfect Progressive: ___*I will have been choosing*___

1. talk (conjugated with *he*)

_____

_____

_____

_____

_____

_____

2. sing (conjugated with *we*)

_____

_____

_____

_____

_____

_____

▶ **Exercise 3**   **Conjugating the Emphatic Forms of Verbs.**   Conjugate the emphatic forms of the two verbs below in the manner shown in the example.

EXAMPLE: choose (conjugated with *I*)

Present Emphatic: ___*I do choose*___

Past Emphatic: ___*I did choose*___

1. own (conjugated with *she*)_____   _____

2. sell (conjugated with *they*)_____   _____

22.1 Expressing Time Through Tense (Uses of Tense in Present Time) • Practice 1

Uses of Tense in Present Time   The three forms of the present tense show present actions or conditions as well as various continuous actions or conditions.

USES OF TENSE IN PRESENT TIME		
Verb Forms	Uses	Examples
Present	Present action Present condition Recurring action Recurring condition Constant action Constant condition	There *goes* the balloon. The band *sounds* wonderful. I *pack* my own lunch. The paramedics *are* prompt to arrive. The earth *rotates* on its axis. Pluto *is* the most distant planet.
Present Progressive	Continuing action Continuing condition	I *am studying* for a math test. Lenny *is being* stubborn today.
Present Emphatic	Emphasizing a statement Denying an assertion	I *do hope* for sun this weekend. Despite the rumors, we *do have* school tomorrow.

▶ **Exercise 1**   **Identifying the Uses of Tense in Present Time.**   Identify the use of the verb in each sentence, using the labels in the chart above.

EXAMPLE: Paul practices the piano before school every day.   _____recurring action_____

1. Jim certainly does study hard. _____

2. The Mississippi River begins in Minnesota. _____

3. Kyle mows the lawn during summer vacation. _____

4. All of these dishes taste alike tonight. _____

5. I hear a noise in the basement. _____

6. Grandpa is taking a nap. _____

7. A perpetual flame burns in Arlington Cemetery. _____

8. Regardless of earlier reports, Ed does plan to enter the race. _____

9. Mom commutes sixty miles every day. _____

10. My brother is going to school in Ohio now. _____

▶ **Exercise 2**   **Using Present Tense Forms in Sentences.**   Complete each sentence by filling in an appropriate form showing present time.

EXAMPLE: Terri _____walks_____ two miles every morning.

1. Sid _____ the cows now, but he will finish soon.

2. Although she is new in town, Beth _____ quite a few friends.

3. Our neighbors _____ to Alaska.

4. These sweet rolls _____ delicious.

5. Uncle Jack always _____ a nap after lunch.

6. I _____ *The Wind in the Willows* to my younger brother.

7. In spite of its high prices, the shop _____ many customers.

8. A hurricane _____ off the Florida coast.

9. Some people _____ to see you now.

10. Dan _____ German.

22.1 # Expressing Time Through Tense (Uses of
Tense in Present Time) • Practice 2

Uses of Tense in Present Time

USES OF THE PRESENT
Present action: Here they *come*.
Present condition: The air in the room *is* stale.
Regularly occurring action: Grandfather *sings* in the shower.
Regularly occurring condition: I *am* most alert in the morning.
Constant action: Animals *need* air to breathe.
Constant condition: The heart *is* a pump.

USES OF THE PRESENT PROGRESSIVE
Long continuing action: My uncle *is building* a sailboat.
Short continuing action: I *am whistling* a tune from *Oklahoma*.
Continuing condition: Gloria *is being* extra helpful this week.

USES OF THE PRESENT EMPHATIC
Emphasizing a statement: I *do believe* you dropped this.
Denying a contrary assertion: Despite the review's claim, that diner *does bake* its own pies.

▶ **Exercise 1** **Identifying the Uses of Tense in Present Time.** Identify the use of the underlined verb in each sentence, using the labels in the charts above.

EXAMPLE: Carl drives his mother to church every Sunday. _____*regularly occurring action*_____

1. My brother is picking up Father at the station. _____
2. I hear loud noises next door. _____
3. Now the president approaches the podium.
4. I jog three miles every morning. _____
5. In spite of warnings, my sister still chews her nails. _____
6. The weather is bad along the entire east coast today. _____
7. The members of the club are raising funds through many different activities this year. _____
8. Mumps and measles are widespread this year. _____
9. My old aunt walks to town almost every morning at the same time. _____
10. I do see a ship in the distance. _____
11. Al is writing a novel. _____
12. The windshield wiper blade is worn. _____
13. No matter what you think, I do practice the piano daily. _____
14. The cats are most active at night. _____
15. Ross sleeps without a pillow. _____
16. Brandon is playing a video game. _____
17. Green plants need sunshine to aid in photosynthesis. _____
18. Most of an iceberg is under water. _____
19. Jan is being very patient with the disobedient dog. _____
20. I do wish you'd make less noise. _____

22.1 Expressing Time Through Tense (Uses of Tense in Past Time) • Practice 1

Uses of Tense in Past Time   The seven forms that express past time show actions and conditions beginning in the past.

USES OF TENSES IN PAST TIME		
Verb Forms	**Uses**	**Examples**
Past	Indefinite past time Definite past time	Jake *mowed* the lawn. Tim *was* sick yesterday.
Present Perfect	Indefinite past time Continuing to present	Janet *has finished* her paper. Grandma *has been* busy all day.
Past Perfect	Completed before another past event	The caller *had hung* up by the time I got to the phone.
Past Progressive	Continuous past event	The sun *was shining* yesterday.
Present Perfect Progressive	Event continuing to present	I *have been studying* all weekend.
Past Perfect Progressive	Continuous past event before another	Before the storm, we *had been enjoying* our picnic.
Past Emphatic	Emphasizing a statement	I *did finish* in time. Despite Brenda's account, Ali *did* *complete* the event.

▶ **Exercise 1**   **Identifying the Uses of Tenses in Past Time.**   Identify the use of the verb in each sentence, using the labels in the chart above.

EXAMPLE: The cast has been rehearsing for a month.   *event continuing to present*

1. Before the opening, the producers had hoped for a hit. _____
2. Bruno was sleeping on the front porch. _____
3. Doris baby-sat for the Holmans. _____
4. We have visited Niagara Falls. _____
5. Several patients were angry about the long wait. _____

▶ **Exercise 2**   **Using Tenses in Past Time.**   Write the correct form of the verb in parentheses.

EXAMPLE: The host _____*served*_____ a fine meal last night. (served, has been serving)

1. I _____ my homework and crawled into bed. (was finishing, had finished)
2. Bernie _____ my best friend since kindergarten. (has been, was being)
3. When we got to the station, the train _____. (has left, had left)
4. The new play _____ last night. (opened, has opened)
5. When I met Lydia, she _____ in a fabric store. (has worked, was working)
6. Andrea protested that she _____ the present. (was liking, did like)
7. The candidate _____ signatures on the petition since dawn. (has been gathering, gathered)
8. Cori _____ for the job yesterday. (applied, has applied)
9. I _____ for the bus when Kim came by. (waited, was waiting)
10. Ken and Bill _____ to repair the wall since Monday. (were working, have been working)

22.1 Expressing Time Through Tense (Uses of Tense in Past Time) • Practice 2

Uses of Tense in Past Time

USES OF THE PAST
Completed action: Judy *finished* her science project.   *Completed condition:* Father *was* terribly depressed.

USES OF THE PRESENT PERFECT
Completed action (indefinite time): Sue *has washed* her hair.   *Completed condition (indefinite time):* She *has been* ill.   *Action continuing to present:* I *have worked* here a year.   *Condition continuing to present:* She *has been* here since May.

USES OF THE PAST PERFECT
Action completed before another past action: Bob *had studied* all the college catalogs before he filled out any applications.   *Condition completed before another past condition:* I *had been* a member of the club long before you were.

USES OF PROGRESSIVE TO EXPRESS PAST TIME	
Past Progressive	*Long continuing action in the past:* Last summer my brother *was working* in Florida. *Short continuing action in the past:* I was *making* omelets this morning. *Continuing condition in the past:* Frank *was being* careful with the pesticide.
Present Perfect Progressive	*Action continuing to the present:* Bob *has been studying* college catalogs.
Past Perfect Progressive	*Continuing action interrupted by another:* The wheat crop *had been thriving* until it was attacked by locusts.

> **Exercise 1** **Using the Past, the Present Perfect, and the Past Perfect.** Underline the correct form of the verb in parentheses.

EXAMPLE: Marie (<u>came</u>, has come) home yesterday.

1. Joshua (has been reading, <u>had read</u>) all of the book before the quiz yesterday.
2. The train (<u>pulled</u>, has pulled) into the station hours ago.
3. Katherine (had been working, <u>has been working</u>) on that poem for a month, and it's still not finished.
4. Every day last week the mail carrier (<u>brought</u>, has brought) me at least one letter.
5. When we drank the soda, we noticed it (has lost, <u>had lost</u>) its fizz.
6. Before he spoke, the demonstrators (<u>rushed</u>, have rushed) down the aisle.
7. The young children never (have seen, <u>had seen</u>) a bald eagle before yesterday.
8. I (<u>developed</u>, have developed) this process a week ago.
9. The judge (has granted, <u>granted</u>) the lawyer's request for leniency yesterday.
10. Mr. Suarez (<u>was working</u>, worked) when a thunderstorm suddenly began.

> **Exercise 2** **Identifying the Uses of Tense in Past Time.** Identify the use of each underlined verb, using the labels in the charts above.

EXAMPLE: He <u>has been</u> in Miami for a year now. _____*condition continuing to present*_____

1. I <u>have seen</u> that movie. _____
2. Lou <u>finished</u> his assignment this morning. _____
3. The actors <u>have been rehearsing</u> the new play for three months. _____
4. I <u>had read</u> the book before it was assigned to the class. _____
5. Keith <u>has finished</u> three paintings. _____

22.1 Expressing Time Through Tense (Uses of Tense in Future Time) • Practice 1

Uses of Tense in Future Time   The four forms that express future time show future actions or conditions.

USES OF TENSES IN FUTURE TIME		
Verb Forms	**Uses**	**Examples**
Future	Future event	Grandma *will visit* us next week.
Future Perfect	Future event before another	We *will have finished* our chores before lunch.
Future Progressive	Continuing future event	The scouts *will be selling* cookies all of next month.
Future Perfect Progressive	Continuing future event before another	By opening night, the actors *will have been rehearsing* for six weeks.

▶ **Exercise 1**   **Identifying the Uses of Tenses in Future Time.**   Identify the use of the verb in each sentence, using the labels in the chart above.

EXAMPLE: The weather tomorrow will be perfect. ___*future event*___

1. The circus will be coming to town next week. _____

2. The roofers will have delivered the shingles by noon. _____

3. The stores will be starting their white sales next week. _____

4. The whole family will go out for dinner. _____

5. Soon we will have been waiting here for an hour. _____

6. A new catalog will be arriving shortly. _____

7. Jason will have completed his research by then. _____

8. Next year, Ali will have been performing for a decade. _____

9. Jodi will be visiting several colleges next weekend. _____

10. By dinnertime, the gelatin will have set. _____

▶ **Exercise 2**   **Using Tenses in Future Time.**   Fill in each blank with the indicated form of the verb in parentheses.

EXAMPLE: The President ___*will address*___ Congress tonight. (address, *future*)

1. A local restaurant _____ the party. (cater, *future progressive*)

2. A real disc jockey _____ records. (play, *future progressive*)

3. By midnight, they _____ on the flagpole for seventeen hours. (sit, *future perfect progressive*)

4. The shipment you ordered _____ soon. (arrive, *future progressive*)

5. Surely you _____ Tanya to the party. (invite, *future*)

6. Before the play, we _____ the town with posters. (paper, *future perfect*)

7. This term, I _____ six credits. (take, *future progressive*)

8. By the time we get there, all the singers _____. (perform, *future perfect*)

9. The team _____ its first game on Saturday. (play, *future progressive*)

10. Mom _____ your call when she gets back. (return, *future*)

22.1 Expressing Time Through Tense (Uses of Tense in Future Time) • Practice 2

Uses of Tense in Future Time

FORMS EXPRESSING FUTURE TIME	
Future	She will speak.
Future Perfect	She will have spoken.
Future Progressive	She will be speaking.
Future Perfect Progressive	She will have been speaking.

USES OF THE FUTURE AND THE FUTURE PERFECT	
Future	*Future action:* We *will race* in the main event.
	Future condition: The room *will be* warm soon.
Future Perfect	*Future action completed before another:* I *will have finished* the book by the end of the week.
	Future condition completed before another: My sister *will have been* out of school five years by the time I graduate.

USES OF PROGRESSIVE TO EXPRESS FUTURE TIME	
Future Progressive	*Continuing future action:* The team *will be practicing* during July and August.
Future Perfect Progressive	*Continuing future action completed before another:* By the time of our first game, I *will have been practicing* for two months.

> **Exercise 1** **Identifying the Uses of Tense in Future Time.** Identify the use of each underlined verb, using the labels in the charts above.

EXAMPLE: Louise will have finished her report before I begin. _____*future action completed before another*_____

1. Mr. Drake will be visiting our class this afternoon. _____
2. Clare will tell you her decision tomorrow. _____
3. I will have been studying for two hours before you arrive. _____
4. He will have been here a year next June. _____
5. The company will provide free refreshments at the party. _____
6. The buses will be late today because of the snow. _____
7. Ethel will be practicing this afternoon. _____
8. He will have left by the time we get there. _____
9. I will have been driving all night when I reach Maine. _____
10. To be kind, some people will tell you only pleasant things. _____

> **Exercise 2** **Using Tense in Future Time.** Fill in each blank with the indicated form of the verb in parentheses.

EXAMPLE: Carol _____*will deliver*_____ her speech tonight. (deliver/*future*)

1. The plane _____ in about two hours. (arrive/*future*)
2. By the time I return home in September, I _____ for six months. (travel/*future perfect progressive*)
3. Before school ends, Steven _____ his career decision. (make/*future perfect*)
4. We _____ parts of Canada in June. (visit/*future progressive*)
5. In another ten years, they _____ the time capsule. (open/*future*)

22.1 Expressing Time Through Tense (Shifts in Tense, Modifiers That Help Clarify Tense) • Practice 1

Shifts in Tense   When showing a sequence of events, do not shift tenses unnecessarily.

Unnecessary (Incorrect) Shifts	Correct Sequence
I *had promised* to help Sylvia, but I *forget*.	I *had promised* to help *Sylvia*, but I *forgot*.
Our cat *has* its own basket. The dog *slept* on my bed.	The cat *has* its own basket. The dog *sleeps* on my bed.
If you *look* carefully, you *saw* the brush strokes.	If you *look* carefully, you *will see* the brush strokes.

Modifiers That Help Clarify Tense   Use modifiers to help clarify the time expressed by a verb.

MODIFIERS EXPRESSING TIME
I *often* study in the library.
That rock group has become very popular *recently*.
Someone will install the telephone *before noon*.

▶**Exercise 1**   **Recognizing and Correcting Unnecessary Shifts in Tense.**   Rewrite each sentence below that has an unnecessary shift in tense. If a sentence is correct as written, write *correct* on the line.

EXAMPLE: I will drive you to school if you needed a ride.

_____ *I will drive you to school if you need a ride.* _____

1. We never watch television until we finished our homework.

   _____

2. My brother will study law when he will graduate from college.

   _____

3. Phil started jogging before he warms up.

   _____

4. We found the library book right where we were leaving it.

   _____

5. I will have finished my report long before it is due.

   _____

▶**Exercise 2**   **Using Modifiers to Help Clarify Tense.**   Fill in each blank with a modifier that helps to make clear the tense of the sentence.

EXAMPLE: _____ *Late last night* _____ I heard a strange sound in the attic.

1. We will return your book before you go on vacation _____.

2. The baby has been cranky _____ because she missed her nap.

3. _____, Laura became an outstanding gymnast.

4. When we got to the gate, the plane had _____ left.

5. I will be there _____ to watch you play.

22.1 Expressing Time Through Tense (Shifts in Tense, Modifiers That Help Clarify Tense) • Practice 2

▶ **Exercise 1** **Avoiding Unnecessary Shifts in Tense.** Rewrite each sentence, correcting tense problems by changing the second verb.

EXAMPLE: When I finished my work, Jim comes in.

When I finished my work, Jim came in.

1. My father growled at the salesman and tells him to leave.
   _____ " and told him _____

2. I landed in Stockholm and arrive an hour later at my hotel.
   _____ arrived _____

3. Beethoven conducted the first performance of his Ninth Symphony when he is already deaf.
   _____ was _____

4. It has been several years since I last see my grandfather.
   _____ saw _____

5. I walked into the room and find no one there.
   _____ found _____

6. As soon as the operation was over, I visit him.
   _____ visited _____

7. He exercises in the health spa before he left for work.
   _____ leaves _____

8. The visitor stayed two hours and then leaves abruptly.
   _____ left _____

9. The first story Hemingway wrote was "Up in Michigan," and the last is "Old Man at the Bridge."
   _____ was _____

10. The referee asked a question or two and stops the fight.
    _____ stopped _____

11. The car has front-wheel drive and came with power brakes and power steering.
    _____ had _____

12. If Susan wins first prize, she will have been getting many offers to perform.
    _____ will be _____

13. They were sailing to Bermuda when you are on your trip.
    _____ were _____

14. My family had dinner at a Japanese restaurant, and then they go to the movies.
    _____ went _____

15. When she completed the assignment, she achieves a first for an American architect.
    _____ achieved _____

22.2 # Active and Passive Voice (Differences Between Active and Passive Verbs, The Forms of Passive Verbs)

• Practice 1

Differences Between Active and Passive Verbs   *Voice* is the form of a verb that shows whether or not the subject is performing the action. A verb is active if its subject performs the action. A verb is passive if its action is performed upon the subject.

Active Voice	Passive Voice
Uncle Lou *met* our plane.	Our plane *was met* by Uncle Lou.
My aunt *taught* me to play the piano.	I *was taught* to play the piano by my aunt.

The Forms of Passive Verbs   A *passive verb* is made from a form of *be* plus the past participle of a transitive verb.

THE VERB *CATCH* IN THE PASSIVE VOICE		
Tense	**Basic Forms**	**Progressive Forms**
Present	I am caught.	I am being caught.
Past	I was caught.	I was being caught.
Future	I will be caught.	
Present Perfect	I have been caught.	
Past Perfect	I had been caught.	
Future Perfect	I will have been caught.	

▷ **Exercise 1**   **Distinguishing Between the Active and Passive Voice.**   After each sentence, write *active* or *passive* to describe the verb.

EXAMPLE: The test flight was made over the desert. ___*passive*___

1. The ambulance has been called. ___passive___
2. This bread was baked by my grandmother. ___passive___
3. The doctor warned against using too much salt. ___active___
4. A new slate of officers has been nominated. ___passive___
5. The movie was reviewed favorably by several critics. ___passive___
6. The manufacturer will advertise the new product heavily. ___active___
7. A new strain of bacteria has been identified. ___passive___
8. I have been having trouble concentrating today. ___active___
9. Despite her years of training, Michelle has never performed publicly. ___active___
10. Several city officials have been asked to resign. ___passive___

▷ **Exercise 2**   **Forming Tenses of Passive Verbs.**   Write the basic forms of each of the following verbs in the passive voice.

1. **find** (with *you*)

you are found
you were found
you will be found
you have been found
you had been
you will have been

2. **make** (with *it*)

it is made
it was made
it will be
it has been
it had been
it will have been

3. **see** (with *he*)

he is seen
he was seen
he will be
he has been
he had been
he will have been

4. **like** (with *they*)

they are liked
they were
they will be
they have been
they had been
they will have been

22.2 Active and Passive Voice (Differences Between Active and Passive Verbs, The Forms of Passive Verbs) • Practice 2

▷ **Exercise 1** **Distinguishing Between the Active and Passive Voice.** Identify each verb as *active* or *passive*.

EXAMPLE: The movie was seen by our whole family. ____*passive*____

1. The letter was obviously signed by a stranger. ____passive____
2. The gates in front of the embassy were closed each night. ____passive____
3. Several business people raced through the airport to catch their flights. ____active____
4. I try to watch as little television as possible. ____active____
5. Most of the books have been chosen by the librarians. ____passive____
6. All four of these symphonies were composed by Brahms. ____passive____
7. The next morning we began our long trek through the steaming jungle. ____active____
8. The air conditioner was delivered later in the day. ____passive____
9. The mayor asked for volunteers to serve on the new committee for planning the city's holiday festival. ____active____
10. A decaying tooth was extracted by my dentist. ____passive____
11. The patient was being taken by ambulance to the plane. ____passive____
12. With wild abandon the players charged across the field. ____active____
13. My mother saves manufacturers' discount coupons. ____active____
14. On a trip across country, the car will have been driven by several people. ____passive____
15. The guest speaker explained his theory to a rather uninterested audience. ____active____

THE VERB *DRIVE* IN THE PASSIVE VOICE			
Present	he is driven	**Past Perfect**	he had been driven
Past	he was driven	**Future Perfect**	he will have been driven
Future	he will be driven	**Present Progressive**	he is being driven
Present Perfect	he has been driven	**Past Progressive**	he was being driven

▷ **Exercise 2** **Forming the Tenses of Passive Verbs.** Conjugate each verb in the passive voice, using the chart above as your model.

1. give (with *we*)

   we are given
   we were given
   we will be given
   we have been given
   we had been given
   we will have been given
   we are being given
   we were being driven

2. tell (with *they*)

   they are told
   they were told
   they will be told
   they have been told
   they had been told
   they will have been told
   they are being told
   they were being told

22.2 Active and Passive Voice (Using Voice Correctly)
• Practice 1

Using Voice Correctly   Use the active voice whenever possible. Use the passive voice to emphasize the receiver of an action rather than the performer of an action. Also use the passive voice to point out the receiver of an action whenever the performer is not important or not easily identified.

VERBS IN THE PASSIVE VOICE	
Unnecessary Passive	**Appropriate Passive**
Our table *was served* first by the waiter.	The President's speech *will be carried* by all the networks.
	The visiting dignitaries *were seated* in the royal box.

▶ **Exercise 1**   **Distinguishing Between Appropriate and Unnecessary Uses of Passive Voice.**
Label *A* the appropriate uses of the passive in the following sentences. Label the other sentences *U*.

EXAMPLE: We were kept after school by the principal. ___U___

1. A roar was given by the crowd. ___U___
2. The actor was acclaimed for his performance. ___A___
3. The phone was answered by Lauren. ___U___
4. A concert was presented by the orchestra and chorus. ___U___
5. That new store will be closed on Saturdays. ___A___
6. Tonight dinner was cooked by Dad. ___U___
7. All contest entries must be mailed by December 31. ___A___
8. A concert was presented by the orchestra and chorus. ___U___
9. A kite was being flown by the children. ___U___
10. The arrival of the British troops was announced by Paul Revere. ___U___

▶ **Exercise 2**   **Using the Active Voice.**   Rewrite five of the sentences that you labeled *U* in
Exercise 1. Change or add words as necessary to put each verb into the active voice.

EXAMPLE: *The principal kept us after school.*

1. _The crowd gave a roar._
2. _Lauren answered the phone._
3. _A friend of mine won a blue ribon_
4. _Dad cooked dinner tonight_
5. _The children were flying a kite_

22.2 Active and Passive Voice (Using Voice Correctly)
• Practice 2

▶ **Exercise 1** **Correcting Unnecessary Use of the Passive Voice.** Rewrite the following paragraph, changing at least five uses of the passive voice to active.

EXAMPLE: The uses of aspirin have been studied by scientists for many years.

Scientists have studied the uses of aspirin for many years.

(1) After over a century of use, aspirin today is still regarded as a "wonder drug." (2) Aspirin, acetylsalicylic acid, was first developed as a painkiller by Felix Hoffman, a German chemist, in 1893. (3) He had been asked by his father, who was suffering from rheumatism, to develop a pain reliever that would not irritate the stomach. (4) Though the formula worked, how it worked could not be told by scientists. (5) Since its introduction, aspirin has been used successfully to reduce fever, pain, and inflammation. (6) Not long ago, a new use for aspirin was uncovered by researchers. (7) The one major drawback of aspirin has always been its tendency to cause intestinal bleeding. (8) This drawback now has been turned into an advantage. (9) It has been discovered that this quality of aspirin may prevent blood clots that often lead to heart attacks and strokes. (10) This is welcome news to the aspirin industry.

1) After over a century of use, many people still regard asprin as a "wonder drug".
2) Felix Huffman, a German chemist, first developed asprin, acetylsalicylic acid, as a painkiller in 1893.
3) His father, who was suffering from rheumatism, asked him to develop a pain-reliever that wouldn't irritate the stomach.
4) Though the formula worked, scientists couldn't tell how it work
5) Since it's introduction, many people have used asprin successfully to reduce, fever, pain, and inflammation.

▶ **Writing Application** **Using the Active and Passive Voice in Writing.** Write a short description of something exciting that happened to you recently. Include two sentences using the passive voice appropriately. Make sure all the other sentences use the active voice.

23.1 The Cases of Pronouns (The Three Cases)
• Practice 1

The Three Cases   Case is the form of a noun or a pronoun that indicates its use in a sentence. The three cases are *nominative*, *objective*, and *possessive*.

CASE FORMS OF PRONOUNS		
Case	**Use in Sentence**	**Forms**
Nominative	subject, predicate nominative	I; you; he, she, it; we; they
Objective	direct object, indirect object, object of preposition	me; you; him, her, it; us; them
Possessive	to show ownership	my, mine; your, yours; his; her, hers; its; our, ours; their, theirs

▶ **Exercise 1**   **Identifying Case.**   Write the case of each underlined pronoun.

EXAMPLE: Before vigorous exercise, <u>we</u> always warm up. _____nominative_____

1. Did the usher give <u>you</u> a program? _____
2. Thomas has lent me <u>his</u> history notes. _____
3. Mandy is bringing <u>her</u> famous brownies to the party. _____
4. Do all of these cookies have nuts in <u>them</u>? _____
5. The book on the table is <u>yours</u>. _____
6. A movie that <u>I</u> want to see is playing at the Bijou. _____
7. The doctor is redecorating <u>her</u> office. _____
8. Ben said that you told <u>him</u> about the party. _____
9. The cat curled up in <u>its</u> basket. _____
10. Uncle Jim lent <u>us</u> his projector. _____

▶ **Exercise 2**   **Identifying Pronoun Case and Use.**   Write the case of each underlined pronoun. Then write the abbreviation that describes how the pronoun is used in the sentence: *S* (subject), *PN* (predicate nominative), *DO* (direct object), *IO* (indirect object), *OP* (object of a preposition), *O* (to show ownership).

EXAMPLE: The strongest candidates are Beth and <u>you</u>. _____nominative, PN_____

1. Ms. Emmons showed <u>us</u> a new glazing technique. _____
2. Peter and <u>he</u> rotate at first base. _____
3. Did I get a call from Donna or <u>him</u>? _____
4. Each book should have a code number on <u>its</u> spine. _____
5. <u>They</u> ordered the car in plenty of time. _____
6. We felt bad because no one invited <u>us</u>. _____
7. Alicia practiced <u>her</u> piece for the recital. _____
8. The new hall monitors are Harry and <u>I</u>. _____
9. My grandparents have offered us <u>their</u> summer cottage. _____
10. Jason will be spending the weekend with <u>us</u>. _____

23.1 The Cases of Pronouns (The Three Cases)
• Practice 2

▶ **Exercise 1**   **Identifying Case.**   Write the case of each underlined pronoun. Then write its use.

EXAMPLE: The witness finally told the truth about them.   _objective (object of a preposition)_

1. Father and he will meet Mother at the station. _____
2. Please give him the letter now. _____
3. Our reasons are not really important. _____
4. The doctor agreed to discuss the symptoms with them. _____
5. Between you and me, I think Bill is telling the truth. _____
6. The team captain is she. _____
7. Our poster is the best so far. _____
8. In the morning, they began to cross the lake. _____
9. Are you sure that's her work? _____
10. The principal spoke to us. _____
11. My friends and I collected funds for cancer research. _____
12. Your congressional representative just phoned. _____
13. This unpleasant matter is between him and them. _____
14. I gave her a number of ideas about the campaign. _____
15. Bring the reports to us at once. _____
16. Won't you tell the reporters what really happened? _____
17. Undoubtedly, those keys belong to them. _____
18. We want to pay for the gift. _____
19. A special effort was made by her. _____
20. I know my books are there. _____

▶ **Exercise 2**   **Identifying Pronouns and Pronoun Case.**   Underline the pronoun in each sentence. Then write the case of the pronoun and the abbreviation that describes how the pronoun is used in the sentence: *S* (subject), *PN* (predicate nominative), *DO* (direct object), *IO* (indirect object), *OP* (object of a preposition), *O* (to show ownership).

EXAMPLE: She looked up and saw a flock of wild geese.   _She, nominative, S_

1. He wants to get a driver's license soon. _____
2. Kate said the red book is yours. _____
3. Kevin gave her a bracelet for Mother's Day. _____
4. Yesterday was her fifteenth birthday. _____
5. Having climbed the mountain before, Stan climbed it more easily this time. _____
6. The person on the telephone is she. _____
7. Sharon bought a magazine for him. _____
8. Florence gave her a long lecture on good manners. _____
9. Patrick saw me at the train station. _____
10. Please give the blue bowl back to us. _____

23.1 The Cases of Pronouns (The Nominative Case, The Objective Case) • Practice 1

The Nominative Case   Use the nominative case for the subject of a verb or for a predicate nominative. When a pronoun used as a subject or predicate nominative is followed by an appositive, the nominative case is still used.

USES OF NOMINATIVE CASE	
Subject	Janet and *she* are sharing an apartment. *We* players pay for our own uniforms.
Predicate Nominative	I think the caller was *she*. The first team up is *we* Sockers.

The Objective Case   Use the objective case for the object of any verb, preposition, or verbal.

USES OF OBJECTIVE CASE	
Direct Object	The course will train *us* in CPR. Dad drove Jed and *me* to the fire station. They announced *us* gymnasts one by one.
Indirect Object	The judges awarded *her* a blue ribbon . Mom ordered Sue and *me* new shoes. The guide showed *us* tourists the White House.
Object of a Preposition	I mailed an invitation to *him* yesterday. You may leave the package with Dan or *me*. The announcer seemed to speak directly to *us* viewers.
Object of a Verbal	Encouraging *us*, she waved from the sidelines. Mr. Koch liked eating tomatoes but not growing *them*. Molly considered the new book and decided to give *it* a try.

▷ **Exercise 1**   **Identifying Pronouns in the Nominative Case.**   Circle the nominative pronoun form in parentheses. Then write *S* (subject) or *PN* (predicate nominative) to describe its use.

EXAMPLE: Vivian and (ⓗe, him) ordered the shore dinner. ____S____

1. Hal and (I, me) help with many household chores. _____
2. The new student in our homeroom is (he, him). _____
3. The most likely suspects are (they, them). _____
4. (Her, She) offered a large reward for the return of the lost dog. _____
5. Dave or (he, him) can give you directions. _____

▷ **Exercise 2**   **Identifying Pronouns in the Objective Case.**   Circle the objective pronoun form in parentheses. Then write *DO* (direct object), *IO* (indirect object), or *OP* (objective of a preposition) to describe its use.

EXAMPLE: Mme. Karla showed (ⓤs, we) dancers a new step. ____IO____

1. Jenny told (her, she). _____
2. Jo bought this for (he, him). _____
3. Give (we, us) kids a chance. _____
4. Lend (I, me) a hand. _____
5. Are these for Harry or (I, me)? _____
6. I told (them, they) the news. _____
7. Show this to (she, her). _____
8. I have never met (him, he). _____
9. Did you see (us, we)? _____
10. The fans gave (us, we) players a cheer. _____

23.1 The Cases of Pronouns (The Nominative Case, The Objective Case) • Practice 2

Exercise 1 **Identifying Pronouns in the Nominative Case.** Choose the pronoun in the nominative case to complete each sentence. Then write the use of the pronoun.

EXAMPLE: Phyllis and ___*we*___ are giving the party. (us, we) ___*subject*___

1. Terry and _____ went to a movie last night. (me, I) _____

2. _____ sophomores are planning the activities. (We, Us) _____

3. _____ and Robert are the only ones absent. (She, Her) _____

4. The losers were Maureen and _____ . (I, me) _____

5. I can't believe that _____ and Greg are in town. (her, she) _____

6. Your new teacher is _____ . (he, him) _____

7. Craig and _____ cleaned the whole house. (she, her) _____

8. The new students are Cynthia and _____ . (he, him) _____

9. Barry and _____ solved the problem. (I, me) _____

10. The counselor to see about that problem is _____ . (her, she) _____

Exercise 2 **Identifying Pronouns in the Objective Case.** Choose the pronoun in the objective case to complete each sentence. Then write the use of the pronoun.

EXAMPLE: The principal wants to see ___*him*___ immediately. (him, he) ___*object of infinitive*___

1. Larry saw _____ in town yesterday. (I, me) _____

2. Give the apple to _____ . (her, she) _____

3. My uncle sent a letter to _____ . (me, I) _____

4. I had lunch with _____ just last week. (they, them) _____

5. Carol wants to tell _____ about the new program offered by her high school. (him, he) _____

6. Just between you and _____ , I don't think Tim will win. (I, me) _____

7. The woman babysitting _____ was very responsible. (they, them) _____

8. Mary tried to ask _____ about the incident. (he, him) _____

9. The officer found _____ in the playground on the new set of swings. (her, she) _____

10. Please stand in front of _____ . (me, I) _____

23.1 The Cases of Pronouns (The Possessive Case)
• Practice 1

The Possessive Case   Use the possessive case before nouns and before gerunds to show ownership. Use certain possessive pronouns by themselves to indicate possession.

USES OF THE POSSESSIVE CASE	
Before Nouns	Have you found *your* keys? Jared has not chosen *his* courses yet.
Before Gerunds	All of the other students admired *her writing*. *His* whining annoyed all of us.
Alone	The sweater on the yard chair is *hers*, not *his*, Is that desk *yours* or *mine* ?

▶ **Exercise 1**   **Using Pronouns in the Possessive Case.**   Choose the correct word in each set of parentheses to complete the sentences below.

EXAMPLE: Please put the record back into _____*its*_____ jacket. (it's, its)

1. _____ working at night has changed the family's schedule. (Him, His)
2. That statue of a woman on a horse is _____. (mine, my)
3. Mrs. Killian complimented _____ handling of the incident. (our, us)
4. I brought my towel along, but I couldn't find _____. (your's, yours)
5. Louise practiced _____ speech for several days. (her, hers)
6. Have you asked Mr. Hawkins about _____ taking the class pictures? (him, his)
7. We couldn't decide whether to have the party at our house or _____.
   (their's, theirs)
8. _____ solution to the puzzle surprised everyone. (My, Mine)
9. The dog returned the stick to _____ owner. (it's, its)
10. We admired _____ cooking. (them, their)

▶ **Exercise 2**   **More Work with Pronouns in the Possessive Case.**   Write a possessive pronoun in the space provided to complete each of the sentences below.

EXAMPLE: _____*Our*_____ team won the game.

1. Isn't this car _____?
2. Nearly every year _____ Ramblers are in the finals.
3. _____ doing the laundry so late at night woke up the family.
4. I want to know which of those notebooks is _____.
5. Danny begged Marcia to disclose _____ secret.
6. The storm left destruction in _____ wake.
7. The officers were charged with inappropriate tactics in _____ handling of the investigation.
8. Alice claimed that the book was _____.
9. Billy felt that _____ hard work had paid off when he passed the test.
10. The breeders were ecstatic when _____ horse won the race.

23.1 The Cases of Pronouns (The Possessive Case)
• Practice 2

▶ **Exercise 1** Using Pronouns in the Possessive Case. Choose the correct word in each set of parentheses to complete the sentences below.

EXAMPLE: The teacher was tired of ___his___ talking in class. (his, him)

1. I think this book is _____. (yours, your's)

2. The door fell off _____ hinges. (its, it's)

3. _____ a beautiful day today. (Its, It's)

4. _____ answers were unsatisfactory. (Their, Them)

5. The angry woman finally told him that _____ nagging had to stop. (his, him)

6. The camera and the manual are _____. (ours, our's).

7. The dog looked for _____ master. (its, it's)

8. I'm quite sure that this pencil is _____. (mine, mine's).

9. Are all of those gowns _____? (hers, her's)

10. Father wants _____ practicing to stop soon. (their, them)

11. I can't see why you object to _____ borrowing your book for the afternoon (my, me)

12. He thinks that _____ very well prepared. (you, you're)

13. _____ scheduled to arrive in an hour. (They're, Their)

14. _____ dancing did not impress the audience. (Our, Us)

15. Do you know how many of these magazines are _____? (their's, theirs)

16. Mother liked _____ singing. (my, me)

17. _____ leaving the committee meeting now is out of the question. (You're, Your)

18. The insulted woman demanded _____ apology. (his, his's)

19. _____ singing delighted the children. (her, hers)

20. I wonder if _____ raining outside. (its, it's)

▶ **Exercise 2** Using All Three Cases. Choose the correct word in each set of parentheses to complete the sentences below.

1. The doctor told both William and _____ his reasons for prescribing the medicine. (she, her)

2. _____ and _____ make a fine team. (He, Him) (she her)

3. _____ contributions cannot be overestimated. (Their, They're)

4. These sketches are definitely _____. (her's, hers)

5. Mozart and the young Beethoven were similar in _____ musical styles. (their, they're)

6. Why can't we reach David and _____? (they, them)

7. Unquestionably, the outstanding speaker was _____. (she, her)

8. Between _____, nobody expected such a victory. (we, us)

9. Those skates surely are _____. (their's, theirs)

10. The team waited for _____ until _____ arrived. (him, he) (he, him)

23.2 Special Problems with Pronouns • Practice 1

Using *Who* and *Whom* Correctly   *Who* and *whoever* are nominative and are used as subject and predicate nominative. *Whom* and *whomever* are objective and are used as direct object and object of the preposition. For the possessive case, use *whose*, not *who's*.

THE CASES OF *WHO* AND *WHOEVER*	
Nominative	*Who* will bring the dessert? I will support *whoever* the candidate is.
Objective	*Whom* have you told? You may choose *whomever* you want to work with.
Possessive	*Whose* car is that?

Using Pronouns Correctly in Elliptical Clauses   In elliptical clauses beginning with *than* or *as*, use the form of the pronoun that you would use if the clause were fully stated.

Elliptical Clauses	Completed Clauses
Dan sings better than ___?___ . The boss paid Tim more than ___?___ . The coach helped him more than ___?___ .	Dan sings better than *I* [do]. The boss paid Tim more than [the boss paid] *me*. The coach helped him more than *I* [did]. The coach helped him more than [the coach helped] *me*.

▶ **Exercise 1**   **Using *Who* and *Whom* Correctly.**   Write *who* or *whom* to complete each sentence.

EXAMPLE: Mr. Parker is the one ___*whom*___ I came to see.

1. _____ did the teacher appoint as monitor?

2. Lenny Jacobs is a coach _____ gets results.

3. The job is open to anyone _____ can speak German.

4. _____ is your favorite country singer?

5. A good babysitter must be someone _____ likes children.

6. _____ have you invited to the party?

7. _____ will attract more voters?

8. The police spoke to passersby _____ had witnessed the accident.

9. That is the same woman _____ I saw at the rally.

10. Those are the actors _____ the director will audition.

▶ **Exercise 2**   **Using Pronouns in Elliptical Clauses.**   Complete each sentence with an appropriate pronoun.

EXAMPLE: Tom is as tall as ___*I*___ .

1. Paul plays the piano better than _____ .

2. The game pleased Sue as much as _____ .

3. The judges chose Phil rather than _____ .

4. I do not speak Spanish as well as _____ .

5. That comment offended Jenny as much as _____ .

23.2 Special Problems with Pronouns • Practice 2

Exercise 1   **Using *Who* and *Whom* in Questions and Clauses.**   Fill in each blank with the correct pronoun in parentheses.

EXAMPLE: I wonder ____who____ won the election today. (who, whom)

1. With _____ are you arguing? (who, whom)
2. I wonder _____ will win. (who, whom)
3. _____ the spokesperson for the company? (Whose, Who's)
4. The director _____ was fired left the city. (who whom)
5. The shortstop is the player _____, experts feel, will achieve stardom. (who, whom)
6. _____ they select will represent us in Paris. (Whoever, Whomever)
7. Dr. Goodman is the only doctor _____ I know in town. (who, whom)
8. Give _____ arrives this package. (whoever, whomever)
9. _____ has been your delegate to the convention? (Who, Whom)
10. About _____ were they talking? (who, whom)

Exercise 2   **More Work with *Who* and *Whom*.**   Write *who, whoever, whom, whomever, whose,* or *who's* to complete each sentence.

EXAMPLE: Lee is the one ____who____ told me to come early.

1. She is a teacher _____ we all admire.
2. _____ is your favorite recording star?
3. The policeman asked _____?
4. Tell _____ you want about the discovery.
5. He wonders _____ cheated on the exam.
6. She is the artist _____, I feel, has the least talent.
7. _____ the trainer of the hockey team?
8. A person _____ is persistent has a chance of success.
9. _____ wants tickets should see the manager.
10. _____ do you intend to visit in Chicago?
11. With _____ were you planning to go?
12. Only those _____ arrive early will get seats.
13. Bring the package to _____ you were told.
14. With _____ have you raced?
15. I cannot promise to support _____ will be selected.
16. Is it she to _____ I should report?
17. Those _____ train diligently usually finish the event.
18. _____ dictionary is this?
19. They are actors _____ can play a variety of roles.
20. Under _____ authority was this order issued?

Name _____   Date _____

 24.1

Subject and Verb Agreement
(Number: Singular and Plural, Singular and Plural
Subjects) • Practice 1

Number: Singular and Plural   *Number* refers to the two forms of a word: singular and plural. Singular words indicate one; plural words indicate more than one.

NUMBER OF WORDS			
Part of Speech	**Singular**	**Plural**	**Singular or Plural**
Nouns	bakery, woman	bakeries, women	elk, trout, reindeer
Pronouns	I, he, she, it	we, they	you
Verbs	explores, has,		(I, you, we, they)
	does, am, is, was		explore
			(I you, we, they)
			have, do
			(you, we, they)
			are, were

Singular and Plural Subjects   A singular subject must have a singular verb. A plural subject must have a plural verb. A phrase or clause that interrupts a subject and its verb does not affect subject-verb agreement.

SUBJECT-VERB AGREEMENT	
Singular	**Plural**
John likes Chinese food.	They prefer Italian cooking.
A vase of flowers is on the table.	The flowers in the vase are roses.
That reindeer has a red nose.	Eight reindeer pull the sleigh.

▶ **Exercise 1**   **Determining the Number of Words.**   Label each item below as *singular, plural,* or *both.*

EXAMPLE: have found _____*both*_____

1. vegetables _____
2. were studying _____
3. deer _____
4. attorneys _____
5. closes _____

6. admire _____
7. children _____
8. spine _____
9. entertains _____
10. have lost _____

▶ **Exercise 2**   **Making Subjects and Verbs Agree.**   Complete each sentence by writing the verb form given in the parentheses that agrees with the subject. Then label each sentence *S* if the subject is singular or *P* if it is plural.

EXAMPLE: Some members of that club ____*do*____ volunteer work. (do, does) ___*P*___

1. That musical by Rodgers and Hart _____ popular. (remain, remains) _____

2. Our neighbors at the end of the street _____ building a deck. (is, are) _____

3. The plants she likes best _____ tropical. (is are) _____

4. The lawyer for the plaintiffs _____ more time. (need, needs) _____

5. That first edition of Frost's poems _____ valuable. (is, are) _____

Subject and Verb Agreement (Number: Singular and Plural, Singular and Plural Subjects) • 133

24.1 Subject and Verb Agreement
(Number: Singular and Plural, Singular and Plural Subjects) • Practice 2

▷ Exercise 1 Determining the Number of Nouns, Pronouns, and Verbs. Label each item as *singular, plural,* or *both*.

EXAMPLE: writes ___*singular*___

1. animals _____
2. we _____
3. child _____
4. is _____
5. candle _____
6. tempt _____
7. it _____
8. they _____
9. geese _____
10. gives _____
11. delivers _____
12. river _____
13. have _____
14. apples _____
15. were _____
16. has agreed _____
17. tulips _____
18. collapses _____
19. elephant _____
20. shatter _____

▷ Exercise 2 Making Subjects Agree with Their Verbs. Fill in the blank with the verb in parentheses that agrees with the subject of each sentence.

EXAMPLE: The twins ___*were*___ dressed alike. (was, were)

1. The red and brown boxes _____ destroyed in the fire. (was, were)
2. The concert _____ at eight. (begins, begin)
3. Of all of my subjects, woodworking _____ my favorite. (is, are)
4. Old clocks _____ interesting histories. (has, have)
5. My grandfather often _____ to the adult center. (goes, go)
6. In desperation, the heroine _____ for air. (clutches, clutch)
7. Marilyn _____ finally finished her work. (has, have)
8. Yesterday, both dictionaries _____ on that desk. (was, were)
9. I guess this _____ the only possible explanation. (is, are)
10. Lately, our evergreen plants _____ been yellowing. (has, have)

▷ Exercise 3 Making Separated Subjects and Verbs Agree. Fill in the blank with the verb in parentheses that agrees with the subject of each sentence.

1. The old books in the attic _____ thrown away. (was, were)
2. The climates of both countries _____ very good. (is, are)
3. A carton of grapefruits from Florida _____ delivered. (was, were)
4. The vegetables in the stew _____ unusually tasty. (is, are)
5. The men working on the platform _____ quitting early. (is, are)
6. Flights from this airport _____ infrequently. (leaves, leave)
7. Our neighbor, who was abroad, _____ returned. (has, have)
8. The pages of the book _____ in poor condition. (is, are)
9. The bouquet of flowers _____ a nice aroma. (has, have)
10. The speakers in my stereo sound system _____ poorly balanced. (is, are)

24.1 Subject and Verb Agreement
(Compound Subjects) • Practice 1

Compound Subjects   A singular subject after *or* takes a singular verb. A plural subject after *or* takes a plural verb. Compound subjects joined by *and* take a plural verb unless they are thought of as one thing or modified by *every* or *each*.

AGREEMENT WITH COMPOUND SUBJECTS	
Joined by *or* or *nor*	Jason, Jen, or Pat *does* the dishes every night.
	Neither the Bombers nor the Raiders *are* likely to finish first.
	Either the owners or the realtor *has* the keys.
	Either the realtor or the owners *have* the keys.
Joined by *and*	Kim and Sally *are* coming for dinner.
	Dad and I *are* planning the menu.
	Chicken and dumplings *sounds* good.
	Every guest and family member *is* sure to enjoy it.

▶ **Exercise 1**   **Compound Subjects Joined by *Or* or *Nor*.**   Write the verb form given in the parentheses that agrees with the subject in each sentence.

EXAMPLE: My parents or grandparents ____*are*____ about to arrive. (is are)

1. Neither the coach nor the players _____ much hope of winning. (holds, hold)

2. Mom or Dad _____ to my brother every night. (reads, read)

3. The leading actors or the director _____ the film on talk shows. (promotes promote)

4. Lou, Dana, or Sam _____ ordered the pizza already. (has, have)

5. Lemonade, iced tea, or fruit juice _____ a refreshing drink. (is, are)

6. Aunt Ellen or my grandparents _____ for dinner every Sunday. (comes, come)

7. Neither Dan nor his father _____ golf very well. (plays, play)

8. Either a lesser-known singer or the star's backup singers _____ up the audience. (warms, warm)

9. The principal or her assistants _____ detention. (supervises, supervise)

10. Donna or Marco _____ a good choice for student council. (is, are)

▶ **Exercise 2**   **Compound Subjects Joined by *And*.**   Write the verb form given in the parentheses that agrees with the subject in each sentence.

EXAMPLE: Spaghetti and meatballs ____*is*____ today's special. (is, are)

1. The director and stage manager _____ a meeting tomorrow. (has, have)

2. Every nook and cranny _____ thoroughly searched. (was, were)

3. Both the buyer and the seller _____ signed the contracts. (has, have)

4. The couch and draperies _____. (matches, match)

5. Bacon and eggs _____ Laura's favorite breakfast. (was, were)

24.1 Subject and Verb Agreement
(Compound Subjects) • Practice 2

▶ **Exercise 1** Making Compound Subjects Agree with Their Verbs. Fill in the blank with the verb that agrees with the subject of each sentence.

EXAMPLE: Neither Kay nor Irene ___is___ available to babysit. (is, are)

1. Both my boss and her partner _____ coins. (collects, collect)

2. Trish or Kathy _____ to represent us. (plans, plan)

3. Neither Jack nor Tim _____ to make the delivery. (wants, want)

4. Snow, hail, and sleet _____ been forecast for today. (has, have)

5. Fruits and vegetables _____ many minerals. (provides, provide)

6. Spaghetti and meatballs _____ her favorite dish. (is, are)

7. A train or several buses _____ available on Sundays. (is, are)

8. Both the twins and Greta _____ visiting Grandmother. (is, are)

9. Either my uncle or my aunt _____ each week. (phones, phone)

10. Books and magazines _____ appreciated by the patients. (is, are)

11. Neither the sedan nor the truck _____ a spare tire. (has, have)

12. Three men and a woman _____ approaching the door. (was, were)

13. The two sons and their father _____ very close. (is, are)

14. The lamps or the end tables _____ on sale tomorrow. (is, are)

15. Every apple and pear _____ eaten by the guests. (was, were)

16. Franks and beans _____ what I want for dinner. (is, are)

17. Phil or Mary usually _____ the office each day. (opens, open)

18. Three candles or a flashlight _____ needed. (is, are)

19. Either Jim or John _____ the anthem. (sing, sings)

20. Each boy and girl _____ a prize. (receive, receives)

▶ **Exercise 2** Using Compound Subjects in Sentences. Write a sentence for each compound subject.

EXAMPLE: Billy and Joanne

_____*Billy and Joanne work on their science project together.*_____

1. Both my mother and my aunt

_____

2. Blue paint or flowered wallpaper

_____

3. Neither Kyle nor Tracy

_____

4. Peas, lima beans, and spinach

_____

5. Knee pads and helmets

_____

24.1 Subject and Verb Agreement
(Confusing Subjects) • Practice 1

Confusing Subjects Always check certain kinds of subjects carefully to make sure they agree with their verbs.

AGREEMENT WITH CONFUSING SUBJECTS	
Subject After Verb	Atop each cookie *was* a fancy *candy.* Near the horizon *tower* the *masts* of the sailboats.
Subject Versus Predicate Nominative	*Cookies are* always a treat. A *treat* in our house *is* blueberry turnovers.
Collective Nouns	The *family camps* every summer. (as a group) The *family share* household chores. (as individuals)
Plural Form with Singular Meaning	German *measles is* also known as rubella. *Physics is* the science of matter and energy.
Amounts	Six *weeks is* the length of our health course. Two *yards* of fabric *sounds* like a lot.
Titles	*Two Gentlemen of Verona is* not often performed.
Indefinite Pronouns	*Either* of these scarves *matches.* (always singular) *Several* of these ties *are* stained. (always plural) *All* of the fabric *is* too bright. *All* of the chairs *need* slipcovers.

▶ **Exercise 1** **Deciding on the Number of Subjects.** Assume that each item below is to be the subject of a sentence. Label each one *S* if it needs a singular verb or *P* if it needs a plural verb.

EXAMPLE: *Little Women* _____S_____

1. Some of the tourists _____
2. Few of them _____
3. *The Three Musketeers* _____
4. Either of the students _____
5. Mumps _____

6. Each of the women _____
7. *Wuthering Heights* _____
8. One dollar _____
9. Both of the candidates _____
10. Some of the meat _____

▶ **Exercise 2** **Choosing Verbs to Agree with Difficult Subjects.** Write the correct verb form in parentheses to complete each sentence.

EXAMPLE: Here _____*are*_____ the notes I borrowed. (is, are)

1. The World Series _____ played in October. (is, are)
2. The group _____ disagreeing among themselves about the results. (is, are)
3. Severe thunderstorms _____ a threat to life and property. (is, are)
4. Half of the brownies _____ nuts in them. (has, have)
5. The commission _____ its own chairperson. (elects, elect)
6. The jury _____ polled individually. (is, are)
7. The only difference between the dishes _____ the sauces. (was, were)
8. There _____ always been a strong bond between us. (has, have)
9. At the top of the bank _____ a mass of wildflowers. (blooms, bloom)
10. *Romeo and Juliet* _____ not my favorite play. (is, are)

24.1 Subject and Verb Agreement
(Confusing Subjects) • Practice 2

▶ **Exercise 1**   **Making Confusing Subjects Agree with Their Verbs.**   Fill in the blank with the verb in parentheses that agrees with the subject of each sentence.

EXAMPLE: Some of the money ___*was*___ missing. (was, were)

1. Physics _____ my brother's favorite subject. (is, are)
2. _____ a raincoat and umbrella in the closet. (There's, There are)
3. In the back of the cupboard _____ two light bulbs. (is, are)
4. The United States _____ one nation indivisible. (is, are)
5. Here _____ three examples of the Romantic Period. (is, are)
6. The news _____ changed for days. (hasn't, haven't)
7. Smallpox _____ once a serious disease. (was, were)
8. Storms at sea _____ a reason for extreme caution. (is, are)
9. Social studies _____ my best subject. (is, are)
10. Another cause of accidents _____ poor, unlit roads. (was, were)
11. Someone among them _____ to assume leadership. (has, have)
12. There _____ been three attempts on his life. (has, have)
13. A group of pilgrims _____ wending its way toward the shrine. (is, are)
14. Finally, the jury _____ made its decision. (has, have)
15. Local politics _____ caused many problems here. (has, have)
16. After the long, impressive hallway _____ two elevators. (is, are)
17. All of the soup _____ spilled on the new floor. (was, were)
18. _____ one last question from the director. (Here's, Here are)
19. The acoustics in the studio _____ excellent. (was, were)
20. The committee _____ taken their seats. (has, have)
21. A candidate's ethics _____ an important consideration. (is, are)
22. Near the fence between two tires _____ the treasure. (lies, lie)
23. Fifty cents _____ not much of a tip these days. (is, are)
24. Not one of the tomatoes _____ ripened. (has, have)
25. *Wuthering Heights* _____ Emily Bronte's only novel. (is, are)

▶ **Exercise 2**   **More Work with Confusing Subjects.**   Fill in the blank with the verb in parentheses that agrees with the subject of each sentence.

1. There _____ several weaknesses in that survey. (was, were)
2. Most of the reports _____ of poor quality. (was, were)
3. Civics _____ always been a favorite subject of mine. (has, have)
4. At the top of the hill _____ two majestic oaks. (stands, stand)
5. *The Brothers Karamazov* _____ as a great novel. (rank, ranks)
6. The audience _____ not given its verdict. (has, have)
7. Each of the turntables _____ a drawback. (has, have)
8. Dirty streets _____ just one of our complaints. (is, are)
9. The couple always _____ with each other. (disagrees, disagree)
10. Where _____ my new pliers? (is, are)

24.2 Pronoun and Antecedent Agreement
(Between Personal Pronouns and Antecedents) • Practice 1

Agreement Between Personal Pronouns and Antecedents A personal pronoun must agree with its antecedent in person, number, and gender. Use a singular personal pronoun with two or more singular antecedents joined by *or* or *nor*. Use a plural personal pronoun with two or more antecedents joined by *and*. When dealing with pronoun-antecedent agreement, do not shift either person or gender. When gender is not specified, use the masculine or rewrite the sentence.

PRONOUN-ANTECEDENT AGREEMENT

My father has a CB radio in *his* truck.

This air mattress has a leak in *it*.

Francine got an A on *her* essay.

Beth or Ellen will have the party at *her* house.

Tim, Aaron, and Steve rode *their* bikes to the fair.

Each candidate stated *his* position clearly.

Both candidates expressed *their* positions clearly.

▶**Exercise 1** **Choosing Personal Pronouns to Agree with Antecedents.** Assume that each item below is an antecedent for a personal pronoun. After each, write *his, her, its,* or *their* to show which pronoun you would use to refer to it.

EXAMPLE: David or Goliath ___*his*___

1. several parents _____
2. the new bike _____
3. either Jack or Bill _____
4. Pam, Ali, or Elise _____
5. only one woman _____

6. Erik and Marc _____
7. each actor _____
8. most experiments _____
9. the new report _____
10. the ballerina _____

▶**Exercise 2** **Pronoun-Antecedent Agreement in Sentences.** Write an appropriate personal pronoun to complete each sentence.

EXAMPLE: Pete and I enjoyed ___*our*___ trip to Washington, D.C.

1. Although Ben had studied hard, _____ was still nervous about the test.
2. The pool is beautiful, but no one uses _____.
3. Neither Dora nor Carol uses _____ calculator very often.
4. The candidate and her staff revised _____ travel plans.
5. Uncle Al takes _____ dog everywhere.
6. Pete hopes that _____ will get the part.
7. All students must show proof that _____ have been immunized.
8. Liz, may I borrow _____ history notes?
9. Mary has been practicing all week for _____ recital.
10. Maybe Chuck or Don will lend you _____ bike.

(24.2) Pronoun and Antecedent Agreement
(Between Personal Pronouns and Antecedents) • Practice 2

▶ **Exercise 1** **Making Personal Pronouns Agree with Their Antecedents.** Write an appropriate personal pronoun to complete each sentence.

EXAMPLE: Neither Kevin nor Bill rode ___*his*___ bike to school.

1. Aunt Marie sent us _____ best wishes.

2. My brother and sister explained _____ objections.

3. Each boy designed _____ own poster.

4. Lisa briefly told us about _____ experiences in Paris.

5. Neither Bob nor Jerry wanted to drive _____ car to work.

6. I ordered two crates of fruit, but _____ have not arrived.

7. The waiter asked me for _____ choice of salad dressing.

8. The delegates rose and thundered _____ approval.

9. Sam and Jill urged us to use _____ summer cottage.

10. The car has trouble with _____ transmission.

11. Darlene gave me _____ old ski pants.

12. Mabel and Marcia presented _____ project to the class.

13. Each girl suggested _____ own idea for the dance routine.

14. Edward showed us the pictures from _____ camping trip.

15. Neither my grandfather nor my uncle could find _____ sunglasses.

16. Because the party guests are so late, Steven thinks _____ must be lost.

17. After she graded my paper, the teacher handed it back to _____.

18. Because the car needed servicing, Brad brought _____ to the dealer.

19. My cousins want me to visit _____ this weekend.

20. Sam and Red went to the batting cage to practice _____ skills.

▶ **Exercise 2** **Making Personal Pronouns Agree with Their Antecedents.** Rewrite each of the following sentences, correcting any error in pronoun and antecedent agreement. If a sentence has no error, write correct.

EXAMPLE: Neither Jill nor Ann brought their lunch to school.

_____*Neither Jill nor Ann brought her lunch to school.*_____

1. If you need more information, I will be glad to send them.

_____

2. I feel sorry for Fred, an only child, because they must be lonely.

_____

3. If Dean doesn't understand the directions, he should ask the teacher to explain it to him.

_____

4. Neither Dolly nor Karen enjoys her after-school job.

_____

5. George writes his assignments in a notebook, a habit that helps you remember them.

_____

24.2 Pronoun and Antecedent Agreement (With Indefinite Pronouns, With Reflexive Pronouns) • Practice 1

Agreement with Indefinite Pronouns   Use a singular personal pronoun when the antecedent is a singular indefinite pronoun. Use a plural personal pronoun when the antecedent is a plural indefinite pronoun. With an indefinite pronoun that can be either singular or plural, agreement depends on the antecedent of the indefinite pronoun.

AGREEMENT WITH INDEFINITE PRONOUNS
Each of my sisters has *her* own room.
Both of the players have *their* own distinctive styles.
Some of the bread has mold on *it*. (*bread* = singular antecedent)
Some of the students lost *their* note cards. (*students* = plural antecedent)

Agreement with Reflexive Pronouns   A reflexive pronoun must agree with an antecedent that is clearly stated.

REFLEXIVE PRONOUN AGREEMENT	
Incorrect	**Correct**
The new phone is for my brother and *myself*.	The new phone is for my brother and *me*.

▶ **Exercise 1**   **Making Personal Pronouns Agree with Indefinite Pronouns.**   Write an appropriate personal pronoun to complete each sentence.

EXAMPLE: Neither of the doors has a lock on ____*it*____ .

1. Most of this food has too much salt in _____ .

2. Many of the players provide _____ own shin guards.

3. Few of the parents have given _____ permission.

4. Each of the windows has a candle in _____ .

5. Anyone in the Boy Scout troop will lend you _____ handbook.

6. Several of my classmates have _____ own computers.

7. Little of the oceanfront property has houses on _____ .

8. Somebody from the Women's Club will tell us about _____ hobby.

9. Do all of your books have your name in _____ ?

10. Some of the old vinyl records in my father's collection have scratches
    on _____ .

▶ **Exercise 2**   **Using Reflexive Pronouns Correctly.**   Underline the misused reflexive pronoun in each sentence. Write the correct pronoun on the line.

EXAMPLE: Both Carol and <u>yourself</u> have done a fine job. ____*you*____

1. Jay lacks confidence in June and myself. _____

2. Grandma took my cousins and ourselves to the beach. _____

3. Please do not tell himself about this. _____

4. Jan bought a ticket for herself and yourself. _____

5. Donna and myself went out for dinner. _____

24.2 # Pronoun and Antecedent Agreement (With Indefinite Pronouns, With Reflexive Pronouns) • **Practice 2**

> **Exercise 1**   **Making Personal Pronouns Agree with Indefinite Pronouns.**   Fill in the blank with the correct pronoun from the choices in parentheses.

EXAMPLE: Each of the men signed _____*his*_____ name. (his, their)

1. Both of the trucks had delivered _____ shipments. (its, their)
2. Each, of the girls made _____ own dress. (her, their)
3. All of the students completed _____ assignments. (his, their)
4. Several of the dancers promised _____ autographs. (her, their)
5. Neither of the girls offered to lend me _____ notes. (her, their)
6. One of the victims volunteered to tell _____ story. (his, their)
7. All of the members agreed to give _____ support. (his, their)
8. Many of the witnesses offered _____ opinions. (his, their)
9. Few of the reporters have _____ credentials with them. (her, their)
10. Only one of the women explained _____ reasons. (her, their)
11. Each of the musicians has _____ music ready. (his, their)
12. Which one of the women wanted _____ coat? (her, their)
13. Some of the townspeople have voiced _____ approval. (its, their)
14. Neither of my uncles will bring _____ car. (his, their)
15. All of the students have found _____ books. (his, their)
16. Not one of the girls was tired after _____ speech. (her, their)
17. All of the children want to take _____ naps. (his, their)
18. Some of the delegates weren't wearing _____ badges. (his, their)
19. Jim and Scott forgot _____ baseball bats. (his, their)
20. Either Ellen or Mary will recite _____ poem next. (her, their)

> **Exercise 2**   **Using Reflexive Pronouns Correctly.**   Rewrite each sentence, correcting the misused reflexive pronoun.

EXAMPLE: Either Mark or myself will provide the punch.
            _____*Either Mark or I will provide the punch.*_____

1. Christine wants Bob and myself to make a presentation.

    _____

2. I'm sure that the right actor for this part is yourself.

    _____

3. Herself is the person with the best chance for success.

    _____

4. The nurse thought he had hurt both himself and myself.

    _____

5. Neither Ginger nor myself was willing to go alone.

    _____

24.2 Pronoun and Antecedent Agreement (Four Special Problems in Pronoun Agreement) • Practice 1

Four Special Problems in Pronoun Agreement A personal pronoun should always have a clear, single, close, and logical antecedent, either stated or understood.

Problems	Corrections
They are predicting rain for tonight.	The forecasters are predicting rain for tonight.
Dad told Uncle Al that *he* had a flat tire.	Dad told Uncle Al that Dad had a flat tire.
	Dad told Uncle Al that Uncle Al had a flat tire.
Mom told Vera what *she* needed.	Mom told Vera what Mom needed
	Mom told Vera what Vera needed.
In Paris *you* can see the Eiffel Tower.	Visitors to Paris can see the Eiffel Tower.

▷ **Exercise 1** **Solving Special Problems in Pronoun Agreement.** Underline the word or words in parentheses that more clearly complete each sentence.

EXAMPLE: (They, <u>The sportscasters</u>) say the Cats don't stand a chance.

1. The rules specify that (you, entrants) must be 16 years of age.
2. Dad called Mr. Sims back as soon as (he, Dad) got home.
3. Please get the hamburgers and the napkins and put (them, the hamburgers) into the cooler.
4. The guards object if (you, visitors) touch the exhibits.
5. The scouts and their leaders decided that (they, the scouts) would sell candy bars.
6. On all flights (you, passengers) get first-class service.
7. The patient was relieved when (they, the doctors) told her the news.
8. Mr. Kelly told Bruce what (his, Bruce's) new job would involve.
9. Regular exercise is important to (your, everyone's) good health.
10. When will (they, the networks) begin the new season?

▷ **Exercise 2** **Correcting Special Problems in Pronoun Agreement.** Rewrite each sentence below to correct any problems in pronoun agreement.

EXAMPLE: Tom told Ed that he should have known better.

Tom told Ed that Ed should have known better.

1. What did they say when you called the hospital?

_____

2. That platter of food looks pretty with the parsley on it.

_____

3. In that ballet school, they expect you to practice four hours a day.

_____

4. Debbie assured Maureen that her report would be excellent.

_____

5. Why do they tell you to keep your seatbelts loosely fastened?

_____

24.2 Pronoun and Antecedent Agreement (Four Special Problems in Pronoun Agreement) • Practice 2

Exercise 1 **Correcting Special Problems in Pronoun Agreement.** Fill in the blank with the word or words in parentheses that best complete each sentence.

EXAMPLE: The bulletin says ___students___ must register now. (you, students)

1. Sue gave Kay the present after _____ arrived. (she, Kay)
2. The film was good because _____ had a surprise ending. (they, it)
3. Sam angered Todd, but _____ didn't say what happened. (he, Todd)
4. I hid the key in the jar, but now I can't find _____ . (it, the key)
5. Going to camp is good for _____ . (you, a youngster)
6. The end of the book was confusing because _____ didn't explain what happened to the hero. (they, the author)
7. We cleaned the whole house for him, but he didn't even thank us for _____ . (it, our work)
8. _____ showed the film out of focus. (They, The theater)
9. Ken told Bill that _____ had been made captain. (he, Ken)
10. Deciding on a career is a big step in _____ life. (your, one's)

Exercise 2 **More Work with Special Problems in Pronoun Agreement.** Rewrite each sentence, correcting the error in pronoun agreement.

EXAMPLE: I was delayed because they were having a parade.

_____I was delayed because the city was having a parade._____

1. Take the papers from the folders and then file them.

_____

2. At school, they expect students to be on time for class.

_____

3. Marge told Gloria about the bazaar, and they decided not to go today. She said that perhaps they could go another time.

_____

4. The quarterback faded to pass. The receiver and the defender converged on the ball, and he dropped it.

_____

5. When Mother spoke to Alice, she nodded.

_____

6. Take the breadbox off the table and clean it.

_____

7. The ad says that you should be able to type.

_____

8. My brothers chased the intruders until they fell.

_____

9. Going to college out of town makes you feel lonely.

_____

10. When I visited Athens in 1968, you could still walk inside the Parthenon.

_____

25.1 Degrees of Comparison (Recognizing Degrees of Comparison, Regular Forms) • Practice 1

Recognizing Degrees of Comparison   Most adjectives and adverbs have three different forms to show degrees of comparison.

DEGREES OF COMPARISON			
	Positive	**Comparative**	**Superlative**
Adjectives	smooth	smoother	smoothest
	luxurious	more luxurious	most luxurious
	many	more	most
Adverbs	close	closer	closest
	rapidly	more rapidly	most rapidly
	far	further	furthest

Regular Forms of Comparison   Use *-er* or *more* to form the comparative degree and *-est* or *most* to form the superlative degree of comparison of most one- and two-syllable modifiers. Use *more* and *most* to form the comparative and superlative degrees of all modifiers with three or more syllables.

REGULAR FORMS OF COMPARISON			
One- and two-syllable modifiers	strange	stranger	strangest
	silly	sillier	silliest
	graceful	more graceful	most graceful
Three or more syllables	amazing	more amazing	most amazing
	happily	more happily	most happily

> **Exercise 1**   **Recognizing Degrees of Comparison.**   Identify the degree of comparison of the underlined word by writing *pos.* (positive), *comp.* (comparative), or *sup.* (superlative). .

EXAMPLE: Amy is <u>shorter</u> than her younger sister.   _____comp._____

1. The baby's fever is <u>lower</u> this morning. _____
2. The weather has been perfectly <u>beautiful</u> all week. _____
3. This has been the <u>wettest</u> June on record. _____
4. The Jacksons' house is the <u>oldest</u> one on our street. _____
5. Kevin took the news <u>more calmly</u> than the rest of us. _____
6. The Smiths have the <u>most carefully</u> trimmed shrubs on the block. _____
7. The host greeted each guest <u>warmly</u>. _____
8. Pete just ate the <u>biggest</u> sandwich I had ever seen. _____
9. Louise felt <u>better</u> after she had talked things over. _____
10. The crowd gave an <u>enthusiastic</u> roar. _____

> **Exercise 2**   **Comparing Adjectives and Adverbs.**   Write the missing forms of each modifier.

EXAMPLE: gloomy _____*gloomier*_____ _____*gloomiest*_____

1. cautious _____ _____
2. _____ _____ loudest
3. _____ more slowly _____
4. soft _____ _____
5. sadly _____ _____

25.1 Degrees of Comparison (Recognizing Degrees of Comparison, Regular Forms) • Practice 2

Exercise 1 **Recognizing Positive, Comparative, and Superlative Degrees.** Identify the degree of each underlined modifier by writing *pos.* (positive), *comp.* (comparative), or *sup.* (superlative).

EXAMPLE: She is the <u>tallest</u> player on the team. _____sup._____

1. My father is <u>more industrious</u> than I am. _____
2. Sometimes it is <u>best</u> not to argue. _____
3. I think she is <u>hungry</u> now. _____
4. This novel by Charles Dickens is one of the <u>most impressive</u> I've ever read. _____
5. You will be <u>more agreeable</u> after a nap. _____
6. I like baseball <u>better</u> than football. _____
7. Her <u>swollen</u> arm requires treatment. _____
8. The banker is the <u>richest</u> person in town. _____
9. This is the <u>most informative</u> article I've read about Laos. _____
10. He has <u>more</u> money now than when he returned from college. _____
11. For those who want to work, this course is <u>challenging</u>. _____
12. Who do you think is <u>prettier</u>? _____
13. Laura is the <u>happiest</u> person I know. _____
14. You are <u>better</u> at statistics than he is. _____
15. Beth is the <u>fussiest</u> person in our family. _____
16. Unfortunately, he is <u>more talkative</u> than he used to be. _____
17. Judy apparently is <u>sleepy</u> this morning. _____
18. In your opinion, which photo is <u>more attractive</u>? _____
19. Clark was the <u>most qualified</u> candidate in the group. _____
20. That meal was the <u>most satisfying</u> I've had in a long time. _____

Exercise 2 **Forming Regular Comparative and Superlative Degrees.** Write the comparative and superlative form of each modifier.

EXAMPLE: small _____smaller, smallest_____

1. beautiful _____
2. cold _____
3. fast _____
4. slowly _____
5. fruitful _____
6. exciting _____
7. light _____
8. likeable _____
9. pretty _____
10. weak _____
11. informative _____
12. popular _____
13. impressive _____
14. complex _____
15. quickly _____
16. fattening _____
17. hungry _____
18. demanding _____
19. sad _____
20. safe _____

25.1 Degrees of Comparison (Irregular Forms)
• Practice 1

Irregular Forms   The irregular comparative and superlative forms of certain adjectives and adverbs must be memorized.

IRREGULAR MODIFIERS		
Positive	**Comparative**	**Superlative**
bad	worse	worst
badly	worse	worst
far (distance)	farther	farthest
far (extent)	further	furthest
good	better	best
ill	worse	worst
late	later	last *or* latest
little (amount)	less	least
many	more	most
much	more	most
well	better	best

▶**Exercise 1**   **Forming Irregular Comparative and Superlative Degrees.**   Write the appropriate form of the modifier in parentheses to complete each sentence.

EXAMPLE: The Bombers have a ____*better*____ chance of winning than the Stingers do. (good)

1. The dish he prepares _____ than any other is Beef Wellington. (well)

2. Perry swam _____ than anyone else on the team. (far)

3. Sadie's cold was even _____ the second day. (bad)

4. The _____ noise in the house keeps Chris awake. (little)

5. We caught the _____ train before the power went off. (late)

6. Mr. Pella said I should develop the second paragraph _____ . (far)

7. That mosaic is the _____ thing I have ever made in art. (good)

8. Grandpa feels _____ today than yesterday. (ill)

9. Barnaby sang _____ of all when his throat was sore. (bad)

10. Some people need _____ sleep than others. (much)

▶**Exercise 2**   **Using Adjectives and Adverbs to Make Comparisons.**   Use each modifier in a sentence that shows a clear comparison. Use three comparative forms and two superlatives.

EXAMPLE: (many) ____*Len has more clothes than anyone else I know.*____

1. (bad) _____

   _____

2. (badly) _____

   _____

3. (good) _____

   _____

4. (little) _____

   _____

5. (well) _____

   _____

25.1 Degrees of Comparison (Irregular Forms)
• Practice 2

▶ **Exercise 1** **Forming Irregular Comparative and Superlative Degrees.** Write the appropriate form of the underlined modifier to complete each sentence.

EXAMPLE: I am still ill, but I was ____worse____ yesterday.

1. Cherry pie is good, but pecan pie is even _____.

2. I played better than Sue, but Katy played the _____ of all.

3. There were many flowers in the garden and even _____ in the greenhouse.

4. Mother felt bad last night, but today she feels _____.

5. We were late for dinner, but Rita was even _____.

6. Tucson is farther from here than Denver, but Los Angeles is the _____ of the three.

7. Practice went well today, but it went _____ yesterday.

8. I did badly on the test, but Sam did even _____.

9. The school library has more books than the church library, but the public library has the _____ books in town.

10. She has little interest in opera and even _____ in jazz.

11. The lawn needs much care, but the garden needs _____.

12. Sue came later than Tim and was the _____ to arrive.

13. I had much care, but the garden needs _____.

14. We had hiked quite far, but we hadn't much _____ to hike.

15. The first performer was bad, but the second was _____.

16. I had less money than Sam, but Lou had the _____.

17. Jan Peerce was a good tenor, but Caruso was _____.

18. Craig is better than Robert, but Nancy is the _____.

19. Greg did worse than Jim, but Chris did the _____ of all.

20. I have less talent than Jane, but Lou has the _____ talent.

▶ **Writing Application** **Using Adjectives and Adverbs to Make Comparisons.** Use each modifier in a sentence of your own.

EXAMPLE: most ambitious

_____Clark is the most ambitious person in our class._____

1. strongest _____

2. best _____

3. friendliest _____

4. hardest _____

5. slower _____

6. good _____

7. well _____

8. bad _____

9. badly _____

10. better _____

25.2 # Clear Comparisons (Using Comparative and Superlative Degrees) • Practice 1

Using Comparative and Superlative Degrees Use the comparative degree to compare two people, places, things, or ideas. Use the superlative degree to compare three or more people, places, things, or ideas.

Comparative (comparing two)	Superlative (comparing three or more)
If you had called *earlier*, I could have talked. You will feel *better* after a nap. Jan is *more graceful* than her sister.	Jim arrived *earliest* of all the guests. I feel *best* after exercising. Jan is the *most graceful* dancer in the corps.

> **Exercise 1** **Using the Comparative and Superlative Degrees Correctly.** Underline the correct form in each sentence.

EXAMPLE: Dad cooks (better, best) than Mom does.

1. All the rooms need painting, but the living room is the (less, least) dingy.

2. That white frame chapel is the (older, oldest) building in town.

3. Coastal regions usually have (more, most) moderate temperatures than the interior sections.

4. I wish I had proofread my essay (more carefully, most carefully).

5. Jenny has the (longer, longest) hair of anyone I know.

6. Timmy is a (more, most) active youngster than his brother.

7. The engine runs (more, most) smoothly since it was overhauled.

8. Latin IV has the (fewer, fewest) students of any class.

9. The SST is the (faster, fastest) airliner.

10. Of the three candidates, Barker is the (more, most) likely to win.

> **Exercise 2** **Using the Comparative and Superlative Degrees in Sentences.** Use each of the following modifiers in two sentences, first in the comparative degree and then in the superlative degree.

EXAMPLE: (pretty) _____ *Cara's photographs are prettier than mine.* _____

_____ *Daisy's photographs are the prettiest I have ever seen.* _____

1. (successful) _____

_____

2. (hard) _____

_____

3. (young) _____

_____

4. (tame) _____

_____

5. (dangerous) _____

_____

25.2 Clear Comparisons (Using Comparative and Superlative Degrees) • Practice 2

▶ **Exercise 1** Using the Comparative and Superlative Forms Correctly. Fill in the blank in each sentence with the correct comparative or superlative form in parentheses.

EXAMPLE: Of the two, Glenda is the _____faster_____ swimmer. (faster, fastest)

1. Boston is the _____ historic of all American cities. (more, most)

2. His condition is _____ this week than last. (poorer, poorest)

3. Which of the triplets is the _____? (prettier, prettiest)

4. Mr. Willis gave him a _____ introduction than her. (better, best)

5. This is the _____ I can do for you. (less, least)

6. Which of the three cars is the _____? (cheaper, cheapest)

7. She is _____ willing to help than I. (more, most)

8. Is this the _____ case you have seen? (worse, worst)

9. Of the two brothers, which is the _____? (faster, fastest)

10. She is the _____ able legislator in the Senate. (more most)

▶ **Exercise 2** Supplying the Comparative and Superlative Degrees. Write the appropriate comparative or superlative degree of the modifier in parentheses.

EXAMPLE: Alfred is the _____youngest_____ of all their children. (young)

1. Marianne is the _____ of the two sisters. (old)

2. He is the _____ hair stylist I know. (capable)

3. Gladys is the _____ person on the staff. (warm)

4. Charles is the _____ member of the string quartet. (talented)

5. This camera is _____ than that one. (good)

6. The temperature today is _____ than it was yesterday. (low)

7. Grandfather is _____ this morning than he was last night. (ill)

8. Harold is the _____ member of our school's wrestling team. (strong)

9. Which of the twins is _____? (tall)

10. Mr. Adler is the _____ person in town. (generous)

11. Rita is _____ about computers than Rick. (knowledgeable)

12. I think *My Antonia* is the _____ of the two books. (good)

13. Karen speaks Italian _____ than I do. (well)

14. Uncle Sid is my _____ living relative. (old)

15. The Pattersons arrived _____ than the Andersons. (late)

16. Louise is the _____ person in our class. (shy)

17. The cellar is the _____ room in the house. (cold)

18. This coffee is the _____ I've ever tasted. (good)

19. Pat's house is _____ from school than Joe's. (far)

20. Stewart was the _____ person in the audience. (alert)

25.2 **Clear Comparisons** (Logical Comparisons)
• **Practice 1**

Logical Comparisons   Make sure that your sentences compare only items of a similar kind.

Unbalanced Comparisons	Correct
This car rides smoother than *Dad*. A *parrot's plumage* is more colorful than a parakeet.	*This car* runs smoother than *Dad's*. A *parrot's plumage* is more colorful than *a parakeet's*.

When comparing one of a group with the rest of the group, use the word *other* or the word *else*.

Illogical	Correct
Brian has a *higher* strike-out record *than any* pitcher. My brother always eats *more than anyone in our family*.	Brian has a *higher* strike-out record *than any other pitcher*. My brother always eats *more than anyone else in our family*.

▶ **Exercise 1**   **Making Balanced Comparisons.**   Rewrite each sentence, correcting the comparison.

EXAMPLE: My mosaic was larger than Jason.

        My mosaic was larger than Jason's.

1. Aunt Lena's spaghetti sauce is spicier than Mom.

   Aunt Lena's spaghetti sauce is spicier than Mom's.

2. Laura's corn has grown faster than Phil.

   Laura's corn has grown faster than Phil's.

3. Ken's class picture was better than Mike.

   Ken's class picture was better than Mike's.

4. Marc's clothes were even muddier than Steve.

   Marc's clothes were even muddier than Steve's.

5. Julie's job is more demanding than Hal.

   Julie's job is more demanding than Hal's.

▶ **Exercise 2**   **Using *Other* and *Else* in Comparisons.**   Rewrite each sentence, correcting the comparison.

EXAMPLE: Audrey studies harder than anyone in the class.

        Audrey studies harder than anyone else in the class.

1. Often my homework takes me longer than anyone in my class.

   _____

2. That restaurant is more expensive than any place in town.

   _____

3. My friend Marcia writes better than anyone I know.

   _____

4. The intersection at Elm and Main is more dangerous than any in town.

   _____

5. Is there anyone who works as hard as Eric?

   _____

25.2 Clear Comparisons (Logical Comparisons)
• Practice 2

▶ **Exercise 1** **Making Balanced Comparisons.** Rewrite each sentence, correcting the unbalanced comparison.

EXAMPLE: Ginger's essay was better than Albert.

Ginger's essay was better than Albert's

1. Aren't my new pants more attractive than Jacqueline?
   " Jacqueline's?

2. The truck's engine is more powerful than the station wagon.
   " wagon's

3. Trish's debating record is better than Mary.
   " Mary's

4. My father's coin collection is better than my uncle.
   " uncle's

5. At the meeting last night, Bruce's presentation was better than John.
   " John's

6. A larger orchestra is needed to perform Bruckner's symphonies than Haydn.
   " Haydn's

7. Harry's telescope is stronger than Edward.
   " Edward's

8. My jacket is warmer than Steven.
   " Steven's

9. Maine's winters are much colder than Florida.
   " Florida's

10. An infection of the liver is as dangerous as the kidneys.
    " as an ifection of the kidney's

▶ **Exercise 2** **Using *Other* and *Else* in Comparisons.** Rewrite each sentence, correcting the illogical comparison.

EXAMPLE: Richard is more talkative than anyone in class.

Richard is more talkative than anyone else in class.

1. Mount Everest is higher than any mountain.
   " any other mantain

2. My friend William plays baseball with more enthusiasm than anyone I know.
   " anyone else I know.

3. Our apartment is longer than any in the building.
   " any other one in the building

4. Your charitable contribution to the emergency fund was more than any we received.
   " anyone we recieved

5. My room is colder than any in the house.
   " any one in the house

26.1 **Negative Sentences • Practice 1**

Recognizing Double Negatives   Do not write sentences with double negatives.

Double Negatives	Correct Negative Sentences
I *haven't* seen *no one*.	I *haven't* seen anyone.
	I have seen *no one*.
I *haven't* done *nothing* wrong.	I *haven't* done anything wrong.
	I have done *nothing* wrong.
We *don't* have *no* school today.	We *don't* have school today.
	We have *no* school today.

Forming Negative Sentences Correctly   Use only one negative word in a single clause. Do not use *but* in its negative sense with another negative. Do not use *barely, hardly,* or *scarcely* with another negative.

More Double Negatives	Correct Negative Sentences
Didn't Ann say she *couldn't* find *nobody* ?	Didn't Ann say she *couldn't* find anybody?
	Didn't Ann say she could find *nobody*?
I *haven't but* a dollar.	I have *but* a dollar.
	I *haven't* more than a dollar.
We *didn't* have *hardly* any food left.	We had *hardly* any food left.
	We *didn't* have any food left.

▶ **Exercise 1**   **Avoiding Problems with Negatives.**   Underline the word(s) in parentheses that make each sentence negative without creating a double negative.

EXAMPLE: I couldn't find my keys (<u>anywhere</u>, nowhere).

1. You shouldn't have told (<u>anybody</u>, nobody) where we were going.

2. We (<u>could</u>, couldn't) hardly make our way through the brush.

3. Are you sure you (don't have, have) but one day free this week?

4. There wasn't (a, no) cloud in the sky.

5. Jo didn't have (any, no) trouble choosing a topic.

6. The article didn't include (any, no) biographical information.

7. I don't have room for (but, more than) one elective in my schedule.

8. Kelly can't (ever, never) finish anything on time.

9. There (was, wasn't) scarcely enough breeze to ruffle a leaf.

10. I have hardly (ever, never) been more moved by a play.

▶ **Exercise 2**   **Using Negatives Correctly.**   Write a sentence of your own, correctly using each negative word given.

1. (nothing) _____

2. (but) _____

3. (wouldn't) _____

4. (barely) _____

5. (never) _____

26.1 Negative Sentences • Practice 2

Exercise 1 **Avoiding Double Negatives.** Fill in the blank with the word in parentheses that makes each sentence negative without forming a double negative.

EXAMPLE: Ann didn't go ____anywhere____ last night. (nowhere, anywhere)

1. He hasn't eaten _____ of his food. (none, any)

2. That lady hasn't _____ purchased anything here. (never, ever)

3. She couldn't have told them _____ important. (nothing, anything)

4. No one in the office reviewed _____ of the reports. (any, none)

5. Nobody said _____ to me about a quiz today. (anything, nothing)

6. I did _____ of the work I was supposed to do. (none, any)

7. I don't need _____ money from you. (no, any)

8. The Glenns saved _____ from the wreckage. (nothing, anything)

9. Vegetables shouldn't _____ be cooked too long. (never, ever)

10. Our new car _____ no gas guzzler. (is, isn't)

Exercise 2 **Avoiding Problems with Negatives.** Fill in the blank with the word in parentheses that makes each sentence negative without creating a double negative.

EXAMPLE: There ____is____ but one possible explanation. (is, isn't)

1. You _____ hardly mean what you say. (can, can't)

2. I don't owe the bank _____ . (nothing, anything)

3. My sister _____ reported nobody. (has, hasn't)

4. Cindy couldn't eat _____ for dinner. (anything, nothing)

5. He shouldn't have told _____ about the trip. (anyone, no one)

6. Don't you want _____ from the bazaar? (anything nothing)

7. Ann _____ revealed the strategy to no one. (had, hadn't)

8. The counselors did not have _____ better suggestions. (any, no)

9. I _____ never agree to such a plan. (would, wouldn't)

10. We haven't traveled _____ in South America. (anywhere, nowhere)

Exercise 3 **Correcting Double Negatives.** Rewrite each sentence correcting the double negative.

EXAMPLE: We couldn't barely hear the doorbell. ____We could barely hear the doorbell.____

1. Can't you never do anything right?

_____

2. There hadn't been but two possibilities.

_____

3. This old jalopy isn't never going to run properly.

_____

4. I don't take the bus to school no more.

_____

5. Of course, she doesn't expect nothing.

_____

26.2 Common Usage Problems • Practice 1

Solving Usage Problems   Study the items in the usage glossary in your textbook, paying particular attention to similar spellings, words that should never be used, pairs that are often misused, and problems with verb forms.

TYPES OF PROBLEMS		
Similar Spellings	*all ready* and *already*	*farther* and *further*
Wrong Words	*alot*	*enthused*
Misused Pairs	*anxious* and *eager*	*teach* and *learn*
Verb Forms	*busted* for *burst*	*of* for *have*

▶**Exercise 1**   **Avoiding Common Usage Problems.**   Underline the word in parentheses that correctly completes each sentence.

EXAMPLE: I would (advice, <u>advise</u>) you to be careful what you say to him.

1. The real painting looks quite different (from, than) the reproductions.
2. Because I had (laid, lay, lain) in the sun too long, my skin felt tight.
3. I would (have, of) gotten here sooner if the car hadn't broken down.
4. The new tax bill would (affect, effect) all income levels.
5. The candidate mingled (among, between) the guests at the benefit.
6. Nick watches television endlessly, (irregardless, regardless) of what is on.
7. Last weekend our team (beat, won) the Raiders again.
8. Proper food, rest, and exercise help build (healthful, healthy) bodies.
9. I heard (that, where) the Keenans are moving to Detroit.
10. Did your uncle (learn, teach) you that magic trick?

▶**Exercise 2**   **Avoiding Other Usage Problems.**   Underline the word(s) in parentheses that correctly complete each sentence.

EXAMPLE: Marcia's ideas (<u>about</u>, as to) decorations sounded exciting.

1. We were all (anxious, eager) to begin our vacation.
2. The press has given (all together, altogether) too much attention to the candidate's family.
3. By the time we arrived, there was (nowhere, nowheres) to sit.
4. The van driver (sat, set) the old woman's packages on her porch.
5. (Because, Being that) we overslept, Mom drove us to school.
6. Harry was surprised that his parents (left, let) him go on the trip.
7. Students (who, which) have permission slips may go on the trip.
8. I was surprised that little Teddy could walk such a long (way, ways).
9. Damian studies harder (than, then) many of his classmates.
10. Hilda's grandparents (emigrated, immigrated) from Germany.

26.2 Common Usage Problems • Practice 2

Exercise 1 **Correcting Usage Problems.** Rewrite each sentence, correcting the error in usage.

EXAMPLE: The child was anxious to open her presents. _____The child was eager to open her presents._____

1. Yesterday, I wanted too tell him the truth.

   _____

2. Due to the fact that it was snowing, we postponed our trip.

   _____

3. My grandparents have been healthful for many years.

   _____

4. She can't help but want another chance.

   _____

5. Next, the villain busted into the room in a rage.

   _____

6. The matter was quickly settled among my brother and me.

   _____

7. The affect of the medicine was immediate.

   _____

8. To attend the inauguration of a President is a honor.

   _____

9. Sit the glass to the right of the plate.

   _____

10. Being that you asked, I'll tell you my feeling about him.

    _____

11. The coach sat besides my brother and me.

    _____

12. Their are three boxes in the attic.

    _____

13. Partywise, I have had my fill if you really want to know.

    _____

14. You will find similar problems anywheres you go.

    _____

15. If she were smart, she wouldn't of made up an excuse.

    _____

16. Like I have often told you, I prefer chocolate cake.

    _____

17. There apparently lost in the wilderness.

    _____

18. Everyone accept John passed the exams.

    _____

19. My little brother seen our grandfather only once.

    _____

20. Sara's costume is much different than Evelyn's.

    _____

27.1 Rules for Capitalization (Capitals for First Words) • Practice 1

Rules for Capitalization   Capitalize the first word in a sentence, including complete sentences in quotations and following a colon. Capitalize the first word in interjections and incomplete questions, as well as the words *I* and *O*. Capitalize the first word in each line of most poetry.

CAPITALS FOR FIRST WORDS	
Complete Sentences	When can we expect delivery?
	What a fright you gave me!
Quoted Sentence	The chief shouted, "Sound the alarm."
Sentence After Colon	One thing seems clear: We must act at once.
Interjection	Darn! He left his wallet in his locker.
Incomplete Question	What time?
I and O	Today, O spring, I claim you for myself.
Lines of Poetry	Not marble, nor the gilded monuments
	Of princes, shall outlive this powerful rhyme.

▶ **Exercise 1**   **Using Capitals for First Words.**   Underline the word or words that should be capitalized in each sentence.

EXAMPLE: after dinner i asked, "what's for dessert?"

1. only one solution is possible: we must cut our expenses.

2. what a beautiful sunset we had last night!

3. the tourist asked, "does the Number 4 bus stop here?"

4. that restaurant deserves its reputation, i think.

5. ouch! that rose bush is loaded with thorns.

6. of course i'll meet you after school, but where?

7. a volunteer spoke: food, clothing, and blankets are the greatest needs at present.

8. one student suggested, "couldn't we raise money with a bake sale?"

9. halfway through the movie i began wondering, "when will this end?"

10. several of my classmates are going to computer camp this summer.

▶ **Exercise 2**   **Using Capitalized Words.**   Fill in each blank with an appropriate capitalized word.

EXAMPLE: Tony suggested, "___Certainly___ the town needs a recycling center."

1. _____ did you last see my keys?

2. The teacher said, "_____ your work carefully."

3. The effects of the storm were devastating: _____ trees and other debris were everywhere.

4. _____ can tell me how to get there?

5. James exclaimed, "_____! What a lucky break that was!"

6. _____ parents are very supportive.

7. The situation is this: _____ must find a new source of income.

8. _____ is a good source of calcium.

9. Jessica wondered, "_____ could have left that message?"

10. _____ boy blue, come blow your horn

    _____ sheep's in the meadow; the cow's in the corn.

27.1 Rules for Capitalization (Capitals for First Words) • Practice 2

▶ Exercise 1 **Using Capitalization with First Words.** Underline the word or words that should be capitalized. Some items may require more than one capital.

EXAMPLE: generally, i finish my assignments on time.

1. put the book back on the shelf.
2. where does the Great Wall of China start? and end?
3. good grief, Charlie Brown! you can't do anything right!
4. "o time too swift, o swiftness never ceasing!"—George Peele
5. the team was successful: it won the championship.
6. Mary, Mary, quite contrary,

   how does your garden grow?

   with silver bells and cockleshells

   and pretty maids all in a row.—Mother Goose
7. goodness! that truck is traveling too fast.
8. "in some ways," wrote Henry Wallace, "certain books are more powerful by far than any battle."
9. "whoever is happy will make others happy too," wrote Anne Frank. "he who has courage and faith will never perish in misery!"
10. in studying Latin America, you should not overlook these interesting aspects: the dress, the culture, and the food.
11. please get some broccoli at the store today.
12. did you go snorkeling on your vacation? how about scuba diving?
13. come quick, Ethel! the baby is trying to stand up!
14. hear our pleas, o mighty king!
15. if i give you a dollar, will you be quiet for a while?
16. success is counted sweetest

    by those who ne'er succeed.

    to comprehend a nectar

    requires sorest need.—Emily Dickinson
17. wow! what an amazing performance!
18. "for three years now," said Angela, "this peach tree has not produced any fruit."
19. when buying real estate, you should consider these three things: location, location, and location.
20. the company had a very catchy slogan: it was "we try harder."

▶ Exercise 2 **Using Capitalization with First Words in Passages.** Fill in each blank in the following passage with an appropriate capitalized word.

EXAMPLE: Bill said, "(1) _____Duck_____ your head when you walk under that low branch. (2) _____The_____ three of us continued to move forward cautiously.

(1) _____ we went on a picnic last week, the sun was shining and the weather was perfect. (2) _____, however, the weather is just terrible:

(3) _____ has been raining for the past two days. The woman giving the weather report said, (4) "_____ there will be scattered showers for most of the afternoon."

(5) _____ she said that, I was quite relieved.

27.1 Rules for Capitalization (Proper Nouns, Proper Adjectives) • Practice 1

Capitals for Proper Nouns   Capitalize proper nouns, including each important word in a proper noun of more than one word.

PROPER NOUNS	
Name of People: James A. McCoy	*Geographical Names:* Cedar Street
Names of Animals: Lassie	*Specific Places:* the Chrysler Building
Specific Events: the War of 1812	*Specific Groups:* League of Nations
Religious Terms: Bible	*Awards:* the Cy Young Award
Specific Vehicles: the *Concorde*	*Brand Names:* Photoflex

Capitals for Proper Adjectives   Capitalize most proper adjectives.

PROPER ADJECTIVES	
With Capitals	**Without Capitals**
Proper Adjectives: Chinese food	*Common Terms:* venetian blinds
Brand Names: Speedway motorcycle	*Most Prefixes:* pro-British sentiment
Combinations: Judeo-Christian tradition	*Parts of Compounds:* French-speaking province

▶ **Exercise 1**   **Recognizing Proper Nouns and Proper Adjectives.**   Underline the proper nouns and proper adjectives in each sentence. Rewrite each one correctly on the line at the right.

EXAMPLE: We visited the tower of london last july.   _Tower of London   July_

1. In texas we saw the rio grande and the alamo. _____

2. That hemingway novel is set during the spanish civil war. _____

3. Will the talks reduce iraqi-american tensions? _____

4. Did alex order french fries or a baked potato? _____

5. My neighbor mrs. henderson drives a green chevrolet. _____

6. The league of women voters sponsored the debate. _____

7. Those japanese tourists seem very pro-american. _____

8. The koran is the holy book of islam. _____

9. The baseball hall of fame is in cooperstown, new york. _____

10. We met many english-speaking russians on our trip. _____

▶ **Exercise 2**   **Using Proper Nouns and Proper Adjectives.**   Fill in each blank with a proper noun or proper adjective.

EXAMPLE: The ___*Alps*___ and the ___*Urals*___ are mountain ranges in ___*Europe*___ .

1. My parents are considering buying a(n) _____ computer.

2. The tour will include stops in _____
    and _____ .

3. Several speakers expressed pro-_____ views.

4. I have just finished reading a book by _____ .

5. Our state capital is _____ .

6. The biggest event in baseball is the _____ .

7. Will you ask _____ and _____ to join us?

8. We went skiing in the _____ .

9. The coldest continent is _____ .

10. _____ holiday is in the month of _____ .

27.1 Rules for Capitalization (Proper Nouns, Proper Adjectives) • Practice 2

> **Exercise 1** **Using Capitals in Sentences with Proper Nouns.** Underline the words that should be capitalized in each sentence.

EXAMPLE: We read a poem by <u>edna</u> <u>st. vincent</u> <u>millay</u>.

1. After hearing the news, the united nations called a meeting of the security council.
2. Illustrators of children's books all hope to win the coveted caldecott award.
3. Anyone who loves animal stories should read about the horse known as flicka.
4. Most people in india are hindus and worship brahma.
5. One goddess in mythology that you will read about often is the goddess hera.
6. As he made a purchase from the store called stamp house, inc., I noticed that the russian spoke english very well.
7. If you want passport information, you should contact the state department in washington, d.c.
8. My bluvard watch is now ten years old but still works.
9. The concorde crosses the atlantic ocean in just a few hours.
10. We inducted sixty new members into the national honor society at our school last week.

> **Exercise 2** **Adding Capitals for Geographical Places, Specific Events, Periods of Time, and Other Proper Nouns.** Underline the words that should be capitalized in the following paragraph. Note that some sentences do not need additional capitalization.

(1) The early years of the twentieth century brought with them a variety of new names, exciting events, and far-reaching ideas. (2) The century got off to a flying start when Orville and Wilbur Wright took to the air in december 1903. (3) Excitement continued into the next year when the st. louis world's fair began, bringing over 20,000 visitors flocking to the city. (4) Sports lovers also enjoyed the olympic games that were held in conjunction with the fair that year. (5) Formation of the american baseball league in 1901 had also brought the sports fans joy since it introduced a new level of competition to this popular sport. (6) Many people enjoyed activities in their own communities during the 1900's: Parades and picnics held as part of the july celebration of independence day brought pleasure to people of all ages. (7) Of course, all was not fun and games; many important laws were passed during these years. (8) One of the most influential pieces of legislation in the early 1900's was the pure food and drug act passed in the summer of 1906. (9) Advertisements of many "quack" medical cures came to a quick halt. (10) All this began in those first few years of the twentieth century as america boldly entered the 1900's—the time period labeled by some as the progressive era.

> **Exercise 3** **Using Capitalization with Proper Adjectives.** Underline the words that should be capitalized in each sentence. If a sentence does not need additional capitals, write *correct*.

EXAMPLE: The <u>swedish</u> student spoke the <u>english</u> language. _____

1. Charles Drew, who developed the use of plasma in emergency transfusions, was of african-american heritage. _____
2. The baby sitter hunted for the child's teddy bear. _____
3. That store sells many bottles of shaniel perfume. _____
4. The pro-american speaker at the rally was cheered. _____
5. Did you use photoflex brand equipment to take this photograph? _____

(27.1) Rules for Capitalization (for Titles, in Letters)
• Practice 1

Capitals for Titles   Capitalize titles of people and titles of works.

People	Works
Social: Lord and Lady Grantford	*Book:* Peter Rabbit
Business: Superintendent Meyers	*Periodical:* News Digest
Military: Captain McGrath	*Poem:* "The Raven"
Government: Mayor Jane Sims	*Story:* "A Day's Wait"
Religious: Rabbi Feldman	*Painting:* Christina's World
Compound: Commander-in-Chief	*Music:* The Nutcracker Suite
Abbreviations: Dr., Mrs., Jr., Ph.D.	*Courses:* English Composition II

Capitals in Letters   Capitalize the first word and all nouns in letter salutations and the first word in letter closings.

Salutations	Closings
Dear Aunt Eleanor,	Your loving niece,
Dear Senator Williams:	Sincerely yours,
My dear Friend,	Yours truly,

▶ **Exercise 1**   **Using Capitals in Titles.**   Underline the words that should be capitalized in each sentence.

EXAMPLE: *The prime of miss jean brodie* is set in a girls' boarding school.

1. Has major adams approved the plan?

2. Have you ever read "the ransom of red chief"?

3. Some of the world's most precious jewels belong to the queen of england.

4. We heard professor harold jenkins lecture on politics last night.

5. That is a reproduction of *the last supper.*

6. Leon has misplaced his script for *arsenic and old lace.*

7. The new pastor is father riley.

8. Either mrs. pauling or dr. o'rourke will make the presentation.

9. Have you seen a copy of *undersea world,* the new scuba diving magazine?

10. The first selection will be handel's *water music.*

▶ **Exercise 2**   **Using Capitals for Salutations and Closings.**   Rewrite each of the following letter parts, adding the missing capitals.

EXAMPLE: dear uncle albert,   *Dear Uncle Albert,*

1. dear dr. morgan, _____

2. with deep affection, _____

3. gratefully, _____

4. my dear cousin, _____

5. very truly yours, _____

6. dear professor atkins: _____

7. yours sincerely, _____

8. dear sir or madam: _____

9. my dear marian, _____

10. with all good wishes, _____

27.1 Rules for Capitalization (for Titles, in Letters)
• Practice 2

▶ **Exercise 1** **Using Capitalization with Titles of People.** Underline the titles that should be capitalized in each sentence. If a sentence does not need additional capitalization, write *correct*.

EXAMPLE: My aunt introduced me to David Jones, sr. _____

1. Do you remember your first day of school, grandma? _____
2. The well-known reverend John Hall, jr., spoke at the service, _____
3. With no hesitation, mayor Roberts approached the speaker's platform. _____
4. The president of the United States held a press conference. _____
5. Very few officers in the service ever attain the rank of general. _____
6. May I introduce miss Ann Schmidt and mr. Louis Ward, sr.? _____
7. Here is aunt Louise, who is a professor at the college. _____
8. Please give me advice, rabbi. _____
9. The queen of England will be visiting Australia next week. _____
10. Do you know senator-elect Garcia personally? _____

▶ **Exercise 2** **Capitalizing Titles of Things.** Underline the words that should be capitalized.

EXAMPLE: Play: *fiddler on the roof*

1. Painting: *at the circus*
2. Poem: "lines composed a few miles above tintern abbey"
3. Short story: "before the wolves come"
4. School courses: german, geometry, business 312
5. Sculpture: *variation within a sphere*
6. Opera: *the siege of rhodes*
7. Book: *wellington: the years of the sword*
8. Periodical: *national pictorial*
9. One-act play: "the wonderful ice cream suit"
10. Song: "by the light of the silvery moon"

▶ **Exercise 3** **Using Capitalization in a Letter.** If an underlined word in the following letter requires a capital, write *yes* in the blank with the corresponding number; if it does not, write *no*.

(1) my (2) dear Friends,

Recently I have discovered a brand new hobby—hot air ballooning! (3) what a thrill it is to drift slowly above the farms and housetops! Last week I saw the most spectacular sight: (4) a slender steeple rose majestically above the fog.

Of course, this new hobby is not cheap. (5) do you have any idea how much a hot air balloon costs? Over $5,000! Just taking a ride cost about $50. So far, I've learned that the baskets people ride in are usually constructed from one of four materials: (6) rattan, fiberglass, aluminum, or wood. (7) "it's possible to build a basket," a salesman told me. (8) "however, you'll need to purchase the balloon."

Since my pocketbook is empty, I'll have to settle for an occasional flight. I guess I should try to remember the words of Dorothy in *The Wizard of Oz* when she said, (9) "there's no place like home."

With fondest (10) regards,
Archie

1. _____ 3. _____ 5. _____ 7. _____ 9. _____
2. _____ 4. _____ 6. _____ 8. _____ 10. _____

28.1 End Marks • Practice 1

Basic Uses of End Marks Use a period (.) to end a declarative sentence, a mild imperative, and an indirect question. Use a question mark (?) to end a direct question, an incomplete question, or a statement intended as a question. Use an exclamation mark (!) to end an exclamatory sentence, a forceful imperative sentence, or an interjection expressing strong emotion.

Periods	Question Marks	Exclamation Marks
The sky is clear today.	Is it sunny outside?	How clear the sky is!
Just put your coat here.	What time?	Go for help!
She asked if I was ready.	We really won?	Ouch! That hurt!

Other Uses of End Marks Use a period to end most abbreviations and after numbers and letters in outlines. Use a question mark in parentheses (?) after a fact or statistic to show its uncertainty.

Periods	Question Marks
Mr. L.A. Ransom, Ph.D.	The group raised $25.80(?).
I. Causes of revolt	On January 21 (?) the group will have its first
A. Pay inequities	meeting.

▷ **Exercise 1** **Using End Marks for Sentences and Phrases.** Write the proper end mark at the end of each item.

EXAMPLE: You're kidding. She really said that ___?___

1. What a magnificent performance that was _____

2. Are you going to the game on Saturday _____

3. I wonder how big the crowd will be _____

4. Pete won first prize. Yeah _____

5. Don't ever do that again _____

6. Louis ordered another pizza _____

7. How amazing that such a young child can read so well _____

8. The waiter asked if we wanted dessert _____

9. Don't forget to take your umbrella _____

10. What time is the train due _____

▷ **Exercise 2** **Using End Marks in Your Own Sentences.** Follow the directions to write your own sentences.

EXAMPLE: Write a sentence that contains an interjection.

    Gee! I made a dumb mistake.

1. Write a sentence that suggests uncertainty about a date.

_____

2. Write a sentence that includes an abbreviated title.

_____

3. Write a statement intended as a question.

_____

4. Write a forceful imperative sentence.

_____

5. Write an incomplete question.

_____

28.1 End Marks • Practice 2

Exercise 1 | **Using the Period and Question Mark.** Write all necessary periods or question marks in the following items.

EXAMPLE: I wonder which state was named after a Greek island
I wonder which state was named after a Greek island.

1. Who has more bones—a baby or an adult
2. I have often asked in what country a person can expect to live the longest
3. What was the name of Roy Rogers' horse
4. Which state has produced the most Presidents
5. How many Who
6. The scientist questioned how long a queen termite can live
7. Who knows what Lawrence Welk's license plate said
8. Of all the animal personalities, who was first named to the Animal Hall of Fame
9. Where can you find the tallest living thing in the world
10. I wondered where the name Typhoid Mary came from

Exercise 2 | **Using the Period and Exclamation Mark.** Write all necessary periods or exclamation marks in the following items.

EXAMPLE: Wow That was a spectacular catch
Wow ! That was a spectacular catch !

1. Please bring me that pin cushion
2. His voice is fantastic
3. Don't step on the cat
4. Darn
5. A child is caught in that burning building
6. Do it this minute
7. The house looked fresh after its new paint job
8. Well, I have never been so insulted in my entire life
9. Try to finish those essays for tomorrow, class
10. I just won the Boston Marathon

Exercise 3 | **Using All End Marks.** Add all necessary end marks to the following paragraph.

EXAMPLE: Do you enjoy eating popcorn as much as I do
Do you enjoy eating popcorn as much as I do ?

(1) Hey Get your fresh, hot, buttered popcorn right here (2) The cry of the vendor selling popcorn has been heard for years at circuses, ball games, and county fairs (3) But some may wonder who first learned about this delicacy (4) Even before Columbus sailed to this continent, the Indians of Central and South America were popping little kernels of corn (5) They ate them, made popcorn soup from them, and wore them during religious ceremonies (6) Today popcorn is one of America's favorite snack foods (7) Just how much popcorn do Americans eat in a year (8) According to statistics, they eat an average of two pounds per person each year (9) For the popcorn industry that figure is larger than it sounds (10) As a group, Americans eat an incredible amount of popcorn—almost half a billion pounds each year

28.2 ## Commas (with Compound Sentences, with Series and Adjectives) • Practice 1

Commas with Compound Sentences   Use a *comma* before the conjunction to separate two independent clauses in a compound sentence.

COMPOUND SENTENCES
We worked most of the day, but we didn't finish painting the room.
Not only were we late for the party, but most of the food was gone also.

Commas with Series and Adjectives   Use commas to separate three or more words, phrases, or clauses in a series. Use commas to separate adjectives of equal rank but not adjectives that must stay in a specific order.

With Commas	Without Commas
Mom bought candy, milk, and cookies for the party.	Mom bought milk and cookies for the party.
Eager, devoted fans waited outside the star's dressing room.	Many eager fans waited outside the star's dressing room.

▶ **Exercise 1**   **Using Commas Correctly.**   Add commas where they are needed. One sentence needs no commas.

EXAMPLE: My chores include cleaning my room dusting the living room and taking out the trash.
        My chores include cleaning my room, dusting the living room, and taking out the trash.

1. The actor delivered the soliloquy in a clear, strong voice.
2. My sister goes to college in Ohio, and my brother goes to college in Maine.
3. Parsley sprigs, lemon slices, and tomato wedges formed an attractive border on the platter.
4. The hot, tired campers headed straight for the lake.
5. Janice may bake a cake, or we can order one at Farella's.
6. Have you seen the Jacksons' three new puppies?
7. Our trip was far from perfect, but at least we got home safely.
8. Elmer saw a large, lumpy figure moving through the shadows.
9. Jeremy had planned a special meal, but it was ruined.
10. Will you fly, take the train, or drive to California?

▶ **Exercise 2**   **Understanding Rules for Commas.**   Describe the comma rule for each sentence in Exercise 1 above by writing *compound sentence*, *series*, *equal adjectives*, or *adjectives in order*.

EXAMPLE: ___series___

1. ___e a___   6. ___a i o___
2. ___CS___   7. ___CS___
3. ___S___   8. ___e a___
4. ___e a___   9. ___CS___
5. ___CS___   10. ___S___

28.2 Commas (with Compound Sentences, with Series and Adjectives) • Practice 2

> **Exercise 1** **Using Commas in Compound Sentences.** Add commas where they are needed in the following sentences. If no comma is needed, write *correct*.

EXAMPLE: I practice my typing daily but I still make mistakes.

       I practice my typing daily, but I still make mistakes.

1. The drummers beat the rhythm and the band marched the parade route. _____
2. The photograph shows your feet but your head is cut off. _____
3. Neither did we visit the aquarium nor did we watch the show at the planetarium. _____
4. You may have either hot chocolate or coffee to drink. *correct*
5. Jack and Wendy will lead the songfest. *correct*
6. The hateful mosquito bit me and I have had a huge welt ever since. _____
7. My mother lost her favorite earrings so I will get her another pair for her birthday. _____
8. The airplane circled once and then came in for a landing. *correct*
9. The student saved time for the last essay question yet he found the time was not sufficient. _____
10. The TV blared but the child slept on. _____

> **Exercise 2** **Separating Items in a Series.** Add commas where they are needed in the following sentences. For sentences that need no commas, write *correct*.

EXAMPLE: I added oregano parsley and garlic to the spaghetti sauce.

      I added oregano, parsley, and garlic to the spaghetti sauce.

1. We plan to sing and dance and act in our summer theater troupe. *correct*
2. I carefully watered the philodendrons the ivy and the African violet. _____
3. The crowd sat on the edge of their seats listened with awe and absorbed the speaker's powerful words. _____
4. The politician answered with great patience diplomacy and knowledge. _____
5. I looked under the bed in the closet and through my desk to find my homework. _____
6. Cloris Leachman Henry Fonda and other well-known stars performed in the play. _____
7. I described the symptoms to the doctor: a temperature aching bones nausea and a rash on my legs. _____
8. Send that letter to the President the Secretary of State and the Ambassador to France. _____
9. We went first to pick up Beth and then to find Barry and finally to get Peter. *correct*
10. The sun shone brightly the clouds drifted lazily overhead and we waded in the warm water. _____

28.2 Commas (After Introductory Material, with Parenthetical and Nonessential Expressions) • Practice 1

Commas After Introductory Material   Use a *comma* after an introductory word, phrase, or clause.

INTRODUCTORY MATERIAL
Introductory Word: Yes, that is the book I ordered.
Introductory Phrase: Without a word to anyone, Susan left the house.
Introductory Clause: As the ship sailed away, we waved at Jim.

Commas with Parenthetical and Nonessential Expressions   Use commas to set off parenthetical and nonessential expressions.

PARENTHETICAL EXPRESSIONS
Names of People Being Addressed: Did you know, Tom, that I am a twin?
Certain Adverbs: We hoped, however, that the weather would improve.
Common Expressions: The outcome, in my opinion, looks bleak.
Contrasting Expressions: Those scrolls are from China, not Korea.

Essential Expressions	Nonessential Expressions
My friend the football player is trying for a scholarship.	Jack, a football player, is trying for a scholarship.
The woman now approaching the microphone will introduce the speaker.	Alice, now approaching the microphone, will introduce the speaker.

▶ **Exercise 1**   **Recognizing Introductory Material.**   Write the introductory word, phrase, or clause in each sentence, and add the needed comma.

EXAMPLE: Actually I would rather stay home. _____*Actually,*_____

1. Yes the crocuses have begun to bloom. _____Yes,_____
2. To win the game we need a miracle. _____To win the game,_____
3. Shrugging her shoulders Melody walked away. _____Shrugging her shoulders,_____
4. Before we knew it the movie ended. _____Before we knew it,_____
5. Exhausted we looked for a shady spot to rest. _____Exhausted,_____
6. Although he works hard math is difficult for Bob. _____Although he works hard_____
7. As soon as we got your call we changed our plans. _____As soon as we got your call,_____
8. Alice have you seen my keys anywhere? _____Alice,_____
9. To get to work Mom takes a bus and a train. _____To get to work,_____
10. Frankly I have my doubts about the proposal. _____Frankly,_____

▶ **Exercise 2**   **Using Commas with Parenthetical and Nonessential Expressions.**   Add commas where they are needed. One sentence needs no commas.

EXAMPLE: My mother a doctor hopes that I will follow in her footsteps.
   My mother, a doctor, hopes that I will follow in her footsteps.

1. It was Bill, not Bob whom I met at the concert.
2. The novel *All the King's Men* is set in Louisiana.
3. We agreed, of course, that the party should be a surprise.
4. Mr. Palmeri, our next-door neighbor, grows beautiful roses.
5. T.S. Eliot, who was born in St. Louis, adopted England as his home.

28.2 Commas (After Introductory Material, with Parenthetical and Nonessential Expressions) • Practice 2

▶ **Exercise 1** **Using Commas After Introductory Material.** For each of the following sentences, write the introductory material and the comma, if one is needed.

EXAMPLE: My friend do you know how soap was discovered? ___*My friend,*___

(1) Though we probably do not think about it often we use soap every day. (2) In fact a person who lives in the United States uses an average of twenty-eight pounds of soap and detergent a year. (3) According to old legends soap was invented over three thousand years ago. (4) On top of Sapo Hill in Rome fat from sacrificed animals soaked through the ashes on the altar and into the soil. (5) Soon after the women of Rome discovered that the soil around the altar produced a soapy clay that helped wash their clothes. (6) Working with caustic soda in the 1700's Nicolas Leblanc discovered that an inexpensive soap could be produced from salt. (7) To have soap in the early days of American history most people had to make their own lye soap. (8) When the 1800's arrived the soap industry began. (9) However it was not until 1916 that Fritz Gunther developed the first synthetic detergent for industrial use. (10) In 1933 Procter and Gamble began to produce the first household detergents for the marketplace.

1. _____   6. _____
2. _____   7. _____
3. _____   8. _____
4. _____   9. _____
5. _____   10. _____

▶ **Exercise 2** **Setting Off Parenthetical Expressions.** In the following sentences, insert any commas necessary to set off parenthetical expressions.

EXAMPLE: The story was considered so important, in fact, that it was placed on the front page.

1. We have enough paper plates left over I think.

2. The suit nevertheless needed drastic alterations before I could wear it.

3. When does your ship sail Mr. Harville?

4. I will type up the letter Kim if you get it written by tomorrow.

5. I therefore went out shopping for a bathing suit.

▶ **Exercise 3** **Distinguishing Between Essential and Nonessential Expressions.** If a sentence contains an essential expression, write *essential* in the blank. If the sentence contains a nonessential expression, add commas.

EXAMPLE: Those who tried to make their fortunes as pirates succeeded and failed. ___*essential*___

(1) Pirates those colorful, legendary plunderers of the ocean made many spectacular heists on the high seas. (2) Bartholomew Roberts who allowed no drinking or gambling on board his vessel caught and pirated over 400 ships. (3) Long Ben Avery beginning his pirating career at age twenty captured two million dollars worth of booty—the largest amount of loot ever stolen. (4) The pirates who possessed a very strong code of honor within their own ranks had strict rules for dealing with problems on board. (5) Pirates stealing from their mates had their ears and noses cut off as punishment.

1. _____
2. _____
3. _____
4. _____
5. _____

28.2 Commas (Other Uses) • Practice 1

Other Uses of the Comma   When a date, a geographical name, or an address is made up of two or more parts, use a comma after each item except in the case of a month followed by a day. Use commas to set off a title following a name. Also use commas in the other situations shown in the chart below.

Date	On April 18, 1775, Paul Revere made his famous ride.
Geographical Name	Atlanta, Georgia, was almost totally destroyed by fire during the Civil War.
Address	We are moving to 1678 Main Street, Akron, Ohio.
Name with Title	Alice Evans, Ph.D., will speak on Monday.
Salutation and Closing	Dear Aunt Eleanor,
	Your loving niece,
Numbers	37,500 1,675,758
Elliptical Sentence	Jake excels at baseball; Mike, at basketball.
Direct Quotation	"Soon," mused Paul, "this day will be over."
To Prevent Confusion	Together with Julie, Erin is going to the ballet.

▶ **Exercise 1**   **Adding Commas to Sentences.**   Insert commas where they are needed.

EXAMPLE: Lorraine Hall R.N. will teach the CPR course.
Lorraine Hall, R.N., will teach the CPR course.

1. That family has moved to 721 Barker Street Jefferson Missouri.

2. John ordered swordfish; Paul fried clams.

3. The station's goal is 1235 new subscribers.

4. Jed asked "Is February 13 a good day for the party?"

5. Sarah Marsh L.P.N. prefers hospital work to private duty in homes.

6. Without Ellen Ann was lonely.

7. On June 12 2001 my grandfather celebrated his sixtieth birthday.

8. The new hotel has 1354 rooms.

9. "Whenever you are ready" Pat called "we can leave."

10. After dinner entertainment will be offered.

▶ **Exercise 2**   **Punctuating a Letter.**   Add commas wherever necessary in the following letter.

629 West 4th Street
Montpelier Vermont 05602
December 4 2001

Dear Paulette

    Your letter was waiting for me when we arrived home on Friday November 30 after a short trip. We had gone to Boston Massachusetts to spend Thanksgiving with my grandparents.

    It was odd that you should have asked for Margie's address. I just got a letter from her too—the first one since her family moved on August 1 1999. Her address is Margaret Bayard 289 South Caxton Place Gettysburg Pennsylvania.

    Your plan for a reunion this summer sounds wonderful! I wonder if Beth will be able to come 1700 miles for it though. But as you always used to say "Let's go for it!" Keep me posted on the plans.

Your old friend
Sonya

28.2 Commas (Other Uses) • Practice 2

Exercise 1 **Using Commas in Other Situations.** Add commas where they are needed in the following sentences.

EXAMPLE: Number (702) 555–4818 was billed for $2352.
Number (702) 555–4818 was billed for $2,352.

1. The drive from Seattle Washington to Portland Oregon is a pretty one.

2. He was elected on Tuesday November 5 and inaugurated in January of the next year.

3. There were 52500 people watching the parade.

4. "Please move into the left lane" the officer patiently instructed.

5. My brother asked "Have you eaten dinner yet?"

6. Our class will have Martin Deardorf Ph.D. as our guest.

7. I read the address on the business card: R.P. Mendosa 615 Taggert Lane Cupertino California 95041.

8. The irate customer spoke belligerently; the public relations officer gently.

9. "When I reached the age of eight" the woman recalled "I decided to become a dental hygienist."

10. During the afternoon tea and pastries were always served.

Exercise 2 **Correcting Careless Use of Commas.** Some of the commas have been used incorrectly in the following sentences. Rewrite each sentence, removing any incorrect commas.

EXAMPLE: I knew that I was right, and that they would agree.

_____I knew that I was right and that they would agree._____

1. During the initial training period, the falcon, sits on a gloved hand with a hood covering its head.

_____

2. Bees have existed for about fifty million years, and live everywhere but at the North and South Poles.

_____

3. An interesting fact about the buffalo is, that it was once on the nickel coin.

_____

4. Bill, don't forget to clean the garage, and the deck.

_____

5. The cost of World War II, in deaths and suffering, was enormous.

_____

6. She bought shoes, and presents for her grandparents.

_____

7. If eaten, the beautiful, Christmas poinsettia is poisonous.

_____

8. The crayfish is the freshwater counterpart of the lobster, and is found in freshwater springs and lakes.

_____

9. The queen bee, really does not rule the colony but only serves to reproduce the bees.

_____

10. When new seedlings begin to grow, they need water, and sunshine.

_____

28.3 Semicolons and Colons (Uses of the Semicolon)
• Practice 1

Uses of the Semicolon   Use a semicolon to join independent clauses not already joined by a coordinating conjunction or those separated by a conjunctive adverb or transitional expression. Use semicolons to avoid confusion when independent clauses already contain commas or between items in a series that contains commas.

With Independent Clauses	The chief sounded the alarm; the firefighters raced to their stations.
With a Conjunctive Adverb	Helene has a 4.0 average; consequently, she has a good chance for a scholarship.
With a Transitional Expression	In the first place, Stan loves all sports; in addition, he has excellent coordination.
With Items That Already Have Commas	The judges will include Ms. Haley, the drama coach; Mr. Dakin, the choral director; and Mr. Odem, the local drama critic.

▶ **Exercise 1**   **Using Semicolons Correctly.**   In each sentence, a comma is used where a semicolon is needed. Circle the comma that should be replaced with a semicolon.

EXAMPLE: Jenny has neglected her studies lately (,) consequently, her grades are falling.

1. Since childhood, Amy has loved animals, therefore, her career as a veterinarian is hardly surprising.

2. Cucumbers, carrots, tomatoes, and onions are common in salads, for a change of pace, have you ever tried adding broccoli, eggplant, or corn?

3. When Anna is home from college, all the bedrooms are full, for a change of pace, we can always put up a guest in the playroom, a room that is seldom used.

4. Just put the packages on the porch, we'll have to wait here until someone gets home with the key.

5. Penny had just come off a twelve-hour shift, she was exhausted.

6. We are to supply paper goods, beverages, and snacks, but Tom will provide the main dish, the vegetables, and the salad.

7. The house needs to be painted, in addition, it needs a new roof.

8. This is an ideal time to start out, the roads are not yet crowded.

9. Jason, whom I have known all my life, was a very serious youngster, but he has, surprisingly enough, become the life of every party.

10. Grandma has lived in that old house all her life, no wonder she doesn't want to move.

▶ **Exercise 2**   **Understanding Uses of the Semicolon.**   Give the reason why each of the semicolons in Exercise 1 is needed by writing the appropriate label from the chart.

EXAMPLE: _____conjunctive adverb_____

1. _____   6. _____
2. _____   7. _____
3. _____   8. _____
4. _____   9. _____
5. _____   10. _____

28.3 Semicolons and Colons (Uses of the Semicolon)
• Practice 2

▶Exercise 1 **Using the Semicolon with Independent Clauses.** Add semicolons where needed.

EXAMPLE: I once had a red yo-yo my sister had a green one.
     I once had a red yo-yo; my sister had a green one.

(1) Yo-yos have been enjoyed for years in fact, people in ancient Greece played with toys like yo-yos for entertainment. (2) In France, the popularity of the yo-yo grew quickly for instance, the nobles in seventeenth-century France played with yo-yos in the royal courts. (3) Napoleon's soldiers played with them while waiting to fight France's prisoners supposedly played with them while waiting for the guillotine. (4) Even King George IV is pictured with a yo-yo a cartoonist satirically drew him spinning his top. (5) In Europe they played with yo-yos in the Philippines they used them for more serious purposes. (6) In the sixteenth century, the people of the Philippines hunted with yo-yo-like weapons they sat in trees and sent the yo-yos hurtling down to stun the animals below. (7) History reports that Donald Duncan first promoted the yo-yo in America in 1926 however, recent evidence shows Lothrop Llewellyn selling a metal yo-yo as early as 1906. (8) He sold his yo-yos in Gloucester Llewellyn even took out a patent on his invention. (9) The latest yo-yo craze occurred in the 1960's indeed, Duncan reportedly sold fifteen million in 1961 alone. (10) Today, the most difficult yo-yo trick is the whirlwind it requires performing inside and outside loop-the-loops.

▶Exercise 2 **Using Semicolons with Internal Punctuation.** Add semicolons where they are needed to avoid confusion in each of the following sentences.

EXAMPLE: I baked cookies, made with raisins muffins, made with dates and a cake, made with walnuts.
     I baked cookies, made with raisins; muffins, made with dates; and a cake, made with walnuts.

1. When the milk carton fell, it split but I picked it up before all the milk flowed onto the floor.

2. Joe, Maria, and I drove into the city last night and we went to a delightful concert in the park.

3. As I watched, the tall, thin man reached into the pedestrian's pocket, removing his wallet but before I could even protest, the pickpocket was lost in the crowd.

4. As she tried to lay out the pattern on the material, she finally concluded that she was short of fabric and so she switched to another pattern, one requiring less material.

5. My grandmother knew more about people, places, and life in general than many world travelers yet she never left the state of Nebraska.

6. When the cast was posted, you should have seen the look of joy on Martin's face for to get a lead in the play was his dream.

7. Walking home from the store, I found an injured, frightened cat and I knew, at that moment, he was meant to be mine.

8. I peeked out of my sleeping bag and saw a squirrel, who was busily gathering his winter food a bird, who was welcoming the morning in song and a doe, who was surveying her peaceful domain.

9. During this morning's practice, we have to master the routine or the coach says we will work, work, work all day.

10. I am certain that you will enjoy this class, which is interesting and challenging, and the teacher, Mr. Gray, is excellent.

28.3 Semicolons and Colons (Uses of the Colon)
• Practice 1

Uses of the Colon   Use a colon to introduce a list of items after an independent clause; a quotation that is formal, lengthy, or lacking a "he said/she said" expression; a sentence that summarizes or explains the sentence before it; or a formal appositive that follows an independent clause.

INTRODUCTORY COLONS	
List	The arrangement consisted entirely of spring flowers: irises, daffodils, tulips, and hyacinths.
Quotation	Ellen waved goodbye: "Have a good trip."
Summary Sentence	The paper reported the election results: All three present school board members were unseated.
Formal Appositive	The class play will be an American classic: *Our Town*

In addition, use a colon in the following special situations.

OTHER USES OF THE COLON	
Numerals Giving Time	8:17 A.M. 11:57 P.M.
Periodical References	*National Geographic* XI: 421 (volume: page)
Biblical References	I Corinthians 13: 4–13 (chapter: verse[s])
Subtitles	*Pierre: A Cautionary Tale*
Salutations in Business Letters	Dear Ms. Adamson:
	Gentlemen:
Labels Signaling Important Ideas	Caution: Keep this and all medications out of the reach of children.

> **Exercise 1**   **Using Colons Correctly.**   Add colons where they are needed in the following sentences.

EXAMPLE: The recipe calls for three basic spices garlic, parsley, and thyme.
          The recipe calls for three basic spices: garlic, parsley, and thyme.

1. Jeremy unfolded the note "Meet me in the gym after school."

2. The express, which was due at 8 14, did not arrive until 9 00 P.M.

3. Two actors have refused Academy Awards George C. Scott and Marlon Brando.

4. The three magazines with the largest paid subscriptions last year were these *TV Scene, Reader's Review,* and *National Reflections Magazine.*

5. Warning This cabinet contains dangerous electrical equipment.

> **Exercise 2**   **More Work with Colons.**   Follow the directions in Exercise 1.

1. The text of the sermon was Matthew 10 8.

2. I am reporting on a biography titled *Gandhi Fighter Without a Sword.*

3. Caution Read this manual completely before using your power sled.

4. Flight 401 leaves LaGuardia Airport at 8 40 A.M. each weekday.

5. The president banged the gavel "Let the meeting come to order."

28.3 Semicolons and Colons (Uses of the Colon)
• Practice 2

> **Exercise 1** **Using Colons as Introductory Devices.** In each of the following sentences, add colons where they are needed and underline any words that should be capitalized.

EXAMPLE: You will hear about a man with talent and imagination he is a man whose work you know well.
You will hear about a man with talent and imagination: he is a man whose work you know well.

(1) This man was born December 5, 1901, and until his death in 1966, he carried one of the best-known names in the world Walt Disney. (2) Of course, he is best remembered as the creator of some of our most beloved cartoon characters Mickey Mouse, Pluto, and Donald Duck. (3) Walt Disney studied one subject with diligence he concentrated on art. (4) Walt Disney felt he had to go to the one city where he could possibly become successful he headed to Hollywood. (5) In Hollywood, he made money from his drawings, but he finally hit success with a now-classic Mickey Mouse cartoon short "Steamboat Willie." (6) Disney went on to create many of the following famous films *Snow White and the Seven Dwarfs*, *Fantasia*, and *Mary Poppins*. (7) In 1955, he started something that was to change family entertainment he opened Disneyland. (8) Parents appreciated Walt Disney "Our children can explore the worlds of Frontierland, Fantasyland, Tomorrowland, and Adventureland in a clean environment." (9) Several years later, Disney directed his efforts in a new direction television. (10) Yes, Disney has left us the kind of memorials that will continue to be enjoyed by millions Mickey Mouse, Snow White, Bambi, and the rest of the Disney gang.

> **Exercise 2** **Using Colons for Special Writing Situations.** Add the necessary colons in each of the following items.

EXAMPLE: Our textbook is *Psychology Exploring Behavior*.
Our textbook is *Psychology: Exploring Behavior*.

1. Warning Pull the plug after you finish using the iron.
2. School ended at 235 P.M., and we were expected to be ready for the presentation at 300 P.M.
3. *The Readers' Guide* listed *Green Garden Magazine* 1623, but I could not find that issue.
4. "Dear Mr. Nelson" is the way I started my business letter.
5. The Old Testament reading came from Psalms 1305.
6. I read *Caring for Livestock A Guide for Beginners*.
7. I should be finished with my homework at 1000 P.M.
8. Danger This water is polluted. No swimming is allowed.
9. Note The meeting will begin one hour late.
10. The movie starts at 730 P.M.

28.4 Quotation Marks with Direct Quotations
(Direct Quotations) • Practice 1

Direct Quotations A direct quotation represents a person's exact speech or thoughts and is enclosed in quotation marks (" "). An indirect quotation reports only the general meaning of what a person said or thought and does not require quotation marks. In writing direct quotations, use a comma or colon after an introductory expression and a comma, question mark, or exclamation mark after a quotation followed by a concluding expression. Also use commas to surround interrupting expressions in a direct quotation. Use a comma, question mark, or exclamation mark after a quoted sentence before an interrupting expression and a period after the expression.

Direct Quotations	Indirect Quotations
"Do you think that it will rain?" asked Harry.	Harry wondered whether or not it would rain.
Harry asked, "Do you think that it will rain?"	Harry asked me if I thought it would rain.
"I certainly hope," Cheryl said, "that we will win the game."	Cheryl hoped that we would win the game.
"Slow down!" Max exclaimed.	Max told the driver to slow down because there
"There's an accident ahead."	was an accident ahead.

▶ **Exercise 1** **Distinguishing Between Direct and Indirect Quotations.** Label each sentence below *D* (for direct quotation) or *I* (for indirect quotation).

EXAMPLE: All I know, Sharon said, is that I did my best. ___D___

1. The tourist asked for directions to the World Trade Center. _____

2. Marcia began her letter: Dear Santa, Please bring me a new sled. _____

3. Have you chosen your topic for the report? Darryl inquired. _____

4. Bruce told me not to tell anyone about the party. _____

5. We could go roller skating, Dana suggested, or would you rather see a movie? _____

6. The garden really needs weeding, Mom observed. _____

7. I told the waiter to bring me another fork. _____

8. Amanda suggested that we could organize a scrap paper drive. _____

9. Ouch! Lou cried. That pan is hot! _____

10. The librarian said that our entire card catalog will soon be on a computer. _____

▶ **Exercise 2** **Using Quotation Marks Correctly.** Write each sentence labeled *D* above, adding quotation marks where they are needed. Rewrite each sentence labeled *I* so that it contains a direct quotation. Use quotation marks where they are needed.

EXAMPLE: _"All I know," Sharon said, "is that I did my best."_

1. _____

2. _____

3. _____

4. _____

5. _____

6. _____

7. _____

8. _____

9. _____

10. _____

28.4 Quotation Marks with Direct Quotations
(Direct Quotations) • Practice 2

▶ **Exercise 1** **Indicating Direct Quotations.** Rewrite each sentence that needs quotation marks, adding the necessary marks. If no quotation marks are needed, write *correct.*

EXAMPLE: Ashley Montagu said The cultured man is a wise man.

     Ashley Montagu said, "The cultured man is a wise man."

1. Hain't we got all the fools in town on our side? And ain't that a big enough majority in any town?—Mark Twain

    _____

    _____

2. Ginny told me she did very well on her science test.

    _____

3. Among mortals, Euripides commented, second thoughts are wisest.

    _____

4. Her favorite saying was To each his own.

    _____

5. James Martineau once said, Religion is no more possible without prayer than poetry without language or music without atmosphere.

    _____

    _____

6. Wit has truth in it; wisecracking is simply calisthenics with words.—Dorothy Parker

    _____

7. My aunt told me I was the only one who remembered her birthday.

    _____

8. Longfellow often expressed this philosophy: People should act in the living present.

    _____

9. I rode this bicycle, Felipe gasped, at least two miles up the hill.

    _____

10. Maybe I can go shopping with you at the mall this afternoon, Carolyn said.

    _____

▶ **Exercise 2** **Indicating and Capitalizing Quotations.** On other paper, rewrite these sentences, making corrections in punctuation and capitalization. Quoted phrases are underlined.

EXAMPLE: as for looking back, I do it reluctantly wrote Joyce Maynard.

    "As for looking back, I do it reluctantly," wrote Joyce Maynard.

1. it is better to wear out than rust out.—Bishop Cumberland
2. in one of her poems, Mary Lamb referred to a child as a young climber-up of knees.
3. sympathy was once described by Charles Parkhurst as two hearts tugging at one load.
4. the greatest powers of the mind are displayed in novels Jane Austen wrote.
5. better late than never has become a favorite proverb for those who never get anything done on time.

28.4 Quotation Marks with Direct Quotations
(Other Punctuation Marks with Quotation Marks,
Quotation Marks in Special Situations) • Practice 1

Other Punctuation Marks with Quotation Marks   Always place a *comma* or a period inside the final quotation marks. Always place a *semicolon* or *colon* outside the final quotation marks. Use the meaning of the whole sentence to determine the placement of question marks and exclamation marks.

PLACING OTHER PUNCTUATION MARKS	
Commas and Periods	"I am sure," Beth said, "that you are right."
Colons and Semicolons	Jill remarked, "We have a problem"; she went on to give details.
Questions Marks and Exclamation Marks	Nina asked, "Isn't she the one?" Didn't Nina say, "She is the one"?

Quotation Marks in Special Situations   Use single *quotation marks* for a quotation within a quotation. When writing dialogue, begin a new paragraph with each change of speaker. For quotations longer than a paragraph, put quotation marks at the beginning of each paragraph but only at the end of the final paragraph.

SPECIAL USES OF QUOTATION MARKS	
Quotation Within a Quotation	Ann answered, "The soliloquy begins, 'To be or not to be,' and it is found in Act III of *Hamlet*."

Dialogue	"Pets are well known to offer benefits to humans. They provide companionship, loyalty, and affection without making difficult emotional demands.
	   "Pets are particularly beneficial," the psychologist continued, "at times of great loss."
	   "However," interrupted the allergist, "there are medical hazards from pets as well."

▶ **Exercise 1**   **Punctuating Direct Quotations.**   Add the missing punctuation marks.

EXAMPLE: Jed asked, Who wrote the line Hope spring eternal?
   Jed asked, "Who wrote the line 'Hope springs eternal'?"

   1. Didn't the travel agent say, All tips are included in the package price?

   2. Jeffrey remarked, She should be here any minute. Then the doorbell rang.

   3. I wonder, Phyllis mused, if we have taken the right action.

   4. Who ordered the pizza? Kelly asked.

   5. The patient winced, That felt like more than just the prick of a pin!

   6. I remember, Grandma reminisced, the day when you were born.

   7. Do you think, Mom asked, that we need more cookies?

   8. Have you ever wondered, the teacher asked, who first said, Eureka?

   9. Carmen announced loudly, I'm starved; just then the waiter arrived.

   10. Perhaps, Phil suggested, we should postpone the party.

▶ **Exercise 2**   **Paragraphing Dialogue.**   On other paper write a short dialogue between you and a friend on a topic such as those listed.

an upcoming school function	a current movie	studying for an important test
a political issue in your town	a book you have recently read	finding a summer job

28.4 Quotation Marks with Direct Quotations
(Other Punctuation Marks with Quotation Marks)
• Practice 2

> **Exercise 1** **Adding Quotation Marks and Other Punctuation Marks.** Add the necessary quotation marks, commas, colons, semicolons, or end marks to these sentences.

EXAMPLE: Did you say Let's meet at four o'clock
Did you say, "Let's meet at four o'clock"?

1. The car keeps overheating she explained to the mechanic

2. We enjoyed perfect skiing weather my friends told me The sun came out and the wind died down

3. We watched the principal on the closed circuit TV I am pleased to announce that one of our own teachers will be on the school board this year

4. Watch that child a driver called out

5. Will you go to the Senior Ball with me asked my friend

6. Ouch Archie yelped I'm having a few problems with this project

7. Doesn't that kite look beautiful floating in the air up there the father asked his young child

8. She explained I got the job at Mervyn's I start working there tomorrow morning

9. I sent the package first class the secretary reported

10. Since the milk has turned sour the clerk apologized let me get you a new quart right away.

> **Exercise 2** **Punctuating and Capitalizing in Longer Selections.** The following dialogue has no paragraphing, quotation marks, capitalization, or punctuation. Each number indicates a new speaker. On another piece of paper, copy the dialogue, indent paragraphs, and add the necessary quotation marks, capitals, and other punctuation.

(1) today we are lucky to have dr. margaret sherman to discuss the subject of dreams (2) it is a pleasure to be with you today dr. sherman began as I talk please feel free to interrupt and ask questions (3) someone in the audience raised a hand will you cover the interpretation of dreams (4) yes the doctor replied but first let me talk about the importance certain cultures place on dreams for instance the cheyenne indians sent their boys out to dream a vision that would reveal their destinies in the ibans tribe in borneo they believe that a secret helper comes in a dream to provide advice (5) i have heard that people have gotten inspirations and inventions from their dreams can you verify this an individual asked (6) the doctor turned to the questioner mozart reported that he saw whole musical pieces composed in his dreams and friedrich kekule solved the structure of benzene based on his dream (7) and did einstein discover the theory of relativity through a dream someone in the back of the room challenged (8) as a matter of fact the lecturer explained he had been sick from overwork he worked out his theory while experiencing a feverish dream (9) i find this fascinating a girl in the front row whispered (10) ten minutes later the speaker concluded we should welcome our dreams—not fear them let me leave you with these words from william wordsworth come blessed barrier between day and day.

Name _____ Date _____

 28.4

Underlining and Other Uses of Quotation Marks • Practice 1

Underlining   Underline the titles of books, plays, periodicals, newspapers, long poems, movies, radio and television series, long musical compositions, albums, and works of art. In addition, underline the names of individual air, sea, space, and land craft; foreign words not yet accepted into English; numbers, symbols, letters, and words used to name themselves; and words that you want to stress.

Titles	Other Uses
Wuthering Heights (novel)	the Concorde (plane)
The Miracle Worker (play)	the Montrealer (train)
Return of the Jedi (movie)	I will keep you au courant.
The Twilight Zone (TV series)	That t should be capitalized.
Madama Butterfly (opera)	Check the spelling of chief.
the Thinker (sculpture	Please leave now!

Quotation Marks   Use quotation marks for the titles of short written works, parts of longer works, songs, and works that are part of a collection.

WORKS WITH QUOTATION MARKS	
"A Day's Wait" (short story)	"Out of My Dreams" (song)
"Ile" (one-act play)	"Floods of Gold" (chapter)
"Mending Wall" (poem)	"Hallelujah Chorus" from The Messiah

Titles Without Underlining or Quotation Marks   Do not underline or place in quotation marks mentions of the Bible and other holy scriptures or their parts. No marking is required for titles of government charters, alliances, treaties, acts, statutes, or reports.

TITLES WITHOUT UNDERLINING OR QUOTATION MARKS
the Bible, the Koran (religious works)
Bill of Rights, Declaration of Independence (government documents)

▶ **Exercise 1**   **Punctuating Different Types of Works.**   Use underlining or quotation marks with the works in each sentence. One item does not require punctuation. Mark it *correct*.

EXAMPLE: The song Shall We Dance? comes from the musical The King and I.

   The song "Shall We Dance?" comes from the musical The King and I.

1. The first book in the New Testament is Matthew.

2. We have just finished reading the Inferno from Dante's Divine Comedy.

3. The background music was The March of the Toys from Babes in Toyland.

4. Each evening, the band on the Queen Elizabeth 2 played God Save the Queen.

5. Did you read the article The Land of the Dead in last week's News Review Magazine?

▶ **Exercise 2**   **Choosing the Correct Form**

Circle the correct form in each item.

1. "Hamlet" or Hamlet

2. Genesis or Genesis

3. "Happy Birthday" or Happy Birthday

4. The Magna Carta or the Magna Carta

5. The "Nutcracker Suite" or the Nutcracker Suite

28.4 Underlining and Other Uses of Quotation Marks • Practice 2

> **Exercise 1** **Underlining Titles, Names, and Words.**   Underline titles, names, or words that require underlining. If a sentence is correct, write *correct*.

EXAMPLE: She graduated magna cum laude.   She graduated <u>magna cum laude</u>.

1. The movie Vertigo was very popular.
2. Many books such as Gone with the Wind have been made into movies.
3. Margot Fonteyn, a famous ballerina, appeared in the production Marguerite and Armand.
4. My favorite CD album is We Are the World.
5. Renoir depicts a summer outing in his painting Luncheon of the Boating Party.
6. The word nice is too often used in place of a more descriptive word.
7. She reads The Daily Tribune every day.
8. Many important historical events occurred in and around Boston's Faneuil Hall.
9. In 1830, the people held a race between a horse and a railroad steam locomotive, the Tom Thumb; the horse won.
10. I thought I heard the clerk say the number fifteen, but she apparently called out the number fifty.

> **Exercise 2** **Using Quotation Marks with Titles.**   In each of the following sentences, enclose the title in quotation marks.

EXAMPLE: The story Rear Window is a classic tale of suspense.
        The story "Rear Window" is a classic tale of suspense.

1. I read the assigned chapter: Building the Affirmative Case.
2. Our foreign visitor had learned The Star-Spangled Banner.
3. The short poem Ozymandias by Shelley conveys the theme that no one can achieve immortality.
4. Woody Guthrie wrote the famous song This Land Is Your Land.
5. I tried out for a part in the one-act play called The Veldt.
6. Road to the Isles is my favorite Jessamyn West story.
7. A Modest Proposal is a satirical essay written by Jonathan Swift in 1729.
8. This month's issue had an interesting article about elephants called What Do You Do with a 300-Pound Nose?
9. Henry David Thoreau's famous essay Civil Disobedience was first published in 1849.
10. The Open Window, a short story by H. H. Munro, has a surprise ending.

> **Exercise 3** **Punctuating Different Types of Titles.**   In each sentence, enclose titles in quotation marks or underline them. If a sentence is correct, write *correct*.

EXAMPLE: The Bill of Rights protects the rights of individuals. (correct as is)

1. I just finished the chapter called Life with Max in the book Agatha Christie: An Autobiography.
2. The magazine Short Story International published Before the Wolves Come by Hugh Munro.
3. I would much rather read short poems like Poe's Dream Within a Dream than long ones like Lord Byron's The Prisoner of Chillon.
4. Waltz of the Flowers is often a featured excerpt from The Nutcracker Suite.
5. The Treaty of Versailles officially ended World War I in 1919.

28.5 Dashes and Parentheses (Dashes) • Practice 1

Dashes Use *dashes* to indicate an abrupt change of thought, a dramatic interrupting idea, or a summary statement. Use dashes to set off a nonessential appositive or parenthetical expression when it is long, when it is already punctuated, or when you want to be dramatic.

USES OF THE DASH	
Change of Thought	I'll be with you in a minute—oh, oh, there's the phone again.
Dramatic Interruption	That musical—the production numbers are spectacular—has been running on Broadway for years.
Summary Statement	Nuts, fruits, and grains—all are nutritious foods.
Nonessential Element	The woman who proposed the plan—a wealthy widow who owns two villas, a Manhattan townhouse, and a yacht—has always had liberal ideas. When Stacy saw the new car—can you believe this?—she fainted.

Exercise 1 **Using the Dash.** Add dashes where they are needed in the following sentences.

EXAMPLE: Tanya's report Ms. Wilson raved about it was heavily documented.
Tanya's report—Ms. Wilson raved about it—was heavily documented.

1. In the first presentation it was just an illusion, of course a small ball was passed through a solid mirror.
2. One of the exhibits you would have loved it depicted colonial baking in a hearth oven.
3. The justices of the Supreme Court, the complete Senate, and the members of the House of Representatives all assembled to hear the State of the Union message.
4. The librarian you know Mrs. Norman was very helpful in finding the information I needed.
5. I know I have that paper somewhere oh, never mind.
6. Whitney Jones an interesting man who has spent most of his life in Saudi Arabia is teaching a course at Rutgers this fall.
7. Reggie Jackson, Ted Williams, Mickey Mantle, Willie Mays all were famous baseball players.
8. They are serving strawberry ice cream your favorite for dessert.
9. The storm seems to be over no, the sky is darkening again.
10. Joe Smith a golfer with a handicap of two is fifty years old.

Exercise 2 **More Work with Dashes.** Follow the instructions for Exercise 1.

1. Actors take particular pride in receiving major awards the Oscar for motion pictures, the Tony for Broadway plays, and the Emmy for television because they are chosen by their peers.
2. I wonder what could be keeping Elena hey, there's her car now.
3. Yesterday's football victory the crowd was ecstatic guarantees us a chance at the state title.
4. The woman I met at the museum I think her name was Barker or Barkus used to work with Mom at the bank.
5. Turkey, stuffing, cranberry sauce, pies all are traditional dishes for an American Thanksgiving dinner.

28.5 Dashes and Parentheses (Dashes) • Practice 2

▶ **Exercise 1** **Using the Dash.** Add dashes where they are needed in the following sentences.

EXAMPLE: I take care of our family pet that is, sometimes.
I take care of our family pet—that is, sometimes.

1. The marching band which has been, I might point out, practicing for weeks won a blue ribbon at the competition.
2. Our new gardener she is a genius with all plants! pruned the roses recently.
3. The scenery long, sandy beaches, desolate lava beds, and fiery sunsets brings many tourists to Hawaii.
4. Cats are lovable and hey, stop eating my plant, you bad cat!
5. To be able to see exotic fish in their natural habitat that provides one of the greatest joys of snorkeling.
6. That runner what was his name? looked tired after his race.
7. We ordered Valentine arrangements carnations, daisies, and roses to be sent to our relatives.
8. The family bookkeeping system which just looks like a jumble of numbers to me is designed to keep me on a budget.
9. Some ski resorts for example, Lake Placid in New York provide for a variety of skiing activities.
10. Baseball, basketball, football, and tennis these probably represent America's favorite sports.
11. Lavender she just loved that color was her choice for the walls.
12. The movie have you seen it yet? has been nominated for several awards.
13. With the arrival of our cousins one never knows how many will come confusion reigns.
14. Sometime in April 1564 no one knows the exact date William Shakespeare was born.
15. Several essays by Thoreau we read them last year in class have been widely quoted.
16. Aunt May or Crankie as my brother and I always called her when we were children has not been feeling well.
17. The stock market see Chapter 10 has really been climbing lately.
18. The first two years of my life were spent in Germany my father was stationed there.
19. Her enthusiastic I should say fanatic devotion to the singer is almost frightening.
20. Elaine prepared quite a feast of Mexican food tamales, burritos, rellenos, and enchiladas.

▶ **Exercise 2** **Using the Dash in Paragraphs.** On another piece of paper, rewrite the paragraph, adding dashes where they are needed. Not every sentence in the paragraph needs a dash.

EXAMPLE: (1) The twins I'm sure you've met them will be here at three.

(1) The twins—I'm sure you've met them—will be here at three.

(1) The party it's been in the planning stages for several weeks now will take place on Saturday. (2) I hope you can be here a little early I'll need help setting up the buffet table. (3) The clown Bojingles Entertainment, Inc., is sending him out will arrive at about four o'clock. (4) By then, all the guests should be here. (5) I've invited the Johnson twins you remember them, don't you? (6) I've also invited Susan Campbell I haven't seen her in months (7) The extra chairs, which I ordered from a party supply house, will be delivered in the morning. (8) In addition to the clown, we'll have other live entertainment a guitar player, a singer, and a magician. (9) This the third party I've ever given will be the best one ever! (10) In a way, I'll be glad when it's over the preparations have really been exhausting.

28.5 # Dashes and Parentheses (Parentheses)
• Practice 1

Parentheses   Use *parentheses* to set off asides and explanations only when the material is not essential or when it consists of one or more sentences. Use parentheses to set off numbers or letters used with items in a series and with certain numerical references such as birth and death dates.

USES OF PARENTHESES	
Phrases	This gray sweater (old and baggy as it is) is my favorite.
Sentences	This summer my friend Marissa is coming for a visit. (She lives in Montana.) We have gone to the same camp for years.
Numbers or Letters	Mom left a list of specific chores: (1) make the beds, (2) set the table, and (3) make a salad.
Dates	The Magna Carta (A.D. 1215) established the right to trial by a jury of peers.

The chart below illustrates the rules for punctuating and capitalizing material in parentheses. Notice, too, the punctuation outside the parentheses.

CAPITALIZATION AND PUNCTUATION WITH PARENTHESES	
Declarative Sentence Interrupting Another Sentence	When Joey cries (he's six months old) and wakes the whole family, we all try to remember we wanted a baby.
Interrogative or Exclamatory Sentence	After I finish my exercise class (Why did I ever sign up?), I am always exhausted.
Sentence Between Sentences	We placed the order six weeks ago. (It was for fifty dollars worth of merchandise.) However, it still has not arrived.

▶ **Exercise 1**   **Using Parentheses.**   Add parentheses wherever they are appropriate.

EXAMPLE: After the assassination of Julius Caesar 44 B.C., a triumvirate ruled Rome.
   After the assassination of Julius Caesar **(**44 B.C.**)**, a triumvirate ruled Rome.

1.   As soon as we had finished dinner it was about 6:30, I started my homework.

2.   We considered several plans for raising funds: a a bake sake, b a bottle drive, or c a plant sale.

3.   In the Battle of Hastings 1066, William of Normandy defeated the English.

4.   Jason's favorite pet he has several unusual ones is a boa constrictor.

5.   Considering the distance between the two cities 3,124 miles, to be exact, driving seems impractical.

▶ **Exercise 2**   **More Work with Parentheses.**   Rewrite each sentence, adding parentheses and capital letters where necessary.

EXAMPLE: Zach's jack-o'-lantern smile he had lost his first tooth was cute.
   Zach's jack-o'-lantern smile (he had lost his first tooth) was cute.

1.   Beth's party what a wonderful party it was! lasted till midnight.
   _____

2.   Benjamin Franklin 1706–1790 was an extremely versatile man.
   _____

3.   The coral reefs what a beautiful underwater sight they make have meant destruction for many unknowing ships.
   _____

4.   I watered the plant which has a water indicator that shows when it needs moisture then, I added some fertilizer to the soil.
   _____

5.   My alarm watch stopped could the battery be dead already and made me late for school.
   _____

28.5 Dashes and Parentheses (Parentheses)
• Practice 2

▶ **Exercise 1** **Using Parentheses.** Add the necessary parentheses to the following sentences.

EXAMPLE: Toni Morrison Have you read any of her books? creates fascinating characters.
Toni Morrison (Have you read any of her books?) creates fascinating characters.

1. We watched the second one-act play "The Devil and Daniel Webster," but then we had to leave.
2. The skater looked confident perhaps more confident than the judges liked as he left the ice.
3. Our new exchange student German speaks English well.
4. Mopeds motorized bicycles first became popular in Europe.
5. Check the boat for the following safety supplies: a extra gas; b life preservers; c flares.
6. Claude Engles 1911–1983 was a wonderful neighbor to us for many years.
7. I must remember to do my homework in these classes 1 algebra; 2 speech; and 3 history.
8. This painting by Picasso see the picture on page 75 is considered one of his best.
9. My report card came today. I've been checking the mail every day. The grades will please my parents.
10. While the lion was completely out the effects of the tranquilizer, the vet entered the cage confidently.

▶ **Exercise 2** **Using Capitals and Punctuation with Parentheses.** Copy each sentence that needs capitalization or punctuation and make the necessary changes. If a sentence is correct, write *correct*.

EXAMPLE: When I finished the assignment (what a tough one it was) I took a nap.
When I finished the assignment (What a tough one it was!), I took a nap.

1. Helmers Electronic firm (did they open up in 1974) showed a 25-percent increase in profits.

   _____

2. The sale went well (over one thousand dollars profit,) and we now have room for the new merchandise.

   _____

3. After the fashion show (held at 11:00 A.M.) a lunch was served.

   _____

4. My antique music box (it was constructed in 1880 in Dusseldorf) operates with a hand wheel.

   _____

5. The cowboy hat (I planned to wear it skiing.) fit perfectly.

   _____

▶ **Writing Application** **Using Dashes and Parentheses in Sentences.** On another piece of paper, write three sentences to illustrate three different ways dashes may be used. Then write two sentences to illustrate two different ways parentheses may be used.

EXAMPLES: I am enjoying this picnic—oh, no, is that thunder?

   Three dogs in the pound (they had the saddest eyes) attracted our attention.

28.5 Hyphens • Practice 1

Using Hyphens Use a *hyphen* when writing out numbers from twenty-one through ninety-nine and with fractions used as adjectives. Also use hyphens with certain prefixes and compound words, with compound modifiers (except those ending with -*ly*) before nouns, and to avoid confusion.

USES OF HYPHENS	
With Numbers	twenty-eight flavors, one-fourth cup
With Prefixes	pro-American, self-conscious, ex-governor
With Compound Nouns	mother-in-law, passer-by, merry-go-round
With Compound Modifiers	best-dressed performer, well-manicured lawn, tie-dyed shirt, carefully maintained yard
For Clarity	re-cover versus recover, five-acre lots versus five acre-lots

Using Hyphens at the Ends of Lines Divide words only between syllables. A word with a prefix or suffix can almost always be divided between the prefix and root or root and suffix. Divide a hyphenated word only after the hyphen. Do not divide a word so that only one letter stands alone. Do not divide proper nouns or adjectives, and do not carry part of a word over to another page.

HYPHENS AT THE ENDS OF LINES						
Correct	thor-ough	un-happy	ex-officer	de-part	ques-tion	English
Incorrect	tho-rough	unh-appy	ex-of-ficer	a-part	ver-y	Eng-lish

▶ **Exercise 1** **Using Hyphens.** Place hyphens where they are needed. (Not all sentences need hyphens.)

EXAMPLE: Jeremy is an all around athlete.
　　　　　　Jeremy is an all-around athlete.

1. The sergeant at arms asked the demonstrators to leave the meeting.

2. Alison's half hearted response disappointed us.

3. Of the twenty four bottles in the case, three were broken.

4. You will need five eighths yard of fabric for the sleeves alone.

5. Like many other commonly held beliefs, this one has no foundation.

6. Even as a young child, Paul was very self sufficient.

7. Several anti government demonstrators were jailed.

8. That hand carved mantel is a masterpiece.

9. We will have several out of town guests with us for the holidays.

10. Twenty seven students in our school were nominated to the National Honor Society.

▶ **Exercise 2** **Hyphenating Words.** Rewrite each word below, using a hyphen at any place where the word could be divided at the end of a line of writing.

EXAMPLE: amusing ___*amus-ing*___ badge ___*badge*___

1. misspell _____

2. Athenian _____

3. create _____

4. Scandinavian _____

5. above _____

28.5 **Hyphens • Practice 2**

Exercise 1 **Using Hyphens in Numbers, Word Parts, and Words.**   In each of the following sentences, add the necessary hyphens. Not every sentence needs a hyphen.

EXAMPLE: The politician congratulated the senator elect.
The politician congratulated the senator-elect.

1. My mother's yoga class is part of her self improvement plan.

2. We had forty three senior citizens on the bus trip.

3. When I was three fourths of the way to Dan's house, I realized I had left behind the folder he wanted.

4. The happy go lucky child played contentedly.

5. The miniature elephant measured only one quarter inch.

6. Each year, many people celebrate the Chinese New Year.

7. A United Nations committee will study the proposals.

8. The all important decision will be handed down tomorrow.

9. At the art gallery, we saw free form sculptures.

10. During the post World War II days, the United States experienced a baby boom.

Exercise 2 **Using Hyphens to Avoid Ambiguity.**   Rewrite the sentences, adding hyphens to make each sentence clear.

EXAMPLE: We had to relay the bricks in the garden wall.
We had to re-lay the bricks in the garden wall.

1. The clay head that I had modeled needed to be reformed.

   _____

2. Eager for the game to start again, he watched the half time clock.

   _____

3. The stairs to the walk up I saw in the ad were tiring.

   _____

4. The six foot soldiers walked across the bridge; one fell off and then there were five.

   _____

5. The dress my mother made was a recreation of an older one.

   _____

6. She gave him five dollar bills to pay for the book.

   _____

7. They had barely enough money to decorate their new coop.

   _____

8. Liking food well done, he refused the half baked potato.

   _____

9. Recoiling the hose took more time than they had expected.

   _____

10. We were told to wait for the express mail clerk.

    _____

28.6 Apostrophes (With Possessive Nouns, With Pronouns)
• Practice 1

Apostrophes with Possessive Nouns   Use the following rules to form the possessives of nouns.

FORMING POSSESSIVE NOUNS	
Add an apostrophe and an -s to most singular nouns	the cat's basket; the scientist's experiment
Add just an apostrophe to plural nouns ending in -s	the cats' paw print; the scientists' discussions
Add an apostrophe and an -s to plural nouns that do not end in -s	the women's jobs; the mice's nest
Make the last word in a compound noun possessive.	the stage manager's clipboard; the Girl Scouts' jamboree
Treat time, amounts, and the word *sake* like other possessives.	a moment's hesitation; ten cents' worth; for Ann's sake; for the Smiths' sake
To show individual ownership, make each noun in the series possessive.	Ted's, Jim's, and Cliff's bunks; the boys' and girls' locker rooms
To show joint ownership, make the last noun in the series possessive.	Ted, Jim, and Cliff's room; the boys and girls' teacher

Apostrophes with Pronouns   Use an apostrophe and an -s with indefinite pronouns to show possession. Do not use an apostrophe with possessive forms of personal pronouns, which are already possessive.

POSSESSIVE FORMS OF PRONOUNS		
Indefinite		**Personal**
either's	no one's	my, mine, our, ours
someone's	each other's	his, her, hers, its, their, theirs
anybody's	one's	your, yours

> **Exercise 1**   **Writing Possessive Forms.**   Write the phrase in the possessive form.

EXAMPLE: the apples from that tree _____ *that tree's apples* _____

1. the toys of the children _____

2. salary for two weeks _____

3. the trunk on the elephant _____

4. the birthday of my sister-in-law _____

5. the apartment of Elinor and her sister _____

> **Exercise 2**   **Using Apostrophes Correctly with Pronouns.**   Underline the correct pronoun in each set in parentheses.

EXAMPLE: The books on the end table must be (<u>yours</u>, your's).

1. Joyce found her sneakers in (their, they're) usual place in her locker.

2. This must be (someone elses', someone else's) notebook.

3. Ben and Andy both made suggestions; we could accept (neithers, neither's)

4. Shall we meet at your house or (ours, our's)?

5. It is (anyone's, anyones') guess who will win the election.

28.6 Apostrophes (With Possessive Nouns, With Pronouns) • Practice 2

▶ **Exercise 1** **Using Apostrophes with Single-Word Possessive Nouns.** Copy the underlined nouns, which may be singular or plural, putting them into the possessive form when necessary. For sentences that do not require possessive forms, just write the underlined word.

EXAMPLE: We will have to borrow Jeff book.   *Jeff's*

1. The kittens string was tangled after they finished playing. _____
2. The lass blond curls framed her cherubic face. _____
3. The skater sloppy leaps cost him the competition. _____
4. The bright canary yellow of the taxis provided a splash of color against the gray of the city buildings. _____
5. The town main offices were located off First Street. _____

▶ **Exercise 2** **Using Apostrophes with Compound Nouns.** Copy the underlined nouns, putting them into the possessive form.

EXAMPLE: He always enjoys his mother-in-law cooking.   *mother-in-law's*

1. The Sierra Club actions pleased environmentalists. _____
2. My great-uncle farm produces many fat Thanksgiving birds. _____
3. The National Honor Society colors are blue and gold. _____
4. Snack-in-the-Box drive-up windows make buying food easy. _____
5. The Director of Transportation recommendations would mean an increase in mass transit fares. _____

▶ **Exercise 3** **Using Apostrophes to Show Joint and Individual Ownership.** Copy the underlined words, changing them to show ownership as indicated in parentheses.

EXAMPLE: Bob and Ann aunt invited them to visit her. (joint)   *Bob and Ann's*

1. The formal style of Rhonda and Emily dresses did not blend with the informal attire of the rest of the guests (individual) _____
2. The sororities and fraternities Greek heritage sets them apart from other clubs. (joint) _____
3. Fred and Marilyn joint tax return is being audited by the IRS. (joint) _____
4. Since Laura and Marcello papers were identical, the teacher accused them of cheating. (individual) _____
5. Doug and Hy desks were covered with graffiti. (individual) _____

▶ **Exercise 4** **Using Apostrophes with Pronouns.** Copy the pronouns that are used incorrectly, making the necessary changes. If a sentence is already correct write *correct*.

EXAMPLE: That sweater is her's.   *hers*

1. Do you think that clearing the table is nobody's job? _____
2. Someone's else's letter came to our address. _____
3. She gave the minutes to the one who's in charge. _____
4. The child gave his' address to the police officer. _____
5. We must not be jealous of one anothers' good fortune. _____

28.6 Apostrophes (with Contractions, Special Uses)
• Practice 1

Apostrophes with Contractions   Use an apostrophe in a contraction to indicate the position of the missing letter or letters. The most common contractions are those formed with verbs.

COMMON CONTRACTIONS			
Verbs with *Not*	isn't (is not)	can't (can not)	won't (will not)
Pronouns with Verbs	I'll (I will)	you'll (you will)	we'll (we will)
	I'm (I am)	you're (you are)	they're (they are)
	I'd (I would)	you'd (you would)	he'd (he would
	I've (I have)	you've (you have)	she's (she is)
Other Kinds of Contractions	o'clock	class of '85 (class of 1985)	
	C'mon (Come on)	comin' (coming)	

Special Uses of the Apostrophe   Use an apostrophe and an -s to write the plurals of numbers, symbols, letters, and words used to name themselves.

EXAMPLE: Dot your *i*'s and cross your *t*'s.
           Avoid using so many *and*'s.

▶ **Exercise 1**   **Writing Contractions.**   Write contractions from the words in parentheses to complete each sentence.

EXAMPLE: _____*He's*_____ been working hard all day. (He has)

1. _____ never seen a cow before. (They had)

2. I wonder if _____ going to be late. (we are)

3. Sandy always says _____ rather stay home. (he would)

4. _____ been waiting for the bus for over an hour. (We have)

5. Uncle Max says _____ his favorite nephew. (I am)

6. Lorna replied that she _____ be able to join us. (will not)

7. Len, _____ you going to eat with us? (are not)

8. I must fix dinner tonight, if _____ not home. (you are)

9. I hope _____ visit us again soon. (you will)

10. I _____ heard from Ellen for several weeks. (have not)

▶ **Exercise 2**   **Using Apostrophes Correctly.**   Add one or more apostrophes to each sentence.

EXAMPLE: The *s indicate items most sorely needed.
           The *'s indicate items most sorely needed.

1. Lou has a strange way of making his *g* s.

2. My father graduated in the class of 66.

3. The concert will begin promptly at eight oclock.

4. I can't tell your *e* s from your *i* s.

5. Michelle makes her 7s in the European style.

28.6 Apostrophes (with Contractions, Special Uses)
• Practice 2

Exercise 1 **Using Apostrophes with Contractions.** Write the two words in each underlined contraction. Write the contraction for two underlined words.

EXAMPLE: Aren't people who regard graphology seriously thought to be silly?

_____ Are not

Graphology, the study of handwriting, (1) is not a new science. Though we (2) don't know with complete certainty, (3) it is believed that it began as far back as 1000 B.C. in China and Japan. Many historical figures (4) did not discount graphology as a "false science." In fact, Shakespeare wrote, "Give me the handwriting of a woman, and I will tell you her character." Other figures who (5) did not regard graphology as silly included Sir Walter Scott, Edgar Allan Poe, Goethe, and both of the Brownings. To prove it (6) was not false, a scientist by the name of Binet tested seven graphologists in the 1800's. He showed them the handwriting of different people and asked, "Who would you pick as intelligent, average, or dull based on their handwriting ?" All the graphologists did better than mere chance would have allowed. Today there are still people (7) who will call it a false science, but (8) that's becoming less frequent. Even the American Medical Association (9) will not call it that. (10) They have written, "There are definite organic diseases that graphodiagnostics can help diagnose.

1. _____   6. _____
2. _____   7. _____
3. _____   8. _____
4. _____   9. _____
5. _____   10. _____

Exercise 2 **Using the Apostrophe in Special Cases.** Underline all items in italics. Then write the italicized words, adding an apostrophe and an -s to numbers, symbols, letters, and words whenever necessary.

EXAMPLE: On my last report card I got all A and B.
On my last report card I got all A's and B's.

1. Hearing all those *Happy New Year* from people has put me in a holiday mood. _____

2. I think you are leaving the *s* and *ed* off the ends of your words. _____

3. We sing eight *do-da* in a row before we get to any lyrics in the song. _____

4. Ten , in one sentence make the sentence too choppy and confusing. _____

5. Europeans put an extra line in their *7* to show they are different from the *1*. _____

6. We both had *H* for our first and last initials. _____

7. The girl said twenty *however* during the course of her short speech. _____

8. I always get carried away writing *!* in my letters. _____

9. He always forgets the *r* in those words. _____

10. The Emporium stores use *E* in various sizes as a symbol of their name. _____

Diagraming Basic Sentence Parts (Subjects, Verbs, and Modifiers) • Practice 1

Subjects, Verbs, and Modifiers   In a sentence diagram, the subject and verb are written on a horizontal line with the subject on the left and the verb on the right. A vertical line separates the subject and verb. Adjectives and adverbs are placed on slanted lines directly below the words that they modify.

SUBJECT AND VERB	ADDING ADJECTIVES AND ADVERBS
George is laughing.	The *very talented* actor moved *quite forcefully*.

Orders and directions whose subject is understood to be *you* are diagramed in the usual way, with parentheses around the understood subject. Inverted sentences are diagramed following the usual subject-verb order with the capital letter indicating which word begins the sentence.

ORDER	QUESTION
Sit still.	*Will* he come, too?

Diagram expletives, interjections, and nouns of direct address by placing them on horizontal lines above the subject.

EXPLETIVE	INTERJECTION
There has been a mistake.	*Oops*, I waited too long.

▶ **Exercise 1**   **Diagraming Subjects, Verbs, and Modifiers.**   On separate paper, diagram each sentence.

1. Beautiful wildflowers grew everywhere.

2. The old dirt road curved sharply.

3. Will the circus parade pass here?

4. Move over.

5. Here is the answer, Nicole.

Diagraming Basic Sentence Parts (Subjects, Verbs, and Modifiers) • Practice 2

▶ **Exercise 1** **Diagraming Subjects, Verbs, and Modifiers.** Correctly diagram each sentence.

1. When does the play begin?

2. Tomorrow I will study all afternoon.

3. The ripe, juicy plums were all eaten.

4. The large dog barked very loudly.

5. The tall corn plants gently swayed.

6. The large truck swerved dangerously.

Diagraming Basic Sentence Parts
(Adding Conjunctions) • Practice 1

Conjunctions are diagramed on dotted lines drawn between the words they connect.

ADDING CONJUNCTIONS
The sleek *but* powerful deer ran quickly *and* gracefully.

Conjunctions that connect compound subjects and compound verbs are also written on dotted lines between the words they connect.

COMPOUND SUBJECT and COMPOUND VERB

Many happy *children* and unhappy *adults* are arriving.   The Hollands *came* early and *stayed* late.

▶ **Exercise 1**   **Diagraming Sentences with Conjunctions.**   Diagram each sentence correctly.

1. The powerful and ruthless tyrant was assassinated.

2. The strong but graceful athlete moved rapidly and effortlessly.

3. Sandy and Dennis have never sung together.

4. The committee met frequently and planned very carefully.

5. Many willing and eager volunteers are working hard.

Diagraming Basic Sentence Parts
(Adding Conjunctions) • Practice 2

> **Exercise 1** **Diagraming Sentences with Conjunctions.** Correctly diagram each sentence.

1. I entered noisily, but the old man did not move.

2. Either his parents or his brother will arrive soon.

3. Janice studies and exercises every day.

4. The students and their parents will arrive shortly.

5. The marigold seedlings will quickly grow and bloom.

6. The old automobile moved slowly and noisily.

Diagraming Basic Sentence Parts (Complements)

• Practice 1

Complements   In diagrams, most complements are placed on the base line after the verb. A straight line that meets the base line separates a direct object from the verb. A slanted line that meets the base line comes before an objective complement or a subject complement. An indirect object is joined to the rest of the sentence below each verb. Compound complements are joined as other compound parts.

<table>
<tr><td>DIRECT OBJECT</td><td>OBJECTIVE COMPLEMENT</td></tr>
</table>

Jan ordered a large *pizza.*

Make Gerry the *leader.*

<table>
<tr><td>PREDICATE NOMINATIVE</td><td>INDIRECT OBJECT</td></tr>
</table>

Ron became the *nominee.*

The mayor gave the *visitor* a very warm welcome.

COMPOUND COMPLEMENTS

Our parents promised *Phil* and *me* either a *puppy* or some other *pet.*

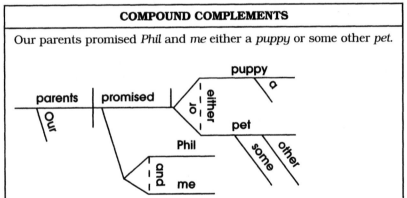

▷ **Exercise 1**   **Diagraming Complements.**   On separate paper, diagram each sentence.

1. The police offered the informers immunity.
2. The referee declared the former champion the winner.
3. Those children show their parents and other adults great respect.
4. Their new single quickly became a hit.

Diagraming Basic Sentence Parts (Complements)
• Practice 2

▶ Exercise 1 **Diagraming Complements.** Correctly diagram each sentence.

1. The young girl crossed the street very carefully.

2. My history teacher plays chess very well.

3. Her brother was elected class president.

4. The warm sun quickly melted the snow.

5. Carol photographs both airplanes and trains.

6. This steak is both juicy and tender.

Diagraming Phrases (Prepositional Phrases, Appositives and Appositive Phrases) • Practice 1

Prepositional Phrases   A prepositional phrase is diagramed to show how it relates the object of the preposition to another word in the sentence. The preposition is written on a slanted line joined to the word the phrase modifies. The object is written on a horizontal line. Modifiers are diagramed as usual.

ADJECTIVE PHRASES	ADVERB PHRASES
A man *with a slight limp* was whistling a song *from a play*.	A vase full *of fresh tulips and daffodils* was delivered *on Monday*.

Appositives and Appositive Phrases   An appositive is diagramed in parentheses next to the noun or pronoun it renames. Any modifiers are diagramed in the usual way.

APPOSITIVE	APPOSITIVE PHRASE
My sister's friend *Linda* is a law student.	We greatly enjoyed the movie, *a comedy with music*.

▶ **Exercise 1**   **Diagraming Prepositional Phrases.**   On separate paper, diagram each sentence.

1. Someone from the agency called you about your tickets.
2. The doll in the window of the shop was bought for a wealthy little girl.

▶ **Exercise 2**   **Diagraming Appositives and Appositive Phrases.**   Diagram the sentences.

1. Doug finally achieved his dream, a house near the ocean.
2. The employer gave Connie, a very hard worker, more responsibility.

[handwritten student work]

Diagraming Phrases (Prepositional Phrases, Appositives, and Appositive Phrases) • Practice 2

> **Exercise 1** **Diagraming Prepositional Phrases.**   Correctly diagram each sentence.

1. A salesperson with a loud voice spoke to the customer.

2. Water plunged downward from the high cliff above the valley.

3. John spoke with much excitement about the price of the new car.

> **Exercise 2** **Diagraming Appositives and Appositive Phrases.**   Correctly diagram each sentence.

1. Her friend Michael is moving to another state.

2. Sally wore her new watch, a gold one with a lighted dial.

3. My neighbor, a restaurant chef, works until nearly midnight.

Diagraming Phrases (Participles and Participial Phrases, Gerunds and Gerund Phrases) • Practice 1

Participles and Participial Phrases The diagram for a participle or a participial phrase looks much like the diagram for a prepositional phrase below the noun or pronoun it modifies. Notice, though, that the participle is written beginning on the slanted line and continuing onto the horizontal line. A nominative absolute is diagramed in the same way an expletive is.

PARTICIPIAL PHRASE	NOMINATIVE ABSOLUTE
Shyly handing the teacher his math paper, Jake asked for help.	*Everything finally ready*, we relaxed. 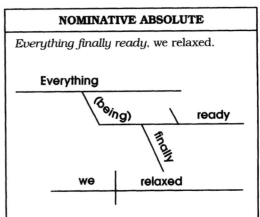

Gerunds and Gerund Phrases When a gerund is used as a basic sentence part, its pedestal is placed on the base line where that sentence part would normally be. The gerund itself is written on a stepped line, and modifiers and complements, if any, are written in their usual positions. When a gerund is used as an indirect object or object of a preposition, it is placed on a stepped line below the main line.

GERUND PHRASE	AS AN INDIRECT OBJECT
Our losing the game was a shock.	Pam gave *writing* all her energy.

▶ **Exercise 1** **Diagraming Participial Phrases and Nominative Absolutes.** Correctly diagram each sentence on separate paper.

1. We approached the table heaped with food.

2. Our spirits confident, we entered the contest.

▶ **Exercise 2** **Diagraming Gerunds and Gerund Phrases.** Correctly diagram each sentence on separate paper.

1. We were disturbed by the wailing of the sirens.

2. Jack's hobby, whittling, became his second career.

Diagraming Phrases (Participles and Participial Phrases, Gerunds and Gerund Phrases) • Practice 2

▶ **Exercise 1** Diagraming Participles and Participial Phrases. Correctly diagram each sentence.

1. Trudging up the path, the hiker appeared exhausted.

2. The work completed, everyone sighed with relief.

3. The radio announcer, filled with excitement, described a thrilling basketball game.

▶ **Exercise 2** Diagraming Gerunds and Gerund Phrases. Correctly diagram each sentence.

1. Her favorite exercise is walking around the block.

2. Winning the contest will be extremely difficult.

3. Bill's hobby, painting landscape scenes, filled him with happiness.

Diagraming Phrases (Infinitives and Infinitive Phrases)

• Practice 1

Infinitives and Infinitive Phrases   An *infinitive* or *infinitive phrase* used as a noun is diagramed on a pedestal in any of the positions a noun or pronoun would occupy. Subjects, complements, or modifiers of the infinitive—if any—occupy normal positions. Notice how an omitted *to* is handled.

INFINITIVE PHRASE	WITH A SUBJECT
To accept help gracefully is a gift.	We watched *Tony run in the marathon.*

An *infinitive* or *infinitive* phrase used as an adjective or an adverb is diagramed in much the same way as a prepositional phrase.

AS AN ADJECTIVE	AS AN ADVERB
The best dish *to serve* is also inexpensive.	We were eager *to see Cary.*

▷ **Exercise 1**   **Diagraming Infinitives and Infinitive Phrases Used as Nouns.**   Correctly diagram each sentence. Refer to the models if necessary.

1. The blackmailer threatened to show the police the photographs.

2. Did you help Logan build that model?

▷ **Exercise 2**   **Diagraming Infinitives and Infinitive Phrases Used as Adjectives and Adverbs.**   Correctly diagram each sentence.

1. Lucy's suggestion is the one to follow.

2. Few people are happy to work in that factory.

Diagraming Phrases (Infinitives and Infinitive Phrases)
• Practice 2

> **Exercise 1** **Diagraming Infinitives and Infinitive Phrases.**   Correctly diagram each sentence.

1. His dream was to visit many countries around the world.

2. To do just one thing at a time is best.

3. To visit the home of Thomas Jefferson at Monticello would be a wonderful experience.

4. Her chief task was to paint the ceiling of the bedroom.

5. The lesson to learn from the experience is painful.

6. To skate in a championship is thrilling.

Diagraming Clauses (Compound Sentences) • Practice 1

Compound Sentences Diagram each independent clause of a compound sentence separately. Then join the verbs with a dotted, stepped line, writing the conjunction or semicolon on the dotted line as shown.

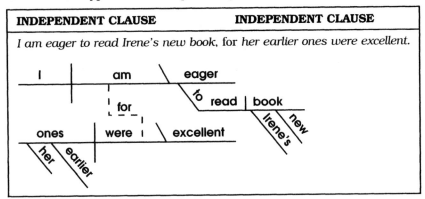

▶**Exercise 1** **Diagraming Compound Sentences.** Diagram each sentence correctly. Refer to the model.

1. Tie the rope securely, or the swing may fall down.

2. Mike advertised the job widely, but no one applied for it.

▶**Exercise 2** **Diagraming Compound Elements and Compound Sentences.** Decide whether each sentence below is a compound sentence or a simple sentence with compound elements. Then diagram each one correctly.

1. Maureen must take the test again or lose credit for the course.

2. Watch your step, for the sidewalk may be slippery.

Diagraming Clauses (Compound Sentences) • Practice 2

▶**Exercise 1** Diagraming Compound Sentences. Correctly diagram each sentence.

1. Crime increased, so the police started patrolling more often.

2. The movie was very entertaining, but Melanie slept through it.

3. We picked apples all day, and in the evening we baked some for dessert.

4. The sky is cloudy, but no rain is expected.

5. The book was wonderful, but the ending was too sad.

6. The chicken was delicious, and the broccoli was fine, but the baked potatoes were undercooked.

Diagraming Clauses (Complex Sentences) • Practice 1

Complex Sentences   Both adjective and adverb clauses are diagramed on a line beneath the independent clause and connected to the independent clause by a dotted line. With an adjective clause, the dotted line extends from the noun or pronoun the clause modifies to the relative pronoun or relative adverb in the clause.

With an adverb clause, the dotted line extends from the word modified to the verb in the adverb clause. The subordinating conjunction is written along the dotted line.

A noun clause is placed on a pedestal extending upward from the position it fills in the sentence. If the introductory word has no function in the sentence, it is written along the pedestal.

 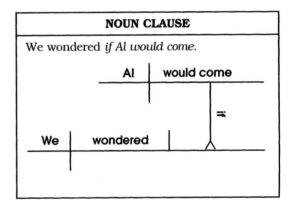

▷ **Exercise 1**   **Diagraming Adjective and Adverb Clauses.**   On separate paper, diagram the sentences.

1. Although you hate the gift, you should write a thank-you note.
2. Edna prepared for the day when she would have her own job.

▷ **Exercise 2**   **Diagraming Noun Clauses.**   On separate paper, diagram the sentences.

1. We promised Mr. Hillyer that we would mow his lawn today.
2. Whatever we decide is likely to displease someone.

Diagraming Clauses (Complex Sentences) • Practice 2

▶Exercise 1 **Diagraming Complex Sentences.** Correctly diagram each sentence.

1. That attorney is a person whom Betty knows quite well.

2. That restaurant is the place where they usually ate dinner on Saturday nights.

3. Andrea moved because her new job required a relocation.

4. They sing as if they were in a chorus.

5. The little boy suspected that his parents would buy him a puppy.

Diagraming Clauses (Compound-Complex Sentences)
• Practice 1

Compound-Complex Sentences When diagraming a compound-complex sentence, begin by diagraming each of the independent clauses. Then diagram the subordinate clause(s).

NOUN CLAUSE	ADVERB CLAUSE

We hoped *that Sandy would join us*, but she stayed home *because she had a cold.*

Exercise 1 **Diagraming Compound-Complex Sentences.** Correctly diagram each sentence.

1. We unloaded the car, and the guide led us through the woods until we found a good campsite.

2. When Julie went to Chicago, she took the train, but when she goes to Los Angeles, she will fly.

Exercise 2 **Diagraming Sentences of Varying Structures.** Diagram the sentences.

1. The doctor who made the initial diagnosis has recommended a second opinion.

2. I do not know where you got your information, but I do know that it is inaccurate.

Diagraming Clauses (Compound-Complex Sentences)
• Practice 2

Exercise 1 **Diagraming Compound-Complex Sentences.** Correctly diagram each sentence.

1. We waited until the rain stopped, and then we went into the stadium where the baseball game would begin.

2. Because they were late, they missed the beginning of the movie that was being shown, but they still understood the plot.

3. Mary hoped that she could buy a new television set, but she did not purchase one because the sets were too expensive.

4. Because traffic was bad, we missed our morning flight, but we took an afternoon flight.

Answers

16.1 Nouns (Names, Compound Nouns) (Page 1)
Practice 1
Exercise 1 Identifying Nouns

1. Constitution, (rights)
2. (concern), hikers, (time)
3. (grace) birds, tourists
4. Paula, (fear) (success)
5. (difference), Lou, Len, (attitude)
6. hunters, deer, elk, moose
7. doctor, Sherry, (advice)
8. article, newspaper, (opening), Marvelle Park
9. sign, auditorium, soloists
10. nurse, hospital, splint, arm

Exercise 2 Recognizing Compound Nouns

1. scientist, (breakthrough), research
2. bird watcher, way, (underbrush)
3. player, (home runs), game
4. host, guests, (dining room)
5. (stepmother), (heart attack)
6. (jack-in-the-box), toy, (two-year-old)
7. (heat wave), records
8. plans, (high school)
9. (Spring-cleaning), chore, people
10. actor, (spotlight)

16.1 Nouns (Names, Compound Nouns) (Page 2)
Practice 2
Exercise 1 Identifying Nouns
1. inventor, imagination   concrete/abstract
2. excitement, zoo   abstract/concrete
3. election, auditorium   abstract/concrete
4. health, child   abstract/concrete
5. animals, captivity   concrete/abstract
6. artist, plan   concrete/abstract
7. boy, future   concrete/abstract
8. average, tests   abstract/concrete
9. team, championship   concrete/abstract
10. memories, Italy   abstract/concrete
11. hunger, children   abstract/concrete
12. fear, airplanes   abstract/concrete
13. quarterback, courage   concrete/abstract
14. ink, memoirs   concrete/abstract
15. mask, sadness   concrete/abstract

Exercise 2 Recognizing Compound Nouns

1. The (maid-of-honor) at the wedding cried during the ceremony.
2. The back of the (station wagon) was loaded with luggage.
3. The gardener and his son filled the (trash bags).
4. Ed enjoyed his visit with his (mother-in-law).

5. Three planes awaited the signal for (takeoff).
6. In the attic the children found a (lampshade).
7. This (railroad) has many bridges and tunnels.
8. Most families still have an (ironing board) and iron.
9. The young cook put too much salt on the (lima beans).
10. Laura held the position of (editor-in-chief).
11. John acted as a (go-between) during the transaction.
12. It was quite a (milestone) when the baby took her first step.
13. Janice shared her (watermelon) with six friends.
14. The car Frank bought has (bucket seats.)
15. Sara joined a (book club) this year.

16.1 Nouns (Common and Proper Nouns) (Page 3)
Practice 1
Exercise 1 Recognizing Proper Nouns
1. Brooklyn Bridge
2. Tower of London
3. Bulldogs
4. Jackson High School
5. California
6. Willow Street
7. Abigail Adams
8. Uncle Mike
9. Montana
10. Mount Rushmore

Exercise 2 Adding Proper Nouns to Sentences
Sample proper nouns are given.
1. Jane Street
2. Vikings
3. Mexico
4. Lincoln Memorial
5. Louise
6. Delaware River
7. Nebraska
8. Garden Spot
9. Rambler
10. Jack London

16.1 Nouns (Common and Proper Nouns) (Page 4)
Practice 2
Exercise 1 Distinguishing Between Common and Proper Nouns
Sample nouns are given.
1. Fremont
2. Spot
3. F. Scott Fitzgerald
4. holiday
5. Oregon
6. Eleanor Roosevelt
7. desert
8. Mississippi
9. king

10. Kiwanis
11. Neil
12. Mars
13. Aunt Lynn
14. Empire State Building
15. continent
16. Brite-o-Brush
17. Mount Whitney
18. country
19. Hereford
20. Spain
21. Thanksgiving
22. girl
23. queen
24. Dr. Jones
25. *Titanic*
26. author
27. James Stewart
28. singer
29. Buddhism
30. lake

Writing Application
Writing Sentences with Nouns
Sample sentences are given.
1. The Central High School football team had an excellent season.
2. People who visit San Francisco enjoy riding the cable cars.
3. Almost anyone with a sense of humor would laugh at that comedian's jokes.
4. In the morning I enjoy grapefruit, toast, and coffee for breakfast.
5. Beijing is the capital of China.

16.2 Pronouns (Antecedents of Pronouns) (Page 5)
Practice 1
Exercise 1   Identifying Antecedents
1. Al
2. critics
3. man, Sally
4. Hannah, bikes
5. Climbing to the top of the Washington Monument
6. trunk
7. students
8. twins
9. Anthony, Mrs. Lee
10. senator, bill

Exercise 2   Adding Pronouns to Match Antecedents
Sample pronouns are given.
1. his
2. its, its
3. you, some
4. their
5. your
6. her
7. who, him
8. their
9. its
10. some, their

16.2 Pronouns (Antecedents of Pronouns) (Page 6)
Practice 2
Exercise 1   Recognizing Antecedents

Pronoun	Antecedent
1. all	work
herself	Betty
2. one	doll
It	doll
3. all	employees
himself	Mr. Jenkins
4. many	audience
it	play
5. that	trees
They	Magnolias
6. who	senator
them	petitions
7. these	potatoes
you	Joe
8. Many	people
their	people
9. themselves	group
their	group
10. he	Matt
himself	Matt
11. she	mother
it	orchid
12. he	Carlito
them	steps
13. you	Diane
it	recipe
14. her	Pamela
him	brother
15. his	Walt
himself	Walt
16. who	Sam
it	money
17. you	Jon
She	teacher
18. her	Sue
all	students
19. herself	Dina
me	Pablo
20. herself	Joanne
they	candles

Exercise 2   Writing Sentences with Pronouns and Antecedents
Sample sentences are given.
1. The kitten was sleeping in its little pet bed.
2. Marion was tired, so she took a nap.
3. Ted bought some roses and gave them to Teresa.
4. The bananas that you bought yesterday are all gone.
5. The maple tree had lost all its leaves by late October.
6. I knew you wanted a skateboard, so I bought this for you.
7. Please serve the guests their dessert now.
8. After viewing the photographs, Sam saved them in his download file.
9. When the water was turned off, we realized how much we used it.
10. The moonlight was so bright that it lit the path for us.

16.2 Pronouns (Personal, Reflexive, and Intensive Pronouns) (Page 7)
Practice 1
Exercise 1   Identifying Personal, Reflexive, and Intensive Pronouns
1. themselves, reflexive
2. my, personal
3. themselves, intensive
4. yourself, reflexive
5. his, personal

6. herself, intensive
7. it, personal
8. himself, intensive
9. themselves, reflexive
10. your, personal

Exercise 2   Adding Personal, Reflexive, and Intensive Pronouns to Sentences
1. them
2. ourselves
3. its
4. myself
5. her
6. his
7. ourselves
8. our
9. themselves
10. herself

16.2   Pronouns (Personal, Reflexive, and Intensive Pronouns) (Page 8)
Practice 2

Exercise 1   Identifying Personal, Reflexive, and Intensive Pronouns
1. you, personal
2. herself, reflexive
3. I, personal
4. we, personal
5. herself, intensive
6. himself, reflexive
7. its, personal
8. themselves, intensive
9. their, personal
10. itself, intensive
11. her, personal
12. himself, reflexive
13. himself, intensive
14. I, personal
15. yourself, reflexive
16. themselves, intensive
17. himself, reflexive
18. them, personal
19. she, personal
20. herself, intensive

Exercise 2   Writing Sentences with Personal, Reflexive, and Intensive Pronouns
Sample sentences are given.
1. The blue jacket is mine.
2. You yourself are responsible for this.
3. Give the book to him.
4. The audience members gave themselves a hand.
5. We should be going soon.
6. The apple pie is hers.
7. I myself picked out these decorations.
8. Is this his idea?
9. Have you seen our backyard?
10. We have nobody to blame but ourselves.

16.2   Pronouns (Demonstrative, Relative, and Interrogative Pronouns) (Page 9)
Practice 1

Exercise 1   Recognizing Demonstrative, Relative, and Interrogative Pronouns
1. demonstrative
2. relative
3. interrogative
4. relative
5. interrogative
6. demonstrative

7. interrogative
8. relative
9. demonstrative
10. relative

Exercise 2   Adding Demonstrative, Relative, and Interrogative Pronouns to Sentences
Sample pronouns are given.
1. Which
2. those
3. whom
4. that
5. Who
6. This
7. Who
8. who
9. which
10. What

16.2   Pronouns (Demonstrative, Relative, and Interrogative Pronouns) (Page 10)
Practice 2

Exercise 1   Recognizing Demonstrative, Relative, and Interrogative Pronouns
1. Who, interrogative
2. who, relative
3. that, relative
4. these, demonstrative
5. which, relative
6. Which, interrogative
7. those, demonstrative
8. which, relative
9. Who, interrogative
10. This, demonstrative

Exercise 2   Writing Sentences with Pronouns
Sample sentences are given.
1. This is the car I want.
2. The song that you like so much is playing now.
3. Whose is this?
4. Did you see that?
5. The woman whom you met yesterday is my aunt.
6. Which of the three songs do you prefer?
7. Are these the bracelets you bought?
8. Darlene, who dances very well, promised to teach me some steps.
9. Who will be going with you to the movies?
10. Those are my favorite colors.
11. The book, which I really enjoyed, will be made into a movie.
12. To whom should I send the letter?
13. Did you know anything about this?
14. The boy who waited on me had red hair.
15. What do you want to do today?

16.2   Pronouns (Indefinite Pronouns) (Page 11)
Practice 1

Exercise 1   Recognizing Indefinite Pronouns
1. Everyone
2. Someone, most
3. Each
4. None, much
5. Few, anything
6. either, other
7. Both, everyone
8. Several, much
9. No one, something
10. Many, everything

Exercise 2   Adding Indefinite Pronouns to Sentences
Sample indefinite pronouns are given.
1. Most
2. either
3. much
4. nothing
5. all
6. others
7. Everything
8. some
9. little
10. Everything

16.2   Pronouns (Indefinite Pronouns) (Page 12)
Practice 2
Exercise 1   Supplying Indefinite Pronouns
Sample indefinite pronouns are given.
1. everything
2. Nothing/anyone
3. anybody
4. all
5. most
6. none/some
7. any
8. much
9. everyone
10. One
11. some
12. many
13. someone
14. All
15. any
16. few
17. Nothing
18. Several
19. another
20. All

Writing Application
Writing Sentences with Pronouns
Sample sentences are given.
1. These were his tools.
2. Whom is she going to call?
3. She planned the entire ceremony herself.
4. All of their possessions are lost.
5. We helped ourselves to the refreshments that were on the table.

16.3   Action Verbs and Linking Verbs (Action Verbs, Transitive and Intransitive Verbs) (Page 13)
Practice 1
Exercise 1   Recognizing Action Verbs
1. thought, M
2. pointed, V
3. swung, V
4. decided, M
5. made, V
6. plays, V
7. sipped, V
8. considered, M
9. drew, V
10. entered, V

Exercise 2   Adding Transitive and Intransitive Verbs to Sentences
Sample verbs are given.
1. ordered, T
2. moved, I
3. grew, I
4. gave, T
5. sells, T
6. put, T
7. gusted, I
8. arrived, I
9. scheduled, T
10. wrote, T

16.3   Action Verbs and Linking Verbs (Action Verbs, Transitive and Intransitive Verbs) (Page 14)
Practice 2
Exercise 1   Supplying Action Verbs
Sample verbs are given.
1. talked (visible)
2. said (visible)
3. bounced (visible)
4. sheltered (visible)
5. mowed (visible)
6. rest (visible)
7. liked (mental)
8. sawed (visible)
9. looked (visible)
10. know (mental)
11. picked (visible)
12. prepared (visible)
13. jumped (visible)
14. enjoy (mental)
15. worked (visible)
16. place (visible)
17. bought (visible)
18. wants (mental)
19. rides (visible)
20. waved (visible)

Exercise 2   Distinguishing Between Transitive and Intransitive Verbs
1. swung (intransitive)
2. crumpled (transitive) letter
3. answered (transitive) question
4. shuddered (intransitive)
5. chewed (transitive) way
6. drop (intransitive)
7. combed (transitive) hair
8. made (transitive) lemonade
9. smiled (intransitive)
10. sizzled (intransitive)

16.3   Action Verbs and Linking Verbs (Linking Verbs) (Page 15)
Practice 1
Exercise 1   Recognizing Forms of Linking Verbs

Linking Verb	Words Linked
1. should be	(Safety—concern)
2. would be	(I—happy)
3. is	(Elaine—late)
4. can be	(Andrew—child)
5. could have been	(What—cause)
6. is	(That—amount)
7. was	(setback—temporary)
8. will be	(Jenny—president)
9. is being	(Jason—polite)
10. was	(Thomas Jefferson—President)

Exercise 2   Identifying Other Linking Verbs

Linking Verb	Words Linked
1. appears	(Kevin—taller)
2. taste	(sausages—spicier)
3. remained	(cause—mystery)
4. looks	(stranger—suspicious)

5. stayed (child—quiet)
6. became (glove—trademark)
7. remains (A. A. Milne—author)
8. turned (hair—gray)
9. smell (books—musty)
10. felt (I—queasy)

16.3 Action Verbs and Linking Verbs (Linking Verbs) (Page 16)
Practice 2
Exercise 1 Recognizing Forms of *Be* Used as Linking Verbs

Linking Verb	Words Linked
1. can be	(Poodles—pets)
2. was being	(Albert—gentle)
3. should be	(chef—creative)
4. is	(knife—one)
5. should have been	(She—star)
6. is	(doughnut—fresh)
7. are being	(They—prompt)
8. was	(sky—pink)
9. will be	(We—customers)
10. had been	(It—day)
11. can be	(bear—animal)
12. is	(library—building)
13. might be	(peak—one)
14. have been	(Bananas—fruit)
15. are	(quills—sharp)

Exercise 2 Identifying Other Linking Verbs

Linking Verb	Words Linked
1. turned	(She—blue)
2. sounded	(foghorn—strange)
3. taste	(apples—bitter)
4. became	(he—doctor)
5. remained	(They—cheerful)
6. stay	(people—partners)
7. smells	(rose—different)
8. appeared	(They—older)
9. felt	(hair—sticky)
10. looks	(coat—small)

16.3 Action Verbs and Linking Verbs (Linking Verb or Action Verb) (Page 17)
Practice 1
Exercise 1 Distinguishing Between Linking Verbs and Action Verbs
1. action
2. linking
3. action
4. action
5. linking
6. linking
7. action
8. linking
9. action
10. linking

Exercise 2 Adding Verbs to Sentences
Sample verbs are given.
1. turns, LV
2. turned, AV
3. grows, AV
4. grown, LV
5. became, LV
6. looked, LV
7. Look, AV
8. tasted, AV
9. tastes, LV
10. sounds, LV

16.3 Action Verbs and Linking Verbs (Linking Verb or Action Verb) (Page 18)
Practice 2
Exercise 1 Distinguishing Between Linking Verbs and Action Verbs
Sample verbs are given.
1. sounds (linking)
2. grow (action)
3. tastes (linking)
4. feels (linking)
5. grows (linking)
6. feel (action)
7. looks (linking)
8. sounded (action)
9. look (action)
10. tasted (action)
11. felt (action)
12. sounds (linking)
13. tastes (linking)
14. felt (action)
15. worked (visible)
16. looks (linking)
17. feel (linking)
18. grow (action)
19. looked (action)
20. grew (linking)

Writing Application
Writing Sentences with Linking Verbs and Action Verbs
Sample sentences are given.
1. He appears tired.
   Smoke appeared on the horizon.
2. She feels fine, now that her bout with the flu is over.
   I felt the piercing cold as I trudged through the snow.
3. Mark grew very tall.
   Corn once grew where those houses now stand.
4. That car looks great.
   Cindy looked everywhere for her keys.
5. The roast beef smells delicious.
   I could smell the burned carrots from the living room.

16.4 Helping Verbs (Page 19)
Practice 1
Exercise 1 Identifying Helping Verbs
1. has (acted)
2. Did (tell)
3. does (ride)
4. Have (traveled)
5. must have (seen)
6. could have (offered)
7. should have (lasted)
8. have (seen)
9. does (hear)
10. could have (succeeded)

Exercise 2 Adding Helping Verbs to Sentences
Sample helping verbs are given.
1. can (answer)
2. have been (studying)
3. must have (seen)

4. could have been (hurt)
5. have been (doing)
6. Will (open)
7. have (expressed)
8. might have (expected)
9. did (begin)
10. had been (working)

16.4 Helping Verbs (Page 20)
Practice 2
Exercise 1 Supplying Helping Verbs
Sample helping verbs are given.
1. was
2. will be
3. must be
4. Have been
5. has been
6. will be
7. may
8. are
9. will have
10. has

Exercise 2 Locating Helping Verbs
1. are finding
2. are considering, should invest, should know
3. have been lost, were being inserted, were being worn
4. should be inserted
5. do drop, will scratch, would be, might damage

Writing Application
Writing Sentences with Helping Verbs
Sample sentences are given.
1. How long has Jennie been talking?
2. He might not know what to do.
3. We never could have sold so much at the garage sale without your help.
4. Will Leslie have left by then?
5. The planet Mars can scarcely be seen without a telescope.

17.1 Adjectives (The Process of Modification) (Page 21)
Practice 1
Exercise 1 Identifying Adjectives

1. Several (families), an outdoor (party), the new (neighbors)

2. The quaint charming old (house), several major (repairs)

3. The wealthy (family), an extensive (collection), antique (glass)

4. The worthy (cause), many generous (contributions)

5. the (end), the first (round), a narrow (lead)

6. Few (people), that (street) young (children)

7. Western (movies) popular, many (years)

8. A good daily (diet), adequate (calcium)

9. many (countries), southern (food), spicier, northern (food)

10. The entire (kingdom), the terrible (spell), the wicked (sorcerer)

Exercise 2 Adding Adjectives to Sentences
Sample adjectives are given.
1. extravagant, several
2. angry, more
3. That, wool
4. first, birthday
5. Two large gray

17.1 Adjectives (The Process of Modification) (Page 22)
Practice 2
Exercise 1 Recognizing Adjectives
1. The, dull, dingy, the, a, somber
2. The, lonesome, a, the
3. gray, hesitant, the, abandoned
4. a, major, a, few
5. the, last, the, an, important, medical
6. enough, the, the
7. the, a, dozen
8. a, good
9. The brilliant, red, callused
10. The, silvery, the, dim
11. The, athletic, young, six, the, scenic
12. The, chilly, pleasant
13. The, large, the, three, hungry
14. The, newborn, tiny, delicate, perfect
15. The, latest, art, famous
16. The, timid, the, icy
17. some, hot, the, chipped
18. A, purple, a, red, the, blue
19. ivory, special
20. The, colorful, the, elaborate, a, rare

Exercise 2 Using Adjectives in Sentences
Sample adjectives are given.
1. four
2. disappointed
3. stressed
4. gift
5. third
6. interesting
7. young
8. colorful
9. glass
10. quick

17.1 Adjectives (Proper and Compound Adjectives, Nouns Used as Adjectives) (Page 23)
Practice 1
Exercise 1 Recognizing Nouns Used as Adjectives, Proper Adjectives, and Compound Adjectives
1. compound
2. compound

3. noun
4. proper
5. noun
6. compound
7. noun
8. compound
9. proper
10. proper (or noun)

Exercise 2 Using Proper and Compound Adjectives to Modify Nouns
1. deep-sea fishing
2. sidewalk sale
3. Asian nation
4. English poet
5. small-town boy
6. Roman villa
7. salt-water pool
8. Persian rug
9. Turkish coffee
10. front-row seat

17.1   Adjectives (Proper and Compound Adjectives, Nouns Used as Adjectives) (Page 24)
Practice 2
Exercise 1 Recognizing Nouns Used as Adjectives
1. storm
2. leather, fur
3. bus
4. school
5. school
6. ski, vacation
7. weather
8. store
9. birthday
10. ski

Exercise 2 Recognizing Proper and Compound Adjectives
1. red-cheeked, Turkish
2. self-evident
3. wide-mouthed
4. Well-qualified, open-heart
5. steadfast
6. Victorian
7. well-liked, out-of-the-way
8. Boston
9. waterproof, Icelandic
10. Scandinavian
11. Russian, sad-looking
12. Irish, never-to-be-forgotten
13. best-known, German
14. good-natured, Spanish
15. Australian, old-fashioned
16. light-haired, British
17. three-bedroom, African
18. little-known, French
19. ever-optimistic, Belgian, run-down
20. Canadian, quick-witted

17.1   Adjectives (Pronouns and Verbs Used as Adjectives) (Page 25)
Practice 1
Exercise 1 Adding Pronouns Used as Adjectives
Sample pronouns are given.
1. that
2. Some
3. Any
4. which
5. his

6. their
7. Each
8. Most
9. Whose
10. these

Exercise 2 Recognizing Verbs Used as Adjectives
1. shattered (windowpane)
2. screaming (baby)
3. talking (dog)
4. fallen (branch)
5. stolen (money)
6. freezing (rain)
7. winning (car)
8. drowning (boy)
9. following (pages)
10. departing (passengers)

17.1   Adjectives (Pronouns and Verbs Used as Adjectives) (Page 26)
Practice 2
Exercise 1 Supplying Pronouns Used as Adjectives
Sample adjectives are given.
1. Each
2. Our
3. those
4. What
5. his
6. my
7. Whose
8. Some
9. neither
10. that

Exercise 2 Recognizing Verbs Used as Adjectives
1. frightened
2. hurrying
3. crying
4. completed
5. growing
6. cheering
7. flying
8. exhausted
9. streaming
10. lost

Writing Application
Writing Sentences with Adjectives
Sample sentences are given.
1. He could not swallow the leftover Chinese food.
2. Mickey bought a wool sweater and a pair of imported pants.
3. The wounded seagull's wing trailed on the shifting sand.
4. She grew flowering plants with lemon-colored berries.
5. Snow covered the drooping branches and frozen ground.
6. Donald finally selected a wind-up toy for his three-year-old sister.
7. They made those posters to announce the spring carnival.
8. A rippling stream flowed past the barbed-wire fence.
9. In the summer evening, flitting fireflies flashed in the darkness.

10. At the Central Park zoo they saw barking seals begging for fish.

17.2 Adverbs (Modifying Verbs, Adjectives, and Other Adverbs; Nouns Used as Adverbs) (Page 27)
Practice 1
Exercise 1   Recognizing Adverbs
1. quite (rapidly), rapidly (melted)
2. surprisingly (good)
3. very (well) well (suits)
4. somewhat , (dissatisfied)
5. truly (festive)
6. fairly (early), early (completed)
7. almost (forgot)
8. very (nearly), nearly (ready)
9. almost (totally), totally (destroyed)
10. exceptionally (clever)

Exercise 2   Identifying Adverbs and Nouns Used as Adverbs
1. not
2. (home)
3. increasingly
4. truly
5. (yesterday)
6. often, (weekends)
7. (Friday)
8. pleasantly
9. (tonight)
10. somewhat

17.2   Adverbs (Modifying Verbs, Adjectives, and Other Adverbs; Nouns Used as Adverbs) (Page 28)
Practice 2
Exercise 1   Recognizing Adverbs
1. soon
2. much
3. definitely
4. too
5. rather sternly
6. not
7. away
8. nearly
9. surprisingly quickly
10. remarkably
11. surprisingly
12. very
13. kindly
14. quite
15. loudly, not

Exercise 2   Recognizing Nouns Used as Adverbs
1. (Evenings) my parents and grandparents would loudly discuss politics.
2. I was sent (home) because I had a very high fever.
3. Tuesday was an extremely bad day, but the things that happened (Wednesday) were worse.
4. You must definitely see a doctor (today).

5. If you decided to visit (tomorrow) ,please come early.
6. (Saturdays) I usually babysit for my brother.
7. I did not see her (yesterday).
8. I ran approximately two miles (Friday).
9. She works (days) and attends school (nights).
10. Winters are always dreadfully cold in that province.
11. (Weekends) Todd likes to sleep late.
12. (Weekdays) , it is usually Jake's job to walk the dog.
13. We saw a remarkably good movie (Tuesday) .
14. Fortunately last (winter) , we stayed at the lake.
15. (Summers) , we always went to the beach.

17.2   Adverbs (Adverb or Adjective?) (Page 29)
Practice 1
Exercise 1   Distinguishing Between Adjectives and Adverbs
1. adverb
2. adjective
3. adverb
4. adjective
5. adverb
6. adjective
7. adverb
8. adverb
9. adjective
10. adjective

Exercise 2   Adding Adverbs and Adjectives to Sentences
1. regularly
2. sore
3. honest
4. carefully
5. frequently
6. regular
7. honestly
8. careful
9. sorely
10. frequent

17.2   Adverbs (Adverb or Adjective?) (Page 30)
Practice 2
Exercise 1   Distinguishing Between Adverbs and Adjectives
1. adjective
2. adverb
3. adverb
4. adjective
5. adverb
6. adjective
7. adverb
8. adjective
9. adjective

10. adverb
11. adverb
12. adjective
13. adjective
14. adverb
15. adjective

Writing Application
Writing Sentences with Adverbs
Sample adverbs are given.
1. Tony will go to the grocery store for us tomorrow.
2. Barn swallows are especially helpful because they eat insects.
3. His poor posture made him seem much shorter than he was.
4. The extremely tired worker yawned and rubbed his eyes.
5. We were quite sad about the end of summer.
6. Many people think snails are truly delicious.
7. The boat carefully docked and lowered its sails.
8. Their enthusiasm slowly faded.
9. Night fell and the celebration finally began.
10. Can a helicopter really rescue those men?

18.1 Prepositions (Words Used as Prepositions, Prepositional Phrases) (Page 31)
Practice 1
Exercise 1 Supplying Prepositions
Sample prepositions are given.
1. throughout
2. amid
3. in addition to
4. next to
5. about
6. by
7. on
8. in place of
9. but
10. In spite of

Exercise 2 Identifying Prepositional Phrases
1. (According to the (paper)), (at (dusk))
2. (for (you)), (next to (mine))
3. (between the two (countries))
4. (of (apples)), (into quarter-inch (slices))
5. (with a northern (exposure)), (for that (plant))
6. (in the (back)), (of the (boat)), (from the (spray))
7. (through a beautiful (courtyard))
8. (down the (street)), (on the (top)), (of its (garage))
9. (into the abandoned (house)), (through a (crack)), (in the (window))
10. (underneath the (woodpile)), (behind the (barn))

18.1 Prepositions (Words Used as Prepositions, Prepositional Phrases) (Page 32)
Practice 2
Exercise 1 Supplying Prepositions
Sample prepositions are given.
1. except
2. on

3. next to
4. Because of
5. within
6. in addition to
7. into
8. across
9. On account of
10. prior to
11. Because of
12. instead of
13. Aside from
14. between
15. instead of
16. With
17. in
18. Without
19. Before
20. in spite of

Exercise 2 Identifying Prepositional Phrases
1. of (birds) and (animals), to their (bodies)
2. Because of their (tails), regarding impending (danger)
3. With its (rattle)
4. Apart from protective (use), with the more practical (side), of (life)
5. with such (agility) without their (tails), for (balance)
6. With their long (tails) of (bird) in the (grass)
7. In addition to these (uses), during (courtship)
8. above (him), in his (mate)
9. by means of his tail (feathers), in front of the (hen)
10. in home (aquariums), in a courtship (dance)

18.1 Preposition (Preposition or Adverb?) (Page 33)
Practice 1
Exercise 1 Distinguishing Between Prepositions and Adverbs
1. adv.
2. adv.
3. prep.
4. prep.
5. adv.
6. prep.
7. adv.
8. adv.

9. prep.
10. prep.

Exercise 2 Adding Prepositions and Adverbs to Sentences
1. a. between
   b. between (states)

2. a. by (hand)
   b. by

3. a. on
   b. on (envelope)

4. a. behind (house)
   b. behind

5. a. past (or by) (library)
   b. past (or by)

18.1 Prepositions (Preposition or Adverb?) (Page 34)
Practice 2
Exercise 1 Distinguishing Between Prepositions and Adverbs
1. adverb
2. adverb
3. preposition
4. preposition
5. adverb
6. adverb
7. adverb
8. adverb
9. preposition
10. adverb
11. adverb
12. preposition
13. adverb
14. preposition
15. adverb
16. adverb
17. preposition
18. preposition
19. preposition
20. adverb

Writing Application
Writing Sentences with Prepositions
Sample sentences are given.
1. We hiked down the mountain path.
2. Andrea gave a report during English class.
3. They'll have dinner about six o'clock.
4. According to my father, tomorrow's weather will be sunny and warm.
5. The only way to get ahead is by means of hard work.

18.2 Conjunctions and Interjections (Different Kinds of Conjunctions) (Page 35)
Practice 1
Exercise 1 Identifying Conjunctions
1. before, subordinating
2. yet, coordinating
3. but, coordinating
4. both/and, correlative
5. while, subordinating
6. than, subordinating
7. Neither/nor, correlative
8. until, subordinating

9. so that, subordinating
10. whenever, subordinating

Exercise 2 Adding Conjunctions in Sentences
Sample conjunctions are given.
1. While
2. both, and
3. but
4. or
5. Although

18.2 Conjunctions and Interjections (Different Kinds of Conjunctions) (Page 36)
Practice 2
Exercise 1 Identifying Conjunctions
1. neither/nor, correlative
2. for, coordinating
3. whenever, subordinating
4. in order that, subordinating
5. not only/but also, correlative
6. yet, coordinating
7. Since, subordinating
8. or, coordinating
9. and, coordinating
10. because, subordinating
11. and, coordinating
12. whether/or, correlative
13. unless, subordinating
14. Wherever, subordinating
15. even though, subordinating
16. so, coordinating
17. Although, subordinating
18. Either/or, correlative
19. but, coordinating
20. Both/and, correlative

Exercise 2 Using Conjunctions in Sentences
Sample conjunctions are given.
1. but, coordinating
2. when, subordinating
3. neither/nor, correlative
4. Even if, subordinating
5. unless, subordinating

18.2 Conjunctions and Interjections (Conjunction, Preposition, or Adverb?) (Page 37)
Practice 1
Exercise 1 Identifying Words as Conjunctions, Prepositions, or Adverbs
1. conj.
2. adv.
3. conj.
4. prep.
5. adv.
6. conj.
7. conj.
8. prep.
9. conj.
10. prep

Exercise 2 Adding Conjunctions, Prepositions, or Adverbs to Sentences
1. before
   a. adv.
   b. conj.
   c. prep.
2. until
   a. prep.
   b. conj.
3. after
   a. prep.

b. conj.
c. adv.
4. Since
a. prep.
b. conj.

18.2 Conjunctions and Interjections (Conjunction, Preposition, or Adverb?) (Page 38)

Practice 2

Exercise 1 Identifying Words as Conjunctions, Prepositions, or Adverbs

1. preposition
2. adverb
3. subordinating conjunction
4. subordinating conjunction
5. adverb
6. subordinating conjunction
7. preposition
8. preposition
9. subordinating conjunction
10. subordinating conjunction
11. subordinating conjunction
12. preposition
13. preposition
14. subordinating conjunction
15. preposition
16. preposition
17. adverb
18. adverb
19. subordinating conjunction
20. preposition

Exercise 2 Using Conjunctions, Prepositions, and Adverbs in Sentences

Sample sentences are given.

1. before
   conjunction You must clean your room before you go out.
   preposition You must clean your room before noon.
   adverb You may go out after you clean your room—not before.
2. since
   conjunction Since I took that computer class, my skills have improved.
   preposition Since that class, my skills have improved.
   adverb My skills have improved since.
3. till
   conjunction Do nothing till you hear from me.
   preposition Do nothing till then.
4. until
   conjunction Mary waited until the cows came home.
   preposition Mary waited until dark.

18.2 Conjunctions and Interjections (Conjunctive Adverbs, Interjections) (Page 39)

Practice 1

Exercise 1 Recognizing Conjunctive Adverbs

1. besides
2. therefore
3. none
4. indeed
5. none
6. nevertheless
7. again
8. then
9. none

10. consequently

Exercise 2 Adding Interjections to Sentences

Sample interjections are given.

1. Ouch
2. Alas
3. Wow
4. Gee
5. Golly
6. Eek
7. Drat
8. Oh
9. Hurray
10. Whew

18.2 Conjunctions and Interjections (Conjunctive Adverbs, Interjections) (Page 40)

Practice 2

Exercise 1 Supplying Conjunctive Adverbs

Sample conjunctive adverbs are given.

1. finally
2. moreover
3. indeed
4. therefore
5. then
6. however
7. also
8. accordingly
9. thus
10. consequently
11. therefore
12. moreover
13. consequently
14. however
15. nevertheless
16. thus
17. furthermore
18. indeed
19. therefore
20. consequently

19.1 Subjects and Verbs (Complete Subjects and Predicates) (Page 41)

Practice 1

Exercise 1 Recognizing Complete Subjects and Predicates

1. zebras | roamed
2. Elena | did
3. game | requires
4. hallway | makes
5. owners | arranged
6. States | was
7. It | continues
8. Children | enjoy
9. elephants | are
10. I | accepted

Exercise 2 More Work with Complete Subjects and Predicates

1. corner | grew
2. behavior | aroused
3. crocodiles | carry
4. Hieroglyphics | were
5. Spectators | applauded
6. boat | takes
7. Day | is
8. pie | is
9. belts | save
10. Jeremy | phoned.

19.1 Subjects and Verbs (Complete Subjects and Predicates) (Page 42)

Practice 2

Exercise 1 Recognizing Complete Subjects and Predicates

Complete subjects appear to the left of the line; complete predicates to the right.

1. The new puppy| won't leave the older dog alone.
2. An old-fashioned spinning wheel| sat in the corner of the room.
3. Seasonal winds in India| are called monsoons.
4. New skin| was grafted onto his burned leg.
5. We| should have been on the road before now.
6. Anyone| could have made a mistake like that.
7. My umbrella handle| is carved from wood.
8. The Sons of Liberty| was a secret society.
9. Mink oil| is excellent for conditioning leather shoes, boots, and baseball mitts.
10. Her stationery| is always simple but elegant.
11. Fourteen squealing children| played in the sprinklers.
12. One of the best exercises you can do| is swim.
13. My aunt's best friend| knit this sweater for me.
14. The two volumes of the series| will be published later this year.
15. The ancient Egyptians| stained their fingernails with henna.

19.1 Subjects and Verbs (Sentence or Fragment?) (Page 43)

Practice 1

Exercise 1 Distinguishing Between Sentences and Fragments

1. F
2. S
3. S
4. F
5. S
6. F
7. F
8. F
9. S
10. S

Exercise 2 Writing Sentences from Fragments

Sample sentences are given.

1. We ordered pizza in spite of Susanna's objections.
4. We had moderate temperatures throughout the summer.
6. Visitors from near and far tour the nation's capital.
7. The player with the highest batting average in the league was honored at the banquet.
8. My mother spends several hours a week on her hobby.

19.1 Subjects and Verbs (Sentence or Fragment?) (Page 44)

Practice 2

Exercise 1 Distinguishing Between Sentences and Fragments

Sample sentences are given.

1. Her gift was a sewing machine with all the frills.
2. He told stories about creatures in the ocean's depths.
3. sentence
4. Patty jumped higher and higher on the trampoline.

5. Few, if any, are going.
6. We watch basketball, the most popular spectator sport.
7. The young man was wearing a white, heavy knit sweater.
8. sentence
9. The rabbit trembled and shook with fear.
10. We sat beside the pool, soaking up the sunshine.

Exercise 2 Converting Fragments to Sentences

Sample sentences are given.

1. We saw a sudden streak of light in the night sky.
2. During the eclipse, the moon seemed to disappear.
3. Wondering how far she had to walk, Jennifer set out.
4. The kids knocked on the door for a full minute.
5. Jason kicked the ball around for hours.

19.1 Subjects and Verbs (Simple Subjects and Predicates) (Page 45)

Practice 1

Exercise 1 Recognizing Simple Subjects and Predicates

(Simple subjects and predicates are both underlined once.)

1. Many ...photographs/had become
2. We /enjoyed
3. organizers ...event/were
4. sound ...vehicles/pierced
5. All ...group/wear
6. You /promised
7. few ...members/did not attend
8. number ...properties/were destroyed
9. Who /volunteered
10. Mom /had not ordered

Exercise 2 Adding Sentence Parts

Sample sentences are given.

1. My (sister) reads several books a week.
2. Every (visitor) to our home receives a friendly welcome.
3. (No one) in my home room takes typing.
4. (Kevin) bats left-handed.
5. The (chef) in that restaurant studied in Paris.
6. These mail-order (items) arrived in record time.
7. United States (senators) are elected to six-year-terms.
8. Every (member) of the club receives a membership card.
9. The (nickname) of our state is the Nutmeg State.
10. (Most) of the animals in the circus have been trained by Gunther.

19.1 Subjects and Verbs (Simple Subjects and Predicates) (Page 46)
Practice 2
Exercise 1   Recognizing Subjects and Verbs

1. Greek literature contains many stories about Amazons.
2. Supposedly living near the Black Sea, the Amazons were a nation of women warriors noted for their strength.
3. Not enjoying the presence of men, the Amazons lived apart in their own cities.
4. Ares, the god of war, was worshipped in their temples.
5. They fought against the Greeks during the Trojan War.
6. They were also fearless hunters.
7. Their bravery made them famous.
8. Many Greek statues of Amazons with bows and arrows can be seen today in museums.
9. These women never really existed, however, according to some scholars.
10. They are merely the product of the Greeks' imagination.

Exercise 2   Using Simple Subjects and Simple Predicates in Sentences
Sample sentences are given.

1. Marina had flown many times before her solo flight.
2. The pilot got ready for the landing.
3. The brave soldiers conquered the enemy.
4. My garden is not very big.
5. The boys were wondering about the assignment.
6. The dentist has a full schedule for today.
7. We have ordered ten boxes of greeting cards.
8. Basketball is Jerry's favorite sport.
9. The taxi might have been here already.
10. The candles burned for hours.

19.1 Subjects and Verbs (Compound Subjects and Verbs) (Page 47)
Practice 1
Exercise 1   Recognizing Compound Subjects
1. Jake, I
2. President, Vice President
3. Senate, House of Representatives, Supreme Court
4. guests, hosts
5. lilacs, roses
6. Shrimp, shellfish
7. Oranges, lemons, limes, grapefruits
8. Paul, I
9. guide, one
10. Measles, mumps

Exercise 2   Recognizing Compound Verbs
1. touched, rolled
2. did give, practiced
3. writes, bats
4. writes, calls
5. added, adjusted, turned
6. clapped, cheered, called
7. put, yawned
8. checked, found
9. overgrew, began
10. retreated, surrendered

19.1 Subjects and Verbs (Compound Subjects and Verbs) (Page 48)
Practice 2
Exercise 1   Recognizing Compound Subjects and Verbs

1. A hat, gloves, and warm coat should be worn in this weather.
2. Our aunt and uncle visit us every year and bring many gifts.
3. Both salt and pepper are used as seasonings.
4. In the summer, my friends and I swim and ride our bicycles on country roads.
5. Moles have very poor eyesight and, therefore, burrow in dark tunnels underground.
6. The team not only had a perfect season but also won the tournament.
7. Hair dyes and lipsticks come in almost every shade.
8. The mother cat and her kittens mewed pitifully and rubbed against our legs.
9. A small airplane was gliding and spiraling above us.
10. Moths cluster on the screen and beat their wings.

Exercise 2   Finding Simple and Compound Subjects and Verbs

	Subject	Verb
1.	nozzle	was clogged
2.	people	have
3.	rats, mice	eat
4.	Aunt Jennie, Uncle Nick	will fly, bring
5.	miners, families	do lead
6.	Max	can hear, whistle
7.	remedies	do help
8.	campfires, matches	can cause
9.	work, honesty	won
10.	Hilary, Miranda, cousin	could dance, sing, play

19.2 Hard-to-Find Subjects (Page 49)
Practice 1
Exercise 1   Finding Subjects in Orders or Directions
Subjects are all (you).
1. (you)^turn
2. (you)^let
3. (you)^Remember
4. (you)^read
5. (you)^remind

Exercise 2   Finding Subjects in Inverted Sentences
1. firefighters
2. we
3. solution
4. errors
5. multitude

19.2 Hard-to-Find Subjects (Page 50)
Practice 2
Exercise 1 Creating Sentences with Understood Subjects
Sample sentences are given.
1. Bill, (you) give me that hammer.
2. Mike, (you) wipe the dishes.
3. Susan, (you) please speak with them.
4. (you) Please wash the dog.
5. (you) Please step carefully across the wet floor.
6. Helen, (you) drive me to the store.
7. (you) Please clean the windows.
8. Jerry, (you) please brush the dog outside.
9. Mary, (you) please rake the leaves.
10. Steve, (you) mix the ingredients for the cake.

Exercise 2 Finding Subjects in Questions
1. Is a tomato a fruit or a vegetable?
2. Where did you put the buttered rolls?
3. Which shade of blue looks best?
4. Should a murderer ever be released from prison?
5. Who won the prize for the silliest costume?
6. May we have a little peace and quiet?
7. Was the key under the mat?
8. How long will you take to decide?
9. Whose honor was at stake?
10. Can we climb these mountains safely?

Exercise 3 Finding Subjects in Sentences Beginning with *There* or *Here*
1. Here are your gloves.
2. There was the leaky pipe.
3. There he was , with no bus fare.
4. Here are some suggestions for your composition.
5. There are two possible answers to that question.
6. There were the lost documents.
7. Here is a new slant on that topic.
8. Here comes Megan.
9. Here is your change from the dollar bill.
10. There are no mistakes in this needlepoint sampler.

19.3 Direct Objects, Indirect Objects, and Objective Complements (Direct Objects) (Page 51)
Practice 1
Exercise 1 Identifying Direct Objects
1. sheets
2. novel, articles
3. bus
4. doorkeeper
5. teacher
6. State Street, High Road
7. daffodils, flowers
8. fabric
9. notes
10. kinds

Exercise 2 More Work with Direct Objects
1. games
2. played
3. party
4. grew
5. steaks , seafood
6. everything
7. moved
8. car
9. horse
10. has ridden

19.3 Direct Objects, Indirect Objects, and Objective Complements (Direct Objects) (Page 52)
Practice 2
Exercise 1 Recognizing Direct Objects
1. lights
2. light
3. bulbs
4. energy
5. lots
6. bulb
7. switches, bulbs
8. amount
9. light
10. methods

Exercise 2 Writing Sentences with Direct Objects
Sample sentences are given.
1. Dolores had an accident.
2. Did you see the walruses and sea lions?
3. The star acknowledged his fans.
4. Do you like dogs or cats?
5. We had muffins, toast, and bagels at breakfast.
6. Did you buy any lotion?
7. We watched the dancers and singers.
8. Have you had a manicure recently?
9. Let's visit the elephants and giraffes.
10. Do you like raisins?

19.3 Direct Objects, Indirect Objects, and Objective Complements (Indirect Objects, The Objective Complement) (Page 53)
Practice 1
Exercise 1 Identifying Indirect Objects
1. Michelle, Joe
2. lawyer
3. guest
4. police
5. Kelly
6. Helen, Kim
7. Boris
8. Mom, Dad
9. Aunt Helen
10. me

Exercise 2 Recognizing Objective Complements
1. satisfying
2. treasurer
3. invalid
4. busy
5. Toby

19.3 Direct Objects, Indirect Objects, and Objective Complements (Indirect Objects, The Objective Complement) (Page 54)

Practice 2

Exercise 1   Recognizing Indirect Objects

1. people
2. none
3. Harriet, Alberta
4. children, me
5. none
6. none
7. him
8. men, women
9. herself
10. none
11. sister
12. none
13. him
14. none
15. man

Exercise 2   Recognizing Objective Complements

1. sissy
2. happy
3. kind, helpful
4. obstinate
5. welcome
6. president
7. red, sore
8. pink
9. chairwoman
10. worthwhile
11. winner
12. cured
13. angel
14. successful, wealthy
15. unattractive

19.4 Subject Complements (Page 55)

Practice 1

Exercise 1   Recognizing Predicate Nominatives and Predicate Adjectives

1. tired, exhilarated, PA
2. tan, muscular, PA
3. bestseller, PN
4. popular, PA
5. distance, PN
6. consultant, PN
7. triplets, PN
8. surgeon, internist, PN
9. thorough, PA
10. constructive, workable, PA

Exercise 2   Writing Sentences with Compound Subject Complements

Sample subject complements are given.

1. practical, PA
2. zesty, PA
3. rich, PA
4. Saints, PN
5. Lou, PN

19.4 Subject Complements (Page 56)

Practice 2

Exercise 1   Recognizing Predicate Nominatives

1. she
2. hockey, football
3. eggs, meat, beans
4. athlete
5. one
6. naturalist, artist
7. metals
8. everything
9. best
10. you, he
11. seventy-five dollars
12. core
13. planet
14. friends
15. capital

Exercise 2   Recognizing Predicate Adjectives

1. muffled
2. stiff, sore
3. important
4. gritty, inedible
5. kinder, understanding
6. difficult
7. unnecessary
8. harsh, impersonal
9. drawn, pale
10. successful
11. skilled
12. destructive
13. popular
14. nervous
15. prepared

20.1 Prepositional Phrases (Page 57)

Practice 1

Exercise 1   Identifying Adjective Phrases

1. (Everyone) in the lab completed the (experiment) on page 30.

2. The new (house) at the (end) of the street is nearly finished.

3. The (gate) in the (fence) around the estate was padlocked.

4. Tomorrow, the mayor will announce her (plans) for the new committee.

5. Exchange (students) from France are visiting a (family) in our neighborhood.

Exercise 2   Identifying Adverb Phrases

1. The nervous applicant (shifted) from one foot to the other.

2. Without any hesitation, Frank (stepped) to the microphone.

3. No unauthorized personnel were permitted (close) to the launch pad.

4. After the game, we (stopped) at the diner on Hudson Street.

5. Hundreds of fans were (eager) for a glimpse of the star.

20.1 Prepositional Phrases (Page 58)
Practice 2
Exercise 1 Identifying Adjective Phrases

Adjective Phrases	Words Modified
1. of mysteries	writer
2. about Native American folklore	article
3. for the play	props
by Ibsen	play
4. with three parts	book
5. near the door	trellis

Exercise 2 Identifying Adverb Phrases

Adverb Phrases	Words Modified
1. from the village	lured
2. for strong bones and teeth	essential
3. inside its skeleton	safe
4. After the ceremony	left
with the groom	left
5. in silent agony	died
on the beach	died

Writing Application
Writing Sentences with Adjective and Adverb Phrases
Sample sentences are given.

1. He lay back in the comfortable seat on the train.
   He read a book on the train.
2. The time before school each day is for eating breakfast.
   Before school, she jogged around the block.
3. The photographs in the attic are of great sentimental value.
   We searched in the attic for a very old chair.
4. The sidewalk in front of the store is cleared of snow.
   I waited in front of the store for the bus to arrive.
5. Those sounds during the night were frightening.
   It rained very hard during the night.

20.1 Appositives and Appositive Phrases (Page 59)
Practice 1
Exercise 1 Identifying Appositives and Appositive Phrases

1. July 14 (Bastille Day)
2. Juan, Linda (person)
3. tuna fish with lettuce and cheese (lunch)
4. a moist, fertile spot in the desert (oasis)
5. her faithful clerk (Jenkins)
6. all (We)
7. Phyllis, Len (captains)
8. a young couple from Paris (neighbors)
9. *Arsenic and Old Lace* (comedy)
10. Pete, Sue, Judy (them)

Exercise 2 Writing Sentences with Appositives and Appositive Phrases

1. The explorers, Lewis and Clark, opened the Northwest Territory.
2. Delaware has only three counties: Kent, Sussex, and New Castle.
3. My cousin lives in Austin, the capital of Texas.

4. A local reporter, Annette Jackson, broke the story.
5. Both finalists, Logan and Bruce, are fine competitors.

20.1 Appositives and Appositive Phrases (Page 60)
Practice 2
Exercise 1 Identifying Appositives

Appositives	Words Renamed
1. food	topic
2. Phyllis	cousin
3. girlfriend	Cara
4. Herman Melville	writer
5. Manx	cat
6. "Snow Fall"	poem
7. blue	color
8. flashlight	item
9. clarinet	instrument
10. Frankenstein	inventor

Exercise 2 Identifying Appositive Phrases

1. Tammy learned a new safety (measure), a technique for saving people from choking.
2. The (bobcat), an endangered species, has been hunted as a pest in the East.
3. At the circus the clown rode a (dromedary), a one-humped camel, rapidly around the ring.
4. He was proud of owning his first (car), an old jalopy.
5. She named Don Jones (chairman), a well-deserved title.
6. I will tell (you), my good friend, an intriguing story.
7. Herb will read (anything): old matchbooks, junk mail, or the backs of cereal boxes.
8. Marsha gave the baby two stuffed (animals): a white, woolly lamb and a huggable teddy bear.
9. My family took our guests to a French (restaurant), one of the best places in the city.
10. Bill excelled in two outdoor (sports), cross-country skiing and ice hockey.

Writing Application
Using Appositives and Appositive Phrases

1. The ostrich, the largest of all birds, is a native of Africa and parts of Asia.
2. Mrs. Gordon had a piano in her parlor, a room for special guests.
3. The restaurant serves lobster in a delicious Newburg sauce, a creamy sauce made with butter and wine.
4. Marjorie, one of the most interesting people I know, is a gourmet, an expert ventriloquist, and a very good poet.
5. Donny's father is a neurologist, a specialist on the nervous system.

20.1 Participles and Participial Phrases (Participles, Verb or Participle?) (Page 61)
Practice 1
Exercise 1   Identifying Participles
1. broken (finger), past
2. crying (baby), present
3. stirring (speech), present
4. injured (bird), past
5. frozen (dessert), past
6. acting (chairman), present
7. drowning (man), present
8. building (permit), present
9. broken (promise), past
10. revised (proposal), past

Exercise 2   Distinguishing Between Verbs and Participles
1. verb
2. participle
3. participle
4. verb
5. participle
6. verb
7. verb
8. participle
9. participle
10. verb

20.1 Participles and Participial Phrases (Verb or Participle?) (Page 62)
Practice 2
Exercise 1   Identifying Present and Past Participles
1. fractured, past
2. fluttering, present
3. swollen, past
4. established, past
5. Drizzling, present
6. pounding, present
7. splattered, past
8. Lisping, present
9. broken, past
10. Disgusted, past
11. closing, present
12. worried, past
13. welcoming, present
14. broken, past
15. speaking, present
16. tattered, past
17. acting, present
18. singing, present
19. corrected, past
20. signed, past

Exercise 2   Distinguishing Between Verbs and Participles
1. verb
2. participle/runners
3. participle/crowd
4. verb
5. participle/Joan
6. verb
7. participle/she
8. verb

9. participle/race
10. participle/Joan

20.1 Participles and Participial Phrases (Participial Phrases) (Page 63)
Practice 1
Exercise 1   Recognizing Participial Phrases
1. visiting the Jackson's (family)
2. signed by Napoleon (letter)
3. Feeling uneasy (babysitter)
4. sold at the farm store (pie)
5. Bought by an eccentric millionaire (car)
6. standing outside the library (Mike)
7. having a pet (Anyone)
8. Confused by the directions (contestant)
9. hanging from the ceiling (plant)
10. lost in the department store (child)

Exercise 2   Writing Sentences with Participial Phrases
1. The person looking in the window is our neighbor.
2. The storm coming from the west is bringing precipitation.
3. Early sketches made by that painter have become valuable.
4. The wallet found on the street had no identification in it.
5. We enjoyed all the food served at the party.

20.1 Participles and Participial Phrases (Essential or Nonessential?) (Page 64)
Practice 2
Exercise 1   Recognizing Participial Phrases
1. (Andrea), waking from a dream, cried fearfully. nonessential
2. Slumped over a chair, (I) could think only of sleep. nonessential
3. The (boat), making large waves, overturned our canoe. nonessential
4. She picked up (debris) thrown by a careless motorist. essential
5. Feeling jaunty in his borrowed tuxedo, (Barney) sauntered into the room. nonessential
6. We stared at the (horizon), broken only by sails. nonessential
7. As Zack fell, he grabbed a (branch) jutting out from the cliff. essential
8. Shivering in anticipation, (I) could hardly wait for the conclusion to Poe's "The Pit and the Pendulum." nonessential
9. She ordered a (plate) piled high with flapjacks. essential
10. She saw in the mirror a (face) streaked with tears. essential

11. The (woman) standing at the end of the line is my cousin Sylvie, essential
12. (Tyler) disappointed by Dana's refusal, felt abandoned, nonessential
13. Ignored by the fans, the (singer) decided to give up on her career, nonessential
14. The (people) fleeing the area are trying to escape a fire, essential
15. The (path) , worn smooth by millions of feet, leads to a spectacular view, nonessential
16. Exhausted by her effort, (Myra) slept for twelve hours, nonessential
17. The (man) working at that desk rarely takes a break, essential
18. (Barry), eating at the counter, looked up to see Susan, nonessential
19. (Grace), being interviewed for a job, wore a blue suit, nonessential
20. The (bird) singing loudly on that branch is a song sparrow, essential

Exercise 2   Using Participial Phrases to Combine Sentences
1. The girls, practicing some new dance steps on the stage, are Laurel, Hillary, and Jamie.
2. The boy walking his dog is headed toward the park.
3. The artist sketching scenes of children at play is my cousin.
4. The Komodo dragon's skin, marked with the scars of many battles, is wrinkled with age.
5. The radio station transmitting this entertaining program is located in Sacramento.

20.1   Participles and Participial Phrases (Nominative Absolutes) (Page 65)
Practice 1
Exercise 1   Recognizing Nominative Absolutes
1. The band continuing to play
2. Hours having passed without any word
3. The patient recovering nicely
4. her right hand broken
5. their best players injured
6. Their chores completed
7. The train having broken down
8. The buffet table looking so tempting
9. Their argument resolved
10. The air conditioning not working

Exercise 2   Writing Sentences with Nominative Absolutes
Sample sentences are given.
1. A parade scheduled for tomorrow, the police put up no-parking signs along the main street.
2. Our decorations complete, the room looked very festive.
3. Her sweater at home, Lucy was chilly at the picnic.
4. We were able to borrow a bike for Kenny, his being broken.
5. The applause having subsided, the speaker was finally able to begin.

20.1   Participles and Participial Phrases (Nominative Absolutes) (Page 66)
Practice 2
Exercise 1   Recognizing Nominative Absolutes
1. Her smile vanishing from her face.
2. its runners skimming over the ice.
3. The furnace broken.
4. Several minutes having gone by.
5. his dog Briar lying at his feet.
6. A bonnet tied around her head.
7. Candles and flowers on every table.
8. Several delays being unavoidable.
9. Midnight striking.
10. His glasses at home.
11. Night having fallen.
12. her performance having been flawless.
13. My homework completed.
14. Her ankle having been sprained.
15. his exercise routine over.
16. Her veil arranged beautifully.
17. Its head caught in the pet door.
18. our arms covered with mosquito bites.
19. The air conditioner broken.
20. Spring coming nearer.

Writing Application
Writing Sentences with Participial Phrases
Sample sentences are given.
1. Telling everyone the good news. Brad had a great time at the party.
2. The dinner cooked by Jason was delicious.
3. Tossed in a bowl, the salad was a perfect appetizer.
4. Working on the highway bridge, two men attached a new section of railing.
5. His flight having left for the Bahamas, Franklin could not be reached at his office.

20.1   Gerunds and Gerund Phrases (Gerunds; Verb, Participle, or Gerund?) (Page 67)
Practice 1
Exercise 1   Recognizing Gerunds
1. Fishing, S
2. coloring, DO
3. flying, OP
4. Losing, S
5. cheating, OP
6. bowling, APP
7. Pruning, S
8. skiing, APP
9. volunteering, IO
10. drawing, OP

Exercise 2   Recognizing Verbs, Participles, and Gerunds
1. G
2. G
3. P
4. V

5. V
6. G
7. P
8. V
9. G
10. P

20.1 Gerunds and Gerund Phrases (Gerunds; Verb, Participle, or Gerund?) (Page 68)
Practice 2
Exercise 1 Identifying Gerunds
1. Gardening (subject)
2. weaving (object of a preposition)
3. running (direct object)
4. counterfeiting (predicate nominative)
5. Milking (subject)
6. sky diving (appositive)
7. eavesdropping (appositive)
8. fencing (object of a preposition)
9. Jogging (subject)
10. vacuuming (subject)
11. Moving (subject)
12. hopping (direct object)
13. eating (predicate nominative)
14. quitting (predicate nominative)
15. Winning (subject)
16. exercising (direct object)
17. walking (appositive)
18. practicing (indirect object)
19. leaving (object of a preposition)
20. napping (appositive)

Exercise 2 Distinguishing Between Verbs, Participles, and Gerunds
1. participle
2. verb
3. gerund
4. verb
5. participle
6. gerund
7. gerund
8. participle
9. gerund
10. verb

20.1 Gerunds and Gerund Phrases (Gerund Phrases) (Page 69)
Practice 1
Exercise 1 Recognizing Gerund Phrases
1. learning French, DO
2. counting to ten, PN
3. Training long hours, S
4. changing her mind about the color for the walls, DO
5. Working for the mayor's reelection, S
6. our working so hard, DO
7. entering the house, OP
8. choosing a good topic, PN
9. finding the buried treasure, OP
10. practicing hard, OP

Exercise 2 Writing Nouns and Pronouns Before Gerunds
1. their
2. Suzi's
3. our
4. His
5. My
6. Her
7. Their
8. his
9. Ken's
10. Your

20.1 Gerunds and Gerund Phrases (Gerund Phrases) (Page 70)
Practice 2
Exercise 1 Identifying Gerund Phrases
1. remembering trivia (object of a preposition)
2. catching a greased pig (appositive)
3. setting the table before dinner (predicate nominative), washing the dishes afterwards (predicate nominative)
4. Caring for pets (subject), earning money (object of a preposition)
5. deep-sea diving (direct object), horseback riding (direct object)
6. Drying fruits and vegetables for winter use (subject), cutting down expenses (object of a preposition)
7. complaining about everyone's faults (predicate nominative), worrying unceasingly (predicate nominative)
8. trading stories (direct object)
9. mowing grass (object of a preposition), raking leaves (object of a preposition), shoveling snow (object of a preposition)
10. Hoarding money under the mattress (subject)
11. baking cakes (object of a preposition)
12. passing this class (appositive)
13. Talking your problems over with your friends (subject)
14. squeezing them first (predicate nominative)
15. talking in the study areas (direct object)

Writing Application
Writing Sentences with Gerund Phrases
Sample sentences are given.
1. He enjoys cooking dinner.
2. Wendy's job is preparing sandwiches.
3. The chemists allotted time for explaining the process.
4. Traveling to distant places takes time and money.
5. The tour guide's job is directing the visitors.

20.1 Infinitives and Infinitive Phrases (Infinitives, Prepositional Phrase or Infinitive?) (Page 71)
Practice 1
Exercise 1 Identifying Infinitives
1. to accept, adv.
2. to work, adj.
3. to learn, adv.
4. to succeed, adv.
5. to try, adv.
6. to fly, n.
7. to watch, adj.
8. to rule, adj.
9. to listen, n.
10. to play, n.

Exercise 2 Distinguishing Between Prepositional Phrases and Infinitives
1. INF
2. PP
3. PP
4. INF
5. PP

6. INF
7. INF
8. PP
9. PP
10. INF

20.1 Infinitives and Infinitive Phrases (Infinitives, Prepositional Phrase or Infinitive?) (Page 72)

Practice 2

Exercise 1   Identifying Infinitives
1. To fantasize (subject)
2. to leave (adverb)
3. to reconsider (direct object)
4. to flee (appositive)
5. to read (adjective)
6. to watch (predicate nominative)
7. To build (subject)
8. To escape (adverb)
9. to abdicate (object of a preposition)
10. to fly (adjective)
11. To teach (subject)
12. to participate (direct object)
13. to paint (direct object)
14. to dance (appositive)
15. to take (adjective)

Exercise 2   Distinguishing Between Prepositional Phrases and Infinitives
1. to bargain (infinitive)
2. to explain (infinitive)
3. to Glenn (prepositional phrase)
4. To believe (infinitive)
5. to friends (prepositional phrase)
6. to rest (infinitive)
7. to China (prepositional phrase)
8. to me (prepositional phrase)
9. to graduate (infinitive)
10. to town (prepositional phrase)
11. to try (infinitive)
12. to the mountains (prepositional phrase)
13. To understand (infinitive)
14. to her sister (prepositional phrase)
15. to learn (infinitive)

20.1 Infinitives and Infinitive Phrases (Infinitive Phrases) (Page 73)

Practice 1

Exercise 1   Recognizing Infinitive Phrases
1. to take seriously, adj.
2. to work harder, adj.
3. to be mailed by Thursday, adj.
4. to try on their new uniforms, adv.
5. to audition for the part, n.
6. to wait till dinnertime, n.
7. to spend the night, adj.
8. to find that game, adj.
9. to sell some of these tickets, n.
10. to apply for the job, n.

Exercise 2   More Work with Infinitive Phrases
1. (to) win
2. to show
3. (to) play
4. (to) practice
5. to come
6. (to) disagree

7. (to) stay
8. (to) bring
9. to run
10. (to) take

20.1 Infinitives and Infinitive Phrases (Infinitive Phrases) (Page 74)

Practice 2

Exercise 1   Identifying Infinitive Phrases
1. To describe the hockey game in an understandable manner (subject)
2. to see one hundred different species during one weekend (predicate nominative)
3. to see the exhibit on Indian art (adverb), to gather material for our reports (adverb)
4. to keep the secret about Injun Joe (direct object)
5. To inhale these fumes (subject), to die instantly (predicate nominative)
6. To pay our bill (adjective), to wash dishes (object of a preposition)
7. To heed his warning (subject), to be prepared for anything (predicate nominative)
8. to become a veterinarian (direct object)
9. to meet on Friday night (adjective)
10. to sink in the leaky boat (object of a preposition), to bail it out (predicate nominative)
11. To visit every state (subject)
12. to go snowboarding for two days straight (predicate nominative)
13. to shop at the farmer's market (direct object), to create a fresh meal for their friends (direct object)
14. to attend the winter dance with him (direct object)
15. To see the waterfall (subject), to be overwhelmed by its beauty (predicate nominative)
16. to improve her relationship with her sister (direct object)
17. to have brunch on Sunday (adjective)
18. to be kind to the stray dog (direct object)
19. to give Al a chance (direct object)
20. to unpack immediately (adjective)

Writing Application

Writing Sentences with Infinitive Phrases

Sample sentences are given.

1. To erase the chalkboard takes little time.
2. The easiest way of understanding the problem is to draw a diagram.
3. Mark made time in his busy schedule to read a short story.
4. Alicia wants to show us her stamp collection.
5. The conductor raised the baton as the concert was about to begin.

20.2   Adjective Clauses (Page 75)

Practice 1

Exercise 1   Recognizing Adjective Clauses
1. where John F. Kennedy was born (house)
2. that I can't identify (spice)
3. for whom I left the message (one)
4. whose mother is the district attorney (one)
5. that cherishes football (state)

6. who inspired me to study chemistry (teacher)

7. I have known since kindergarten (someone)

8. whose work was once ignored (poet)

9. Dad will surely like (something)

10. in which I keep my change (box)

Exercise 2 Recognizing the Use of Introductory Words
1. where, adv.
2. that, DO
3. whom, OP
4. whose, adj.
5. that, S
6. who, S
7. (that), DO
8. whose, adj.
9. (that), DO
10. which, OP

20.2 Adjective Clauses (Page 76)
Practice 2
Exercise 1 Identifying Adjective Clauses and the Words They Modify

1. The (student) whom Mr. Stein chose was first in her class. (essential)

2. Is this the (year) when the planets will align? (essential)

3. Henry VIII was a (king) whose many wives fared badly. (essential)

4. Those were the (years) that I remember best.. (essential)

5. Our school (play) which lasted two hours, was enjoyed by everyone. (nonessential)

6. (Books) that deal with current events in an exciting way often become bestsellers. (essential)

7. My father works in an (office) where everyone helps each other. (essential)

8. People still remember June's last (letter), which arrived twenty years ago. (nonessential)

9. The (position) that Jackie wanted was already filled. (essential)

10. The (man) whose playing you admired is an internationally recognized chess champion. (essential)

Exercise 2 Recognizing the Uses of Relative Pronouns and Relative Adverbs

1. We look forward to a weekend (when) we can rest. (adverb)

2. A sales representative (whose) approach is too insistent may anger potential customers. (adjective)

3. The person with (whom) you spoke is my father. (object of a preposition)

4. In the time (since) Maria returned, she has talked only about her trip. (adverb)

5. My friend (whom) you admired liked you also. (direct object)

6. The play featured too many actors (who) had not learned their lines. (subject)

7. In the centuries (before) the car was invented, people relied on horses for transportation. (adverb)

8. A historian (who) knows the facts can compare the past with the probable future. (subject)

9. Physics is a subject about (which) I know nothing. (object of a preposition)

10. The first person on the moon walked on land (where) no one had ever walked before. (adverb)

20.2 Adverb Clauses (Page 77)
Practice 1
Exercise 1 Identifying Adverb Clauses

1. (if) we are home by eleven

2. (where) it would get the most sun

3. (whenever) he has time

4. (After) the butter has melted

5. (if) you ask her

Exercise 2 Identifying Elliptical Clauses
1. While sick, elliptical
2. than the one before, elliptical
3. as Ben, elliptical
4. as the clerk had promised
5. than jogging, elliptical

20.2 Adverb Clauses (Page 78)
Practice 2
Exercise 1 Identifying Adverb Clauses and the Words They Modify

Adverb Clauses	Words Modified
1. Before she gave the assignment	explained
2. whenever that topic is discussed	gloomy
3. After the sun goes down	drops
4. so that we could enjoy the scenery	to stop
5. since I was young	have lived

Exercise 2 Recognizing Elliptical Adverb Clauses
Sample completed clauses are given.
1. We think our cheerleaders are better than theirs (are).

2. Blake is happier working with people than (he is) working by himself.

3. My younger brother is as tall as I (am).

4. Small children sometimes appreciate classical music more than they (appreciate) nursery jingles.

5. In Riley's backyard you can find junk heaped wherever there is an inch of space.

Writing Application
Using Adverb Clauses to Combine Sentences
Sample sentences are given.
1. The mother called the doctor in the middle of the night because her child's temperature was abnormally high.

2. The crowd looked up in wonder when another brilliant display of fireworks went off.

3. As we toasted marshmallows over the dying embers, we silently shared a feeling of closeness.

4. Randolph will never learn to study <u>unless he will learn to concentrate</u>.
5. Give me some more ideas <u>so that I can think of a topic</u>.

20.2 Noun Clauses (Page 79)
Practice 1
Exercise 1 Identifying Noun Clauses
1. That we arrived just then, S
2. when the last bus leaves, DO
3. whoever wins, IO
4. That she was sick, S
5. which house has more space, PN
6. that you enter the contest again, DO
7. whatever became of Jane, OP
8. whomever you see, IO
9. What Carol reported, S
10. whether he should work or go fishing, PN

Exercise 2 Recognizing the Use of Introductory Words
1. That, NONE
2. when, ADV
3. whoever, S
4. That, NONE
5. which, ADJ
6. that, NONE
7. whatever, S
8. whomever, DO
9. What, DO
10. whether, NONE

20.2 Noun Clauses (Page 80)
Practice 2
Exercise 1 Identifying Noun Clauses
1. Whoever is interested in the past (subject)
2. how it would be possible to please both factions (appositive)
3. what you wore to the party (object of a preposition)
4. That the play is a financial success (subject)
5. whoever is unfortunate enough to sit next to him (object of a preposition)
6. whatever ideas people thought would be workable (appositive)
7. what a tourist can see in Kenya (direct object)
8. when she should expect you to arrive (direct object)
9. whichever ones she orders from the retailer (predicate nominative)
10. whoever came into his store (indirect object)

Exercise 2 Recognizing the Uses of Introductory Words
1. Whoever (subject)
2. how (adverb)
3. what (direct object)
4. that (no function)
5. whoever (subject)
6. whatever (adjective)
7. what (direct object)
8. when (adverb)
9. whichever (adjective)
10. whoever (subject)

Writing Application
Writing Sentences with Noun Clauses
Sample sentences are given.
1. Whoever is the last person in the room should switch off the light.
2. How we begin the project is strictly up to us.

3. I delivered exactly what you requested on the phone.
4. The chief worry of the mountain climbers was whether supplies would be waiting in the shelter.
5. I will support you in whatever way I can.

21.1 Sentences Classified by Structure and Function (The Four Structures of Sentences) (Page 81)
Practice 1
Exercise 1 Distinguishing Between Simple and Compound Sentences
1. compound
2. simple
3. simple
4. compound
5. compound
6. simple
7. compound
8. simple
9. compound
10. simple

Exercise 2 Identifying the Structure of Sentences
1. 3
2. 1
3. 2
4. 2
5. 1
6. 4
7. 1
8. 3
9. 1
10. 4

21.1 Sentences Classified by Structure and Function (The Four Structures of Sentences) (Page 82)
Practice 2
Exercise 1 Identifying the Structure of Sentences
1. simple
2. complex
3. complex
4. compound
5. simple
6. compound-complex
7. complex
8. simple
9. compound
10. compound-complex

Exercise 2 Writing Sentences with Different Structures
Sample sentences are given.
1. The dog ate my homework.
2. I wanted to learn how to do the tango, and Pedro offered to teach me.
3. Because Carol, my cousin who lives in New York, introduced Norma to Carl, she has been invited to their wedding.
4. I hid the key that you gave me under the greenish rock, so you should be able to find it there.
5. Mares eat oats.
6. The artist paints with oil on canvas, and he also sculpts in marble.
7. Mr. Johnson, the teacher who tutors me on Wednesdays, brought his puppets to school today.

8. Salads, as you probably already know, taste better with seasoning, but the only seasonings we have right now are salt and pepper.
9. Little lambs eat ivy.
10. Maria will visit her grandmother, who is active in the local schools, and they will take a class on a field trip.

21.1 Sentences Classified by Structure and Function (The Four Functions of Sentences) (Page 83)
Practice 1
Exercise 1   Identifying the Function of Sentences
1. imperative
2. interrogative
3. interrogative
4. declarative
5. imperative
6. exclamatory
7. imperative
8. declarative
9. declarative
10. interrogative

Exercise 2   Choosing the Correct End Mark by Function
1. (!)
2. (?)
3. (!)
4. (.)
5. (.)
6. (?)
7. (!)
8. (.)
9. (.)
10. (.)

21.1 Sentences Classified by Structure and Function (The Four Functions of Sentences) (Page 84)
Practice 2
Exercise 1   Writing Sentences with Different Structures and Functions
1. imperative (.)
2. declarative (.)
3. exclamatory (!)
4. declarative (.)
5. interrogative (?)
6. interrogative (?)
7. interrogative (?)
8. exclamatory (!)
9. imperative (.)
10. declarative (.)
11. interrogative (?)
12. imperative (!)
13. declarative (.)
14. declarative (.)
15. exclamatory (!)
16. interrogative (?)
17. declarative (.)
18. exclamatory (!)
19. imperative (!)
20. interrogative (?)

Writing Application
Writing Sentences with Different Structures and Functions
Sample sentences are given.
1. That truck is swerving!
2. Shut the door.

3. The sky is dull gray, and snow is starting to fall.
4. Are you coming home tomorrow?
5. Is the store open tonight, and do they have the book I want?

21.2   Sentence Combining (Page 85)
Practice 1
Exercise 1   Combining Sentences
Sample sentences are given.
1. Broadway musicals with large casts and elaborate production numbers are often difficult for amateurs.
2. My favorite breakfast is pancakes and bacon.
3. That is a quality magazine intended for people interested in science.
4. Just by following the directions, Timmy made the birdhouse himself.
5. Today's editorial about toxic waste was quite alarming.
6. Because he works hard in practice and is a very gifted athlete, he is the best player on the team.
7. The band members wanted to leave the stage, but the crowd implored them to continue, so they played another song.
8. After Gerri's children were grown, she went back to school and became a physical therapist.
9. Though Shawn never does well on standardized tests, he gets good grades in school because he works very hard.
10. Because the ice storm lasted for two days and the roads were treacherous, school was canceled for a week.

21.2   Sentence Combining (Page 86)
Practice 2
Exercise 1   Combining Sentences
Sample sentences are given.
1. For seven days, snow fell steadily upon the Acadian Forest.
2. When Jason lost his grip on the rope tow, he slid all the way to the bottom of the hill.
3. Eating balanced meals and exercising regularly are essential for good health.
4. Thomas Jefferson, the third President of the United States, was a key writer of the Declaration of Independence.
5. Horses communicate with each other by snorting and making sounds of different pitch.
6. Reading magazines that give several different viewpoints on a subject is a good way to stay informed.
7. Although a walrus looks clumsy and appears sluggish, it is quite agile when it swims.
8. As the temperature rose, the snowbanks glistened in the sun, and tiny beads of water trickled down the hill.
9. Miles away, we could hear Alan practicing his trumpet.
10. The Tower of London, built about nine hundred years ago, was originally a prison, but today it houses the crown jewels.

21.3   Varying Your Sentences (Expanding Short Sentences, Shortening Long Sentences) (Page 87)
Practice 1
Exercise 1   Adding Details to Short Sentences
Sample sentences are given.
1. Jody, a gifted student, speaks French fluently.

2. The guitarist broke a string in the middle of the band's first song.
3. Jane skied easily and swiftly to the bottom of the hill.
4. Senator Williams came to our school to speak about drug abuse.
5. The weary soldiers marched across the barren field.

Exercise 2   Shortening Long Sentences
A sample revision is given.

Although the doctors had not held out much hope for the surgery, the family remained optimistic throughout the long hours of the operation. They thought that if they wanted it badly enough surely things would work out. They were ecstatic when the surgeon appeared and reported that the operation had indeed been a success.

21.3   Varying Your Sentences (Expanding Short Sentences, Shortening Long Sentences) (Page 88)
Practice 2
Exercise 1   Adding Details
Sample sentences are given.
1. Some of the local residents use the service road at rush hour.
2. The newly discovered treasure aroused most people's curiosity.
3. A fresh coat of white paint brightened my room.
4. Mrs. Hamilton, a wealthy business woman, did her best to influence the town council.
5. Working deftly, the mechanic pried the flat tire from the wheel rim.

Exercise 2   Shortening Long Sentences
Sample sentences are given.
1. Many people laughed at Adam when he first set out to find an old Spanish galleon that had sunk in 1622. Yet within a year he had converted many a disbeliever, because in that short time he had found millions of dollars of submerged treasure.
2. The art of wood carving was perfected so early in history that few records have been preserved, except relics. For example, a recently excavated set of wood carver's tools prove that even before metal was used, people cut and decorated wood with tools of shell, bone, and flint.
3. When I finally saw the movie, I was glad that I read the book first. Important plot details and even some characters that made the story understandable were left out of the movie version.
4. She clutched the letter tightly, refusing to talk about it and refusing to show it to us. Tears streamed down her face and small sobs shook her. We did want to help her, but she was unreachable.
5. In the first few hours of torrential rain, flood waters began to rise, and many people left their homes in search of higher ground. However, most of them got stuck in traffic jams and had to wait out the crisis in their stalled automobiles.

21.3   Varying Your Sentences (Using Different Sentence Openers and Structures) (Page 89)
Practice 1
Exercise 1   Using Different Sentence Openers
Sample sentences are given.
1. For further information phone the box office.
2. Because they had never been camping before, the youngsters were especially excited about their trip.
3. After the game, can you join us for a pizza?
4. After dinner, Uncle John frequently dozes off.
5. To raise money for their trip, the band members will have a bake sale.

Exercise 2   Varying Sentence Structures
A sample revision is given.

Jeremy, who has loved animals all his life, wants to be a veterinarian. As a child, he had a whole menagerie of pets and took excellent care of them. Because he could never bear to see an animal suffer, he nursed several injured chipmunks and other small animals back to health. He has always been a good student, especially in math and science. After he graduates from high school this June, he plans to take pre-med courses at college this fall.

21.3   Varying Your Sentences (Using Different Sentence Openers and Structures) (Page 90)
Practice 2
Exercise 1   Using Different Sentence Openers
Sample sentences are given.
1. Endlessly, oceanographers have worked to study the habits of undersea animals.
2. When the phone began to ring, I lost my concentration.
3. Confused, the tourists stared at the timetable in the train station.
4. On television game shows, lucky contestants have won hundreds of thousands of dollars.
5. From the mouth of Mt. Etna erupted burning coals and boiling lava.
6. Running to answer the phone, Clarissa slipped on a magazine and twisted her ankle.
7. To be a good student and earn high grades, you must fulfill basic requirements.
8. Jagged and menacing, the mountain loomed above us.
9. If it does not meet safety standards, a building can be condemned.
10. However, my uncle would not play golf again.
11. At the concert, there was an audience of nearly ten thousand.
12. Kurt was tired and hungry after skiing all day.
13. Because she wanted the house to look cheerful, Cindy used many colors.
14. Albert will be late for dinner because he has to work overtime.
15. Maggie generously donates four hours a week tutoring poor readers.

Exercise 2   Varying Sentence Structure
A sample revision is given.

Aunt Helen's heirs were an eager group. Sitting around the giant parlor table, eight men and nine women waited anxiously for the lawyer's arrival. Although they had never met before this evening, they exchanged enthusiastic talk of "our dear, departed Helen." Regularly, each pair of eyes glanced toward the parlor doorway. The attorney finally appeared, carrying an impressive-looking document. The heirs suddenly fell silent, and the atmosphere became tense.

21.3 Varying Your Sentences (Using Special Sentence Patterns) (Page 91)

Practice 1

Exercise 1 Using Parallelism

1. Sewing, painting, and cooking gourmet meals are Alice's hobbies.
2. Hank explained his idea clearly, completely, and patiently.
3. Jamie agreed to work at nights and on weekends but not on holidays.
4. Clapping hands, stamping feet, and whistling loudly, the audience demanded an encore.
5. Fran likes to swim and to sail, but not to play baseball.

Exercise 2 Using Special Sentence Patterns

Sample sentences are given.

1. Donna searched through her purse, in her desk, and under the bed.
2. Philosophy is a difficult subject; German is almost as difficult.
3. John liked vacations at the beach; his sister liked vacations in the mountains.
4. She tried her best friends. She tried mere acquaintances. She tried complete strangers. No one would help.

21.3 Varying Your Sentences (Using Special Sentence Patterns) (Page 92)

Practice 2

Exercise 1 Using Patterns for Emphasis

1. parallelism: emphasizes two positive effects of education
2. pattern broken: emphasizes listeners' place in past
3. parallelism
4. pattern broken
5. parallelism

Writing Application

Writing Varied Sentences

A sample revision is given.

(1) Every year, millions of people are injured in their own homes.(2) Any area of your home can possess a safety hazard,(3) and no one can afford to overlook possible hazards.(4) Inspect all rooms of your house; (5) then eliminate all of the dangers you recognize.

(6) You must take special care to ensure safety in your kitchen, where too many home accidents happen. Make sure that electrical appliances are away from the sink, and that their cords cannot slip into the water. In addition, because kitchen fires can occur all too quickly and spread rapidly, keep a fire extinguisher in the room.

(7) You can also help prevent accidents in bathrooms (8) by inspecting them for potential hazards. Remember to keep pills and medicines out of the reach of children and to label all medicines to avoid dangerous mix-ups. Because slippery floors can cause falls, cover the floor with a carpet or bath rug that cannot slip. Most importantly, never place a telephone near the tub or sink.(9) The phone cord can become wet (10) and cause an electrical shock.

21.4 Fragments (Page 93)

Practice 1

Exercise 1 Identifying Sentence Fragments

1. fragment
2. fragment
3. sentence
4. fragment
5. fragment
6. sentence
7. fragment
8. fragment
9. fragment
10. sentence

Exercise 2 Correcting Sentence Fragments

Sample sentences are given.

1. It can be a mistake to believe everything you hear.
2. What can we buy a person who has everything?
4. The woman on the speaker's platform will nominate the presidential candidate.
5. Pete plays the piano with enthusiasm and energy.
7. Heaping platters and bowls of delicacies filled the buffet table.
8. That ballerina gave one of the most exciting performances I have ever seen.
9. Driving along the Pacific Coast was a thrilling experience.

21.4 Fragments (Page 94)

Practice 2

Exercise 1 Correcting Fragments

Sample sentences are given.

1. (series fragment) The children laughed, shouted, and romped.
2. (clause fragment) While she was running after the bus, she slipped.
3. (phrase fragment) Frequent loud interruptions make studying difficult.
4. (phrase fragment) Petrified dinosaur bones were found in the cave.
5. (clause fragment) We found a pond where cattails and reeds grew high.
6. (series fragment) He was sometimes downcast, depressed, or just unhappy.
7. (series fragment) Leopards are skilled at watching, stalking, and pouncing.
8. (clause fragment) He spoke words which recalled a time of carefree days.
9. (phrase fragment) This house must have been abandoned by someone.
10. (clause fragment) She plans to ignore whomever he invites.
11. (series fragment) I spent the afternoon writing letters, reading poetry, and listening to music.
12. (clause fragment) After he took the dog to the vet, he had to get some medicine.
13. (phrase fragment) Look at all those colorful and fragrant bouquets!
14. (phrase fragment) A gallon of lavender paint should be enough for this room.
15. (clause fragment) When dinosaurs ruled the earth, there were no humans.

21.4 Run-ons (Page 95)

Practice 1

Exercise 1 Identifying Run-ons

1. sentence
2. run-on
3. run-on
4. run-on
5. sentence

6. run-on
7. run-on
8. run-on
9. run-on
10. sentence

Exercise 2   Correcting Run-ons
Sample sentences are given.

2. The beach is pleasant during the week, but it is crowded on weekends.
3. The play was excellent although the cast was only mediocre.
4. Jason, my brother, wants to become a teacher.
6. You'll love that book because it's a mystery.
7. Ben applied for a variety of jobs, but everyone said he was overqualified.
8. Although in general I hate exercise, swimming is one thing I do enjoy.
9. When Juliette fell off the swing, she broke her wrist.

21.4   Run-ons (Page 96)
Practice 2
Exercise 1   Correcting Run-ons
Sample sentences are given.

1. Every year at this time the snow melts and the creek flows. In six months, however, it will be dry.
2. They bought an old mill; eventually, they were able to make it into a unique and beautiful home.
3. Jody dropped out of school in her junior year. She received a diploma years later.
4. Days turned into years, and the years seemed endless.
5. Will he leave his job and its security to try his luck at farming? It seems unlikely.
6. Sir Winston Churchill, a brilliant man, was the English Prime Minister during World War II.
7. Catherine II, a Russian empress, was called Catherine the Great.
8. Marty was afraid of bees since he had a severe allergic reaction to their stings.
9. In the spring cardinals and an occasional blue jay come to our bird feeder.
10. Rapunzel, whose name means "lettuce," let her long hair fall to the ground.

Writing Application
Correcting Fragments and Run-ons
A sample revision is given.

The storm had suddenly come upon them, surprising the two boys. Their jackets offered little protection from the rain. Jack led the way to the cabin, which was almost hidden by the trees. Within minutes they stood on the porch. The door opened, and they entered, throwing their backpacks onto the floor. Because the room was cold and damp, they shivered.

They could not see in the darkness, so Jack felt for the lantern, which he knew was on the table. If they had started out earlier, they would not have been caught in the rain or have been unable to reach the cabin before night. A warm fire and supper would certainly help.

When the lantern was lit, Jack gasped. The doors to the cupboard, which his father had filled, were opened, revealing empty shelves. Walking back onto the porch, he stared at the empty place where wood had been stacked. Obviously, someone had been warm and well-fed at their expense. Phil, he knew, would accept his apology, but that was a small consolation for

the uncomfortable night they would have. At least a lesson had been learned. Next time he would prepare for any emergency that might occur.

21.4   Misplaced and Dangling Modifiers (Recognizing Misplaced and Dangling Modifiers) (Page 97)
Practice 1
Exercise 1   Recognizing Misplaced Modifiers
1. with a cry of dismay
2. a dozen times
3. (no misplaced modifier)
4. with deep emotion in his voice
5. with squeals of delight
6. (no misplaced modifier)
7. from the upstairs window
8. in the thrift shop
9. in the principal's office
10. with a secret compartment

Exercise 2   Recognizing Dangling Modifiers
1. Flying low over the treetops
2. Shucking oysters at Caro's Clam Bar
3. (no dangling modifier)
4. Clearing the bar at seventeen feet
5. practicing last week
6. motoring through Vermont
7. Cheered by a taste of success
8. (no dangling modifier)
9. Peering through the keyhole
10. Arriving at the theater an hour late

21.4   Misplaced and Dangling Modifiers (Recognizing Misplaced and Dangling Modifiers) (Page 98)
Practice 2
Exercise 1   Identifying Misplaced and Dangling Modifiers
1. dangling
2. correct
3. misplaced
4. dangling
5. misplaced
6. correct
7. dangling
8. correct
9. misplaced
10. misplaced
11. misplaced
12. dangling
13. correct
14. misplaced
15. misplaced
16. misplaced
17. correct
18. misplaced
19. misplaced
20. correct

Exercise 2   Identifying Misplaced and Dangling Modifiers in Paragraphs
(1) Whistling cheerfully, the bikes were fixed in no time. (2) Then Bob and Marie rode their bikes to the movies that they had just repaired. (3) Waiting in line to get their tickets, it started to rain. (4) Marie waited near the entrance while Bob got the tickets under someone else's big umbrella. (5) Paying with a twenty-dollar bill, the ticket seller handed the tickets to Bob. (6) Getting into the lobby, the line for popcorn was very long. (7) Skipping the popcorn, the seats they found were

good ones. (8) A tall man sat right in front of them coming in late. (9) Twisting into an uncomfortable position, the screen was visible. (10) Getting on their bikes after the movie, the ride home was pleasant and invigorating.

1. dangling
2. misplaced
3. dangling
4. misplaced
5. dangling
6. dangling
7. dangling
8. misplaced
9. dangling
10. dangling

21.4 Misplaced and Dangling Modifiers (Correcting Misplaced Modifiers) (Page 99)

Practice 1

Exercise 1   Recognizing Misplaced Modifiers

1. at 8:00 P.M.
2. with a duck in his mouth
3. using his high-speed camera
4. in an angry voice
5. Cheering wildly
6. in the middle of our trip
7. with small bones in them
8. strolling around the village green
9. with a jelly jar
10. on the enclosed postcard

Exercise 2   Correcting Misplaced Modifiers

Sample corrected sentences are given.

1. Tonight at 8:00 P.M., WCTV presents a special program for viewers interested in changing to new careers.
2. With a duck in his mouth, the retriever swam to his master on shore.
3. Using his high-speed camera, Dad took a picture of a hummingbird.
4. In an angry voice, the customer demanded an explanation.
5. Cheering wildly, the fans greeted the home team.
6. Mom remembered in the middle of our trip that she had not turned the oven off.
7. Please don't give scraps with small bones in them to the dogs.
8. Strolling around the village green, we saw many fine old houses.
9. With a jelly jar, David waited patiently for a bee to come along.
10. Let us know on the enclosed postcard if you plan to make the trip.

21.4 Misplaced and Dangling Modifiers (Correcting Misplaced Modifiers) (Page 100)

Practice 2

Exercise 1   Recognizing and Correcting Misplaced Modifiers

1. The watch that broke was his favorite gift.

2. Lionel sold his bicycle with four speeds to a friend.

3. Brandishing a net in his upraised hand, the zoo keeper captured the escaped iguana.

4. Noticeably trembling, the boys ran from the abandoned house.

5. Brenda put oranges that came from Florida into the punch.

6. Shaking in panic, the deer bounded into the woods.

7. Jed ordered a steak cooked rare and a salad.

8. The fish that we caught were photographed at the pier.

9. The child in a red dress sat perched on top of the counter.

10. We waved farewell to our happy guests leaving the party after midnight.

11. Using red thread, Jill sewed buttons on the jacket.

12. The man wearing a green beret served hot dogs.

13. Passing the building, we saw the graffiti.

14. We saw a herd of cattle grazing peacefully.

15. The women posed by the old building crumbling with decay.

21.4 Misplaced and Dangling Modifiers (Correcting Dangling Modifiers) (Page 101)

Practice 1

Exercise 1   Recognizing Dangling Modifiers

1. Strolling through the narrow streets
2. Searching for the missing contract
3. Doing my homework
4. Before parking in that lot
5. while watching the fireworks display
6. Having sent the suspect to jail
7. approaching the summit of the mountain
8. While farming in Texas
9. Entering the dining room
10. Born into an immigrant family

Exercise 2   Correcting Dangling Modifiers

Sample sentences are given.

1. Strolling through the narrow streets, we found the native quarter picturesque.
2. Searching for the missing contract, the author turned the whole house upside down.
3. Doing my homework, I found the radio next door distracting.

4. Before parking in that lot, a person must purchase a sticker.
5. His wallet was stolen while he watched the fireworks display.
6. Having sent the suspect to jail, the sheriff thought the case was closed.
7. Vegetation became sparse as we approached the summit of the mountain.
8. While farming in Texas, the Gants discovered oil.
9. Entering the dining room, we exclaimed at how appetizing the roast turkey looked.
10. Born into a immigrant family, the young woman thought the White House was an impossible goal for her.

21.4 Misplaced and Dangling Modifiers (Correcting Dangling Modifiers) (Page 102)
Practice 2
Exercise 1 Recognizing and Correcting Dangling Modifiers
Sample sentences are given.

1. Researching that topic, we found three new ideas.

2. Picketing for improved working conditions, the workers continued the strike.

3. Searching for the missing diamond ring, he explored every possible nook and cranny.

4. Swallowing the bitter medicine, she avoided a cold.

5. Lost in a daydream, he failed to hear my words.

6. When Jeremy was nine months old, his father decided that the family should move to Alaska.

7. Driving into Santa Fe, she thought the desert looked like the moon.

8. When he won the race, the losers applauded loudly.

9. When the boys misbehaved, their parents complained.

10. Returning the wallet, she received a reward from the owner.

Writing Application
Correcting Misplaced and Dangling Modifiers
A sample revised paragraph is given.

(1) Sue is a successful architect and interior designer whose custom-built homes stagger the imagination. (2) Priced beyond what the average person can afford, her houses can be seen in many expensive neighborhoods. (3) The front of one house is made entirely of glass.
(4) Potted flowers grow on an elaborate balcony extending outward from the second floor. (5) Within the center of the house, a huge tropical aquarium with exotic fish rests on a marble floor. (6) A wrought iron staircase connecting the first and second stories winds its way around the aquarium. (7) Each room is softly lit by fluorescent lights recessed in the ceiling. (8) Turning a dial in any room, you can hear your favorite kind of music. (9) In the winter, fireplaces provide warmth; in the summer, cool air is circulated by fans. (10) If you have enough money, the house can become yours.

21.4 Faulty Parallelism (Recognizing Faulty Parallelism) (Page 103)
Practice 1
Exercise 1 Recognizing Parallel Ideas
1. cooking, sewing, painting
2. by eating less, by exercising more
3. for originality, for aptness
4. brief, colorful
5. to be true to himself, to value his friends, to keep his own counsel
6. groceries, children's clothing, prescription drugs
7. cutting costs, increasing productivity, improving distribution
8. taking careful notes, reviewing the material daily
9. who could have committed so bizarre a crime, what the motive might have been.
10. imaginative, patient, sympathetic

Exercise 2 Distinguishing Between Correct and Faulty Parallelism
1. F
2. C
3. F
4. C
5. F
6. F
7. F
8. F
9. F
10. C

21.4 Faulty Parallelism (Recognizing Faulty Parallelism) (Page 104)
Practice 2
Exercise 1 Recognizing Parallel Ideas
1. Good speech must be audible, logical, and have clarity. faulty parallelism
2. My paper received a high grade for originality and for neatness. correct parallelism
3. Claire likes hiking for great distances and to climb mountains. faulty parallelism
4. You can adjust the swing by lengthening one rope or you can shorten the other rope. faulty parallelism
5. The insurance agent sold my parents a homeowners' policy and a life insurance policy. correct parallelism
6. The clock is compact, silent, and runs accurately. faulty parallelism
7. The dolls were Russian, Italian, and one from England. faulty parallelism
8. We interviewed the principal, a teacher, and with the nurse. faulty parallelism
9. The football sailed across the yard, over the fence, and into our neighbor's prize dahlias. correct parallelism
10. In India we saw neither the Ganges nor went to Calcutta. faulty parallelism

11. Riding a bike is not only good for your health but it is also fun. faulty parallelism
12. My choices were either to do a dance or singing. faulty parallelism
13. After waiting for hours, pacing the floor, and biting her nails, Sandy was frantic with worry. correct parallelism
14. Judy wanted an after-school job rather than to ask for a raise in her allowance. faulty parallelism
15. Chuck sorted the books neatly and with great efficiency into piles. faulty parallelism
16. To make a good stew, marinate the meat, add plenty of vegetables, and simmer slowly. correct parallelism
17. Joan took classes in history, science, and how to use computers. faulty parallelism
18. The garden includes irises, roses, and it also has lilies. faulty parallelism
19. Barbara is well liked because she is friendly, helpful, and she has a lot of confidence. faulty parallelism
20. You can learn to dance if you sign up for a class, if you attend the class, and if you practice faithfully. correct parallelism

21.4 Faulty Parallelism (Correcting Faulty Parallelism) (Page 105)

Practice 1

Exercise 1 Identifying Faulty Parallelism
1. for being colorless, that he was overly cautious
2. cooking, to clean up afterward
3. who will help in the stockroom, to make deliveries
4. Reading the book, to write a report on it
5. played with great feeling, occasionally hitting some sour notes
6. hiking, to camp out
7. by cutting costs, sell more widgets
8. receiving letters, to write them
9. typing, filing, to do simple bookkeeping
10. on flying, to take a train

Exercise 2 Correcting Faulty Parallelism
Sample sentences are given.
1. The candidate was criticized for being colorless and overly cautious.
2. Paul likes cooking but dislikes cleaning up afterward.
3. Mr. Asforis needs someone who will help in the stockroom and make deliveries.
4. Reading the book was fun, but writing a report on it was hard.
5. The pianist played with great feeling but occasionally hit some sour notes.
6. The scouts especially liked hiking and camping out.
7. The company can become more profitable by cutting costs or by selling more widgets.
8. Nick enjoyed receiving letters but not writing them.
9. The main duties of the job are typing, filing, and doing simple bookkeeping.
10. If you plan on taking a plane or train this weekend, you can expect crowds.

21.4 Faulty Parallelism (Correcting Faulty Parallelism) (Page 106)

Practice 2

Exercise 1 Correcting Faulty Parallelism of Words, Phrases, and Clauses
Sample sentences are given.
1. We were happy to hear the good news and to be the first to congratulate them.
2. The florist arranged the flowers, placing a few ferns here and there and then adding a ribbon.
3. Searching for buried treasure was fun, but finding real pirate booty was astounding.
4. We talked to one another, not about one another.
5. By thinking clearly and being patient, you can unscramble an anagram.
6. The man and his wife were served soup that offended them, a main course that sickened them, and a dessert that nauseated them.
7. My desires were to visit the museum and see everything in the displays.
8. These plants need water and attention.
9. In the pond were small beetles darting to and fro, pollywogs wriggling, and snails climbing up stems.
10. He agreed to participate in the talent show but refused to sing without a microphone.

Writing Application

Writing Sentences with Parallel Structures
1. Tomorrow I will go to the supermarket and to the book store.
2. In the morning I focus on getting ready and leaving the house.
3. You can choose either to live in the country or to live in the city.
4. What you know and what I know are quite different.
5. Listening to the radio is often more interesting than watching television.

22.1 Verb Tenses (The Six Tenses of Verbs, The Four Principal Parts of Verbs) (Page 107)

Practice 1

Exercise 1 Recognizing Tenses and Forms of Verbs
1. followed, past
2. were pulling, past progressive
3. have tried, present perfect
4. will have been visiting, future perfect progressive
5. carries, present
6. will release, future
7. will be waiting, future progressive
8. had planned, past perfect
9. had been investigating, past perfect progressive
10. will have finished, future perfect

Exercise 2 Identifying Principal Parts
1. followed, past
2. pulling, present participle
3. tried, past participle
4. visiting, present participle
5. carries, present
6. release, present
7. waiting, present participle
8. planned, past participle
9. investigating, present participle
10. finished, past participle

22.1 Verb Tenses (The Six Tenses of Verbs, The Four Principal Parts of Verbs) (Page 108)

Practice 2

Exercise 1 Recognizing Basic, Progressive, and Emphatic Forms

1. progressive
2. basic
3. basic
4. progressive
5. progressive
6. basic
7. basic
8. basic
9. basic
10. progressive
11. basic
12. progressive
13. progressive
14. basic
15. progressive
16. progressive
17. basic
18. progressive
19. basic
20. basic

Exercise 2 Recognizing the Six Tenses

1. present progressive
2. past perfect
3. future
4. past progressive
5. past perfect progressive
6. present
7. future
8. past perfect
9. past
10. future perfect progressive
11. present
12. past perfect progressive
13. future progressive
14. present perfect
15. present perfect progressive
16. present progressive
17. past
18. present progressive
19. future
20. past

Exercise 3 Recognizing Principal Parts

1. present participle
2. past participle
3. present
4. present participle
5. present participle
6. present
7. present
8. past participle
9. past
10. present participle
11. present
12. present participle
13. present participle
14. past participle
15. present participle
16. present participle
17. past
18. present participle

19. present
20. past

22.1 Verb Tenses (Regular and Irregular Verbs) (Page 109)

Practice 1

Exercise 1 Writing the Principal Parts of Irregular Verbs

1. begin, began, (have) begun
2. draw, drawing, (have) drawn
3. freezing, froze, (have) frozen
4. run, running, ran
5. put, putting, (have) put
6. think, thought, (have) thought
7. fall, falling, fell
8. catching, caught, (have) caught
9. bind, binding, (have) bound
10. speak, spoke, (have) spoken

Exercise 2 Recognizing Principal Parts of Verbs

1. burst
2. spread
3. thrust
4. dived
5. broken

22.1 Verb Tenses (Regular and Irregular Verbs) (Page 110)

Practice 2

Exercise 1 Learning the Principal Parts of Irregular Verbs

1. fighting, fought, fought
2. letting, let, let
3. splitting, split, split
4. shrinking, shrank, shrunk
5. arising, arose, arisen
6. catching, caught, caught
7. selling, sold, sold
8. slaying, slew, slain
9. costing, cost, cost
10. hanging, hung, hung
11. sitting, sat, sat
12. freezing, froze, frozen
13. swimming, swam, swum
14. drawing, drew, drawn
15. sticking, stuck, stuck
16. teaching, taught, taught
17. singing, sang, sung
18. winning, won, won
19. tearing, tore, tore
20. laying, laid, laid

Exercise 2 Recognizing Principal Parts in Sentences

1. knew
2. paid
3. taught
4. blew
5. chose
6. laid
7. wore
8. led
9. tore
10. stolen

Exercise 3 Choosing Between the Past and Past Participle

1. begun
2. grew
3. gave

4. saw
5. lain
6. came
7. arose
8. knew
9. come
10. went

22.1 Verb Tenses (Conjugating the Tenses) (Page 111)
Practice 1
Exercise 1 Conjugating Verbs
1. I try, I tried, I will try, I have tried, I had tried, I will have tried, I am trying, I was trying, I will be trying
2. he finds, he found, he will find, he has found, he had found, he will have found, he is finding, he was finding, he will be finding.
3. we speak, we spoke, we will speak, we have spoken, we had spoken, we will have spoken, we are speaking, we were speaking, we will be speaking
4. they run, they ran, they will run, they have run, they had run, they will have run, they are running, they were running, they will be running

Exercise 2 Supplying the Correct Verb Form
1. will have tested
2. froze
3. has wound
4. did prepare
5. had promised

22.1 Verb Tenses (Conjugating the Tenses) (Page 112)
Practice 2
Exercise 1 Conjugating the Basic Forms of Verbs
1. climb (conjugated with *we*)
   we climb
   we climbed
   we will climb
   we have climbed
   we had climbed
   we will have climbed
2. say (conjugated with *they*)
   they say
   they said
   they will say
   they have said
   they had said
   they will have said

Exercise 2 Conjugating the Progressive Forms of Verbs
1. talk (conjugated with *he*)
   he is talking
   he was talking
   he will be talking
   he has been talking
   he had been talking
   he will have been talking
2. sing (conjugated with *we*)
   we are singing
   we were singing
   we will be singing
   we have been singing
   we had been singing
   we will have been singing

Exercise 3 Conjugating the Emphatic Forms of Verbs
1. own (conjugated with *she*)

she does own
she did own
2. sell (conjugated with *they*)
   they do sell
   they did sell

22.1 Expressing Time Through Tense (Uses of Tense in Present Time) (Page 113)
Practice 1
Exercise 1 Identifying the Uses of Tense in Present Time
1. emphasizing a statement
2. constant action
3. recurring action
4. present condition
5. present action
6. continuing action
7. constant action
8. denying an assertion
9. recurring action
10. continuing action

Exercise 2 Using Present Tense Forms in Sentences
Sample verb forms are given.
1. is milking
2. is making
3. are moving
4. taste
5. has
6. am reading
7. attracts
8. is forming
9. want
10. is studying

22.1 Expressing Time Through Tense (Uses of Tense in Present Time) (Page 114)
Practice 2
Exercise 1 Identifying the Uses of Tense in Present Time
1. short continuing action
2. present action
3. present action
4. regularly occurring action
5. regularly occurring action
6. present condition
7. long continuing action
8. present condition
9. regularly occurring action
10. emphasizing a statement
11. continuing action
12. present condition
13. denying a contrary assertion
14. regularly occurring condition
15. regularly occurring action
16. short continuing action
17. constant action
18. constant condition
19. continuing condition
20. emphasizing a statement

22.1 Expressing Time Through Tense (Uses of Tense in Past Time) (Page 115)
Practice 1
Exercise 1 Identifying the Uses of Tenses in Past Time
1. completed before another past event
2. continuous past event
3. indefinite past time
4. indefinite past time

5. indefinite past time

Exercise 2 Using Tenses in Past Time
1. had finished
2. has been
3. had left
4. opened
5. was working
6. did like
7. has been gathering
8. applied
9. was waiting
10. have been working

22.1 Expressing Time Through Tense (Uses of Tense in Past Time) (Page 116)
Practice 2
Exercise 1 Using the Past, the Present Perfect, and the Past Perfect
1. had read
2. pulled
3. has been working
4. brought
5. had lost
6. rushed
7. had seen
8. developed
9. granted
10. was working

Exercise 2 Identifying the Uses of Tense in Past Time
1. completed action (indefinite time)
2. completed action
3. action continuing to the present
4. action completed before another past action
5. completed action (indefinite time)

22.1 Expressing Time through Tense (Uses of Tense in Future Time) (Page 117)
Practice 1
Exercise 1 Identifying the Uses of Tenses in Future Time
1. continuing future event
2. future event before another future event
3. continuing future event
4. future event
5. continuing future event before another
6. continuing future event
7. future event before another future event
8. continuing future event before another
9. continuing future event
10. future event before another future event

Exercise 2 Using Tenses in Future Time
1. will be catering
2. will be playing
3. will have been sitting
4. will be arriving
5. will invite
6. will have papered
7. will be taking
8. will have performed
9. will be playing
10. will return

22.1 Expressing Time through Tense (Uses of Tense in Future Time) (Page 118)
Practice 2
Exercise 1 Identifying the Uses of Tense in Future Time
1. continuing future action

2. future action
3. continuing future action completed before another
4. future condition completed before another
5. future action
6. future condition
7. continuing future action
8. future action completed before another
9. continuing future action completed before another
10. future action

Exercise 2 Using Tense in Future Time
1. will arrive
2. will have been traveling
3. will have made
4. will be visiting
5. will open

22.1 Expressing Time Through Tense (Shifts in Tense, Modifiers That Help Clarify Tense) (Page 119)
Practice 1
Exercise 1 Recognizing and Correcting Unnecessary Shifts in Tense
Sample sentences are given.
1. We never watch television until we finish our homework.
2. My brother will study law when he graduates from college.
3. Phil starts jogging before he warms up.
4. We found the library book right where we had left it.
5. correct

Exercise 2 Using Modifiers to Help Clarify Tense
Sample modifiers are given.
1. next week
2. all afternoon
3. After years of practice
4. already
5. tomorrow

22.1 Expressing Time Through Tense (Shifts in Tense, Modifiers That Help Clarify Tense) (Page 120)
Practice 2
Exercise 1 Avoiding Unnecessary Shifts in Tense
Incorrect word in parentheses.
1. (tells) told
2. (arrive) arrived
3. (is) was
4. (see) saw
5. (find) found
6. (visit) visited
7. (left) leaves
8. (leaves) left
9. (is) was
10. (stops) stopped
11. (came) comes
12. (will have been getting) will be getting
13. (are) were
14. (go) went
15. (achieves) achieved

22.2 Active and Passive Voice (Differences Between Active and Passive Verbs, The Forms of Passive Verbs) (Page 121)
Practice 1
Exercise 1 Distinguishing Between the Active and Passive Voice
1. passive

2. passive
3. active
4. passive
5. passive
6. active
7. passive
8. active
9. active
10. passive

Exercise 2   Forming Tenses of Passive Verbs

1. you are found, you were found, you will be found, you have been found, you had been found, you will have been found
2. it is made, it was made, it will be made, it has been made, it had been made, it will have been made
3. he is seen, he was seen, he will be seen, he has been seen, he had been seen, he will have been seen
4. they are liked, they were liked, they will be liked, they have been liked, they had been liked, they will have been liked

22.2   Active and Passive Voice (Differences Between Active and Passive Verbs, The Forms of Passive Verbs) (Page 122)

Practice 2

Exercise 1   Distinguishing Between the Active and Passive Voice

Identify each verb as *active* or *passive*.

1. passive
2. passive
3. active
4. active
5. passive
6. passive
7. active
8. passive
9. active
10. passive
11. passive
12. active
13. active
14. passive
15. active

Exercise 2   Forming the Tenses of Passive Verbs

1. give (with *we*)
   we are given
   we were given
   we will be given
   we have been given
   we had been given
   we will have been given
   we are being given
   we were being given
2. tell (with *they*)
   they are told
   they were told
   they will be told
   they have been told
   they had been told
   they will have been told
   they are being told
   they were being told

22.2   Active and Passive Voice (Using Voice Correctly) (Page 123)

Practice 1

Exercise 1   Distinguishing Between Appropriate and Unnecessary Uses of Passive Voice

1. U
2. A
3. U
4. U
5. A
6. U
7. A
8. U
9. U
10. U

Exercise 2   Using the Active Voice

Sample sentences are given.

1. The crowd gave a roar.
3. Lauren answered the phone.
4. A friend of mine won the blue ribbon.
6. Dad cooked dinner tonight.
8. The orchestra and chorus presented a concert.
9. The children were flying a kite.
10. Paul Revere announced the arrival of the British troops.

22.2   Active and Passive Voice (Using Voice Correctly) (Page 124)

Practice 2

Exercise 1   Correcting Unnecessary Use of the Passive Voice

A sample paragraph is given.

After over a century of use, many people still regard aspirin as a "wonder drug." Felix Hoffman, a German chemist, first developed aspirin, acetylsalicylic acid, as a painkiller in 1893. His father, who was suffering from rheumatism, asked him to develop a pain-reliever that would not irritate the stomach. Though the formula worked, scientists could not tell how it worked. Since its introduction, many people have used aspirin successfully to reduce fever, pain, and inflammation. Not long ago, researchers uncovered a new use for aspirin. The one major drawback of aspirin has always been its tendency to cause intestinal bleeding. Scientists have now turned this drawback into an advantage. They have discovered that this quality of aspirin may prevent blood clots that often lead to heart attacks and strokes. This is welcome news to the aspirin industry.

Writing Application

Using the Active and Passive Voice in Writing

Student descriptions should illustrate the correct use of the active and passive voice.

23.1   The Cases of Pronouns (The Three Cases) (Page 125)

Practice 1

Exercise 1   Identifying Case

1. objective
2. possessive
3. possessive
4. objective
5. possessive
6. nominative
7. possessive
8. objective
9. possessive
10. objective

Exercise 2 Identifying Pronoun Case and Use

1. objective, IO
2. nominative, S
3. objective, OP
4. possessive, O
5. nominative, S
6. objective, DO
7. possessive, O
8. nominative, PN
9. possessive, O
10. objective, OP

23.1 The Cases of Pronouns (The Three Cases) (Page 126)

Practice 2

Exercise 1 Identifying Case

1. nominative (subject)
2. objective (indirect object)
3. possessive (to show ownership)
4. objective (object of a preposition)
5. objective (object of a preposition)
6. nominative (predicate nominative)
7. possessive (to show ownership)
8. nominative (subject)
9. possessive (to show ownership)
10. objective (object of a preposition)
11. nominative (subject)
12. possessive (to show ownership)
13. objective (object of a preposition)
14. objective (indirect object)
15. objective (object of a preposition)
16. nominative (subject)
17. objective (object of a preposition)
18. nominative (subject)
19. objective (object of a preposition)
20. possessive (to show ownership)

Exercise 2 Identifying Pronouns and Pronoun Case

1. He, nominative, S
2. yours, possessive, O
3. her, objective, IO
4. her, possessive, O
5. it, objective, DO
6. she, nominative, PN
7. him, objective, OP
8. her, objective, IO
9. me, objective, DO
10. us, objective, OP

23.1 The Cases of Pronouns (The Nominative Case, The Objective Case) (Page 127)

Practice 1

Exercise 1 Identifying Pronouns in the Nominative Case

1. I, S
2. he, PN
3. they, PN
4. She, S
5. he, S

Exercise 2 Identifying Pronouns in the Objective Case

1. her, IO
2. him, OP
3. us, IO
4. me, IO
5. me, OP
6. them, IO
7. her, OP
8. him, DO
9. us, DO
10. us, IO

23.1 The Cases of Pronouns (The Nominative Case, The Objective Case) (Page 128)

Practice 2

Exercise 1 Identifying Pronouns in the Nominative Case

1. I (subject)
2. We (subject)
3. She (subject)
4. I (predicate nominative)
5. she (subject)
6. he (predicate nominative)
7. she (subject)
8. he (predicate nominative)
9. I (subject)
10. she (predicate nominative)

Exercise 2 Identifying Pronouns in the Objective Case

1. me (direct object)
2. her (object of a preposition)
3. me (object of a preposition)
4. them (object of a preposition)
5. him (object of an infinitive)
6. me (object of a preposition)
7. them (object of a participle)
8. him (object of an infinitive)
9. her (direct object)
10. me (object of a preposition)

23.1 The Cases of Pronouns (The Possessive Case) (Page 129)

Practice 1

Exercise 1 Using Pronouns in the Possessive Case

1. His
2. mine
3. our
4. yours
5. her
6. his
7. theirs
8. My
9. its
10. their

Exercise 2 More Work with Pronouns in the Possessive Case

Sample possessive pronouns are given.

1. yours
2. our
3. Your
4. mine
5. her
6. its
7. their
8. hers
9. his
10. their

23.1 The Cases of Pronouns (The Possessive Case) (Page 130)

Practice 2

Exercise 1 Using Pronouns in the Possessive Case

1. yours
2. its
3. It's
4. Their
5. his
6. ours

7. its
8. mine
9. hers
10. their
11. my
12. you're
13. They're
14. Our
15. theirs
16. my
17. Your
18. his
19. Her
20. it's

Exercise 2 Using All Three Cases
1. her
2. He, she
3. Their
4. hers
5. their
6. them
7. she
8. us
9. theirs
10. him, he

23.2 Special Problems with Pronouns (Page 131)
Practice 1
Exercise 1 Using *Who* and *Whom* Correctly
1. Whom
2. who
3. who
4. Who
5. who
6. Whom
7. Who
8. who
9. whom
10. whom

Exercise 2 Using Pronouns in Elliptical Clauses
Sample pronouns are given.
1. she
2. me
3. me
4. he
5. them

23.2 Special Problems with Pronouns (Page 132)
Practice 2
Exercise 1 Using *Who* and *Whom* in Questions and Clauses
1. whom
2. who
3. Who's
4. who
5. who
6. Whomever
7. whom
8. whoever
9. Who
10. whom

Exercise 2 More Work with *Who* and *Whom*
1. whom
2. Who
3. whom
4. whomever
5. who
6. who

7. Who's
8. who
9. Whoever
10. Whom
11. whom
12. who
13. whomever
14. whom
15. whoever
16. whom
17. who
18. Whose
19. who
20. whose

24.1 Subject and Verb Agreement (Number: Singular and Plural, Singular and Plural Subjects) (Page 133)
Practice 1
Exercise 1 Determining the Number of Words
1. plural
2. plural
3. both
4. plural
5. singular
6. both
7. plural
8. singular
9. singular
10. both

Exercise 2 Making Subjects and Verbs Agree
11. remains, S
12. are, P
13. are, P
14. needs, S
15. is, S

24.1 Subject and Verb Agreement (Number: Singular and Plural, Singular and Plural Subjects) (Page 134)
Practice 2
Exercise 1 Determining the Number of Nouns, Pronouns, and Verbs
1. plural
2. plural
3. singular
4. singular
5. singular
6. both
7. singular
8. plural
9. plural
10. singular
11. singular
12. singular
13. both
14. plural
15. both
16. singular
17. plural
18. singular
19. singular
20. both

Exercise 2 Making Subjects Agree with Their Verbs
1. were
2. begins
3. is
4. have

5. goes
6. clutches
7. has
8. were
9. is
10. have

Exercise 3   Making Separated Subjects and Verbs Agree
1. were
2. are
3. was
4. are
5. are
6. leave
7. has
8. are
9. has
10. are

24.1   Subject and Verb Agreement (Compound Subjects) (Page 135)
Practice 1
Exercise 1   Compound Subjects Joined by *Or* or *Nor*
1. hold
2. reads
3. promotes
4. has
5. is
6. come
7. plays
8. warm
9. supervise
10. is

Exercise 2   Compound Subjects Joined by *And*
1. have
2. was
3. have
4. match
5. was

24.1   Subject and Verb Agreement (Compound Subjects) (Page 136)
Practice 2
Exercise 1   Making Compound Subjects Agree with Their Verbs
1. collect
2. plans
3. wants
4. have
5. provide
6. is
7. are
8. are
9. phones
10. are
11. has
12. were
13. are
14. are
15. was
16. is
17. opens
18. is
19. sings
20. receives

Exercise 2   Using Compound Subjects in Sentences
Sample sentences are given.
1. Both my mother and my aunt are coming to visit.

2. Either blue paint or flowered wallpaper is an excellent choice.
3. Neither Kyle nor Tracy knows how to ski.
4. Peas, lima beans, and spinach are all green vegetables.
5. Knee pads and helmets are required for all skateboarders.

24.1   Subject and Verb Agreement (Confusing Subjects) (Page 137)
Practice 1
Exercise 1   Deciding on the Number of Subjects
1. P
2. P
3. S
4. S
5. S
6. S
7. S
8. S
9. P
10. S

Exercise 2   Choosing Verbs to Agree with Difficult Subjects
1. is
2. are
3. are
4. have
5. elects
6. are
7. was
8. has
9. blooms
10. is

24.1   Subject and Verb Agreement (Confusing Subjects) (Page 138)
Practice 2
Exercise 1   Making Confusing Subjects Agree with Their Verbs
1. is
2. There are
3. are
4. is
5. are
6. hasn't
7. was
8. are
9. is
10. was
11. has
12. have
13. is
14. has
15. have
16. are
17. was
18. Here's
19. were
20. have
21. are
22. lies
23. is
24. has
25. is

Exercise 2   More Work with Confusing Subjects
1. were
2. were

3. has
4. stand
5. ranks
6. has
7. has
8. is
9. disagree
10. are

24.2 Pronoun and Antecedent Agreement (Between Personal Pronouns and Antecedents) (Page 139)

Practice 1

Exercise 1   Choosing Personal Pronouns to Agree with Antecedents

1. their
2. its
3. his
4. her
5. her
6. their
7. his
8. their
9. its
10. her

Exercise 2   Pronoun-Antecedent Agreement in Sentences

1. he
2. it
3. her
4. their
5. his
6. he
7. they
8. your
9. her
10. his

24.2 Pronoun and Antecedent Agreement (Between Personal Pronouns and Antecedents) (Page 140)

Practice 2

Exercise 1   Making Personal Pronouns Agree with Their Antecedents

1. her
2. their
3. his
4. her
5. his
6. they
7. my
8. their
9. their
10. its
11. her
12. their
13. her
14. his
15. his
16. they
17. me
18. it
19. them
20. their

Exercise 2   Making Personal Pronouns Agree with Their Antecedents

1. If you need more information, I will be glad to send it.

2. I feel sorry for Fred, an only child, because he must be lonely.

3. If Dean doesn't understand the directions, he should ask the teacher to explain them to him.

4. correct

5. George writes his assignments in a notebook, a habit that helps him remember them.

24.2 Pronoun and Antecedent Agreement (With Indefinite Pronouns, With Reflexive Pronouns) (Page 141)

Practice 1

Exercise 1   Making Personal Pronouns Agree with Indefinite Pronouns

1. it
2. their
3. their
4. it
5. his
6. their
7. it
8. her
9. them
10. them

Exercise 2   Using Reflexive Pronouns Correctly

1. myself, me
2. ourselves, us
3. himself, him
4. yourself, you
5. myself, I

24.2 Pronoun and Antecedent Agreement (With Indefinite Pronouns, With Reflexive Pronouns) (Page 142)

Practice 2

Exercise 1   Making Personal Pronouns Agree with Indefinite Pronouns

1. their
2. her
3. their
4. their
5. her
6. his
7. their
8. their
9. their
10. her
11. his
12. her
13. their
14. his
15. their
16. her
17. their
18. their
19. their
20. her

Exercise 2   Using Reflexive Pronouns Correctly

1. Christine wants Bob and me to make a presentation.

2. I'm sure that the right actor for this part is you.

3. She is the person with the best chance for success.

4. The nurse thought he had hurt both himself and me.

5. Neither Ginger nor I was willing to go alone.

24.2 Pronoun and Antecedent Agreement (Four Special Problems in Pronoun Agreement) (Page 143)

Practice 1

Exercise 1 Solving Special Problems in Pronoun Agreement

1. entrants
2. Dad
3. the hamburgers
4. visitors
5. the scouts
6. passengers
7. the doctors
8. Bruce's
9. everyone's
10. the networks

Exercise 2 Correcting Special Problems in Pronoun Agreement

Sample sentences are given.

1. What information did you get when you called the hospital?
2. That platter looks pretty with the parsley around the food.
3. Instructors in that ballet school expect students to practice four hours every day.
4. Debbie assured Maureen that Maureen's report would be excellent.
5. Why do flight crews tell passengers to keep their seat belts loosely fastened?

24.2 Pronoun and Antecedent Agreement (Four Special Problems in Pronoun Agreement) (Page 144)

Practice 2

Exercise 1 Correcting Special Problems in Pronoun Agreement

1. Kay
2. it
3. Todd
4. the key
5. a youngster
6. the author
7. our work
8. The theater
9. Ken
10. one's

Exercise 2 More Work with Special Problems in Pronoun Agreement

Sample corrections are given.

1. Take the papers from the folders and then file the folders.
2. At school, teachers expect students to be on time for class.
3. Marge told Gloria about the bazaar, and they decided not to go today. Gloria said that perhaps they could go another time.
4. The quarterback faded to pass. The receiver and the defender converged on the ball, and the receiver dropped it.
5. When Mother spoke to Alice, Alice nodded.
6. Take the breadbox off the table and clean the table.
7. The ad says that an applicant should be able to type.
8. My brothers chased the intruders until my brothers fell.

9. Going to college out of town makes a person feel lonely.
10. When I visited Athens in 1968, tourists could still walk inside the Parthenon.

25.1 Degrees of Comparison (Recognizing Degrees of Comparison, Regular Forms) (Page 145)

Practice 1

Exercise 1 Recognizing Degrees of Comparison

1. comp.
2. pos.
3. sup.
4. sup.
5. comp.
6. sup.
7. pos.
8. sup.
9. comp.
10. pos.

Exercise 2 Comparing Adjectives and Adverbs

1. more cautious, most cautious
2. loud, louder
3. slowly, most slowly
4. softer, softest
5. more sadly, most sadly

25.1 Degrees of Comparison (Recognizing Degrees of Comparison, Regular Forms) (Page 146)

Practice 2

Exercise 1 Recognizing Positive, Comparative, and Superlative Degrees

1. comp.
2. sup.
3. pos.
4. sup.
5. comp.
6. comp.
7. pos.
8. sup.
9. sup.
10. comp.
11. pos.
12. comp.
13. sup.
14. comp.
15. sup.
16. comp.
17. pos.
18. comp.
19. sup.
20. sup.

Exercise 2 Forming Regular Comparative and Superlative Degrees

1. more beautiful, most beautiful
2. colder, coldest
3. faster, fastest
4. more slowly, most slowly
5. more fruitful, most fruitful
6. more exciting, most exciting
7. lighter, lightest
8. more likeable, most likeable
9. prettier, prettiest
10. weaker, weakest
11. more informative, most informative
12. more popular, most popular
13. more impressive, most impressive
14. more complex, most complex

15. more quickly, most quickly
16. more fattening, most fattening
17. hungrier, hungriest
18. more demanding, most demanding
19. sadder, saddest
20. safer, safest

25.1 Degrees of Comparison (Irregular Forms) (Page 147)

Practice 1

Exercise 1 Forming Irregular Comparative and Superlative Degrees

1. better
2. farther
3. worse
4. least
5. last
6. further
7. best
8. worse
9. worst
10. more

Exercise 2 Using Adjectives and Adverbs to Make Comparisons

Sample sentences are given.
1. This is the worst storm that I've ever experienced.
2. Sheila did worse on her history test than she did on her math test.
3. This is the best ice cream I've ever tasted.
4. I think that the thruway is less scenic than the old road.
5. If you rest in bed, you'll feel better tomorrow than you do today.

25.1 Degrees of Comparison (Irregular Forms) (Page 148)

Practice 2

Exercise 1 Forming Irregular Comparative and Superlative Degrees

1. better
2. best
3. more
4. worse
5. later
6. farthest
7. better
8. worse
9. most
10. less
11. more
12. last
13. more
14. farther
15. worse
16. least
17. better
18. best
19. worst
20. least

Writing Application

Using Adjectives and Adverbs to Make Comparisons

Sample sentences are given.
1. That twine is the strongest in the store.
2. Tim is by far the best musician in the class.
3. Your dog is the friendliest I have ever seen.
4. Working outdoors during the cold winter months is the hardest part of the job.
5. That car is slower than a heavy truck.

6. Today has been a good day so far.
7. I hope you're feeling well.
8. Not asking for directions when we were lost was a bad mistake.
9. Mark did badly on the chemistry exam.
10. She is a better swimmer than he is.

25.2 Clear Comparisons (Using Comparative and Superlative Degrees) (Page 149)

Practice 1

Exercise 1 Using the Comparative and Superlative Degrees Correctly

1. least
2. oldest
3. more
4. more carefully
5. longest
6. more
7. more
8. fewest
9. fastest
10. most

Exercise 2 Using the Comparative and Superlative Degrees in Sentences

Sample sentences are given.
1. My uncle is more successful than my father.
   My brother is the most successful of all.
2. Marble is harder than coal.
   A diamond is the hardest natural substance of all.
3. Sue is younger than Bret.
   Genny is the youngest of the three children.
4. Is a dog tamer than a cat?
   Is a lamb the tamest animal you have ever seen?
5. Driving is more dangerous on wet roads than on dry roads.
   Driving is most dangerous on any icy roads.

25.2 Clear Comparisons (Using Comparative and Superlative Degrees) (Page 150)

Practice 2

Exercise 1 Using the Comparative and Superlative Forms Correctly

1. most
2. poorer
3. prettiest
4. better
5. least
6. cheapest
7. more
8. worst
9. faster
10. most

Exercise 2 Supplying the Comparative and Superlative Degrees

1. older
2. most capable
3. warmest
4. most talented
5. better
6. lower
7. worse
8. strongest
9. taller
10. most generous
11. more knowledgeable
12. better
13. better

14. oldest
15. later
16. shyest
17. coldest
18. best
19. farther
20. most alert

25.2 Clear Comparisons (Logical Comparisons) (Page 151)
Practice 1
Exercise 1   Making Balanced Comparisons
1. Aunt Lena's spaghetti sauce is spicier than Mom's.
2. Laura's corn has grown faster than Phil's.
3. Ken's class picture was better than Mike's.
4. Marc's clothes were even muddier than Steve's.
5. Julie's job is more demanding than Hal's.

Exercise 2   Using *Other* and *Else* in Comparisons
1. Often my homework takes me longer than anyone else in my class.
2. That restaurant is more expensive than any other place in town.
3. My friend Marcia writes better than anyone else I know.
4. The intersection at Elm and Main is more dangerous than any other in town.
5. Is there anyone else who works as hard as Eric?

25.2 Clear Comparisons (Logical Comparisons) (Page 152)
Practice 2
Exercise 1   Making Balanced Comparisons
1. Aren't my new pants more attractive than Jacqueline's?
2. The truck's engine is more powerful than the station wagon's.
3. Trish's debating record is better than Mary's.
4. My father's coin collection is better than my uncle's.
5. At the meeting last night, Bruce's presentation was better than John's.
6. A larger orchestra is needed to perform Bruckner's symphonies than Haydn's.
7. Harry's telescope is stronger than Edward's.
8. My jacket is warmer than Steven's.
9. Maine's winters are much colder than Florida's.
10. An infection of the liver is as dangerous as an infection of the kidneys.

Exercise 2   Using *Other* and *Else* in Comparisons
1. Mount Everest is higher than any other mountain.
2. My friend William plays baseball with more enthusiasm than anyone else I know.
3. Our apartment is longer than any other in the building.
4. Your charitable contribution to the emergency fund was more than any other we received.
5. My room is colder than any other in the house.

26.1 Negative Sentences (Page 153)
Practice 1
Exercise 1   Avoiding Problems with Negatives
1. anybody
2. could
3. have
4. a
5. any

6. any
7. more than
8. ever
9. was
10. ever

Exercise 2   Using Negatives Correctly
Sample sentences are given.
1. We saw nothing unusual yesterday afternoon.
2. I had but three minutes to spare before the train arrived.
3. That wouldn't do any good.
4. He barely ate while he had the flu.
5. She had never before seen so many people hurrying to work.

26.1 Negative Sentences (Page 154)
Practice 2
Exercise 1   Avoiding Double Negatives
1. any
2. ever
3. anything
4. any
5. anything
6. none
7. any
8. nothing
9. ever
10. is

Exercise 2   Avoiding Problems with Negatives
1. can
2. anything
3. has
4. anything
5. anyone
6. anything
7. had
8. any
9. would
10. anywhere

Exercise 3   Correcting Double Negatives
Sample sentences are given.
1. Can't you ever do anything right?
2. There had been but two possibilities.
3. This old jalopy is never going to run properly.
4. I don't take the bus to school any more.
5. Of course, she doesn't expect anything.

26.2 Common Usage Problems (Page 155)
Practice 1
Exercise 1   Avoiding Common Usage Problems
1. from
2. lain
3. have
4. affect
5. among
6. regardless
7. beat
8. healthy
9. that
10. teach

Exercise 2   Avoiding Other Usage Problems
1. eager
2. altogether
3. nowhere
4. set
5. Because
6. let
7. who

8. way
9. than
10. emigrated

26.2 Common Usage Problems (Page 156)
Practice 2
Exercise 1   Correcting Usage Problems
1. Yesterday, I wanted to tell him the truth.
2. Because it was snowing, we postponed our trip.
3. My grandparents have been healthy for many years.
4. She can't help wanting another chance.
5. Next, the villain burst into the room in a rage.
6. The matter was quickly settled between my brother and me.
7. The effect of the medicine was immediate.
8. To attend the inauguration of a President is an honor.
9. Set the glass to the right of the plate.
10. Since you asked, I'll tell you my feeling about him.
11. The coach sat beside my brother and me.
12. There are three boxes in the attic.
13. As for parties, I have had my fill if you really want to know.
14. You will find similar problems anywhere you go.
15. If she were smart, she wouldn't have made up an excuse.
16. As I have often told you, I prefer chocolate cake.
17. They're apparently lost in the wilderness.
18. Everyone except John passed the exams.
19. My little brother has seen our grandfather only once.
20. Sara's costume is much different from Evelyn's.

27   Rules for Capitalization (Capitals for First Words) (Page 157)
Practice 1
Exercise 1   Using Capitals for First Words
1. only, we
2. what
3. the, does
4. that, i
5. ouch, that
6. of, i'll
7. a, food
8. one, couldn't
9. halfway, i, when
10. several

Exercise 2   Using Capitalized Words
Sample capitalized words are given.
1. Where
2. Check
3. Downed
4. Who
5. Gosh
6. My
7. We
8. Milk
9. Who
10. Little, The

27   Rules for Capitalization (Capitals for First Words) (Page 158)
Practice 2
Exercise 1   Using Capitalization with First Words
1. put the book back on the shelf.

2. where does the Great Wall of China start? and end?
3. good grief, Charlie Brown! you can't do anything right!
4. "o time too swift, o swiftness never ceasing!"— George Peele
5. the team was successful: it won the championship.
6. Mary, Mary, quite contrary,
   how does your garden grow?
   with silver bells and cockleshells
   and pretty maids all in a row.—Mother Goose
7. goodness! that truck is traveling too fast.
8. "in some ways," wrote Henry Wallace, "certain books are more powerful by far than any battle."
9. whoever is happy will make others happy too," wrote Anne Frank. "he who has courage and faith will never perish in misery!"
10. in studying Latin America, you should not overlook these interesting aspects: the dress, the culture, and the food.
11. please get some broccoli at the store today.
12. did you go snorkeling on your vacation? how about scuba diving?
13. come quick, Ethel! the baby is trying to stand up!
14. hear our pleas, o mighty king!
15. if i give you a dollar, will you be quiet for a while?
16. success is counted sweetest
    by those who ne'er succeed.
    to comprehend a nectar
    requires sorest need.—Emily Dickinson
17. wow! what an amazing performance!
18. "for three years now," said Angela, "this peach tree has not produced any fruit."
19. when buying real estate, you should consider these three things: location, location, and location.
20. the company had a very catchy slogan: it was "we try harder."

Exercise 2   Using Capitalization with First Words in Passages
Sample capitalized words are given.
   (1) When we went on a picnic last week, the sun was shining and the weather was perfect. (2) Now, however, the weather is just terrible: (3) It has been raining for the past two days. The woman giving the weather report said, (4) "Today there will be scattered showers for most of the afternoon." (5) When she said that, I was quite relieved.

27   Rules for Capitalization (Proper Nouns, Proper Adjectives) (Page 159)
Practice 1
Exercise 1   Recognizing Proper Nouns and Proper Adjectives
1. Texas, Rio Grande, Alamo
2. Hemingway, Spanish Civil War
3. Iraqi-American
4. Alex
5. Mrs. Henderson, Chevrolet
6. League of Women Voters
7. Japanese, pro-American
8. Koran, Islam
9. Baseball Hall of Fame, Cooperstown, New York
10. English-speaking Russians

Exercise 2　Using Proper Nouns and Proper Adjectives

Sample proper nouns and proper adjectives are given.

1. Infoswift
2. Rome, Venice
3. Israeli
4. William Faulkner
5. Dover
6. World Series
7. Kim, Terri
8. Rockies
9. Antarctica
10. Thanksgiving, November

27　Rules for Capitalization (Proper Nouns, Proper Adjectives) (Page 160)

Practice 2

Exercise 1　Using Capitals in Sentences with Proper Nouns

1. After hearing the news, the <u>united nations</u> called a meeting of the security <u>council</u>.
2. Illustrators of children's books all hope to win the coveted <u>caldecott award</u>.
3. Anyone <u>who</u> loves animal stories should read about the horse known as <u>flicka</u>.
4. Most people in <u>india</u> are <u>hindus</u> and worship <u>brahma</u>.
5. One goddess in mythology that you will read about often is the goddess <u>hera</u>.
6. As he made a purchase from the store called <u>stamp house</u>, <u>inc.</u>, I noticed that the <u>russian</u> spoke <u>english</u> very well.
7. If you want passport information, you should contact the <u>state department</u> in <u>washington</u>, d.c.
8. My <u>bluvard watch</u> is now ten years old but still works.
9. The <u>concorde</u> crosses the <u>atlantic ocean</u> in just a few <u>hours</u>.
10. We inducted sixty new members into the <u>national honor society</u> at our school last week.

Exercise 2　Adding Capitals for Geographical Places, Specific Events, Periods of Time, and Other Proper Nouns

The early years of the twentieth century brought with them a variety of new names, exciting events, and far-reaching ideas. The century got off to a flying start when Orville and Wilbur Wright took to the air in <u>december</u> 1903. Excitement continued into the next <u>year</u> when the <u>st. louis world's fair</u> began, bringing over 20,000 visitors flocking to the city. Sports lovers also enjoyed the <u>olympic games</u> that were held in conjunction with the fair that year. Formation of the <u>american baseball league</u> in 1901 had also brought the sports fans joy since it introduced a new level of competition to this popular sport. Many people enjoyed activities in their own communities during the 1900's: Parades and picnics held as part of the <u>july</u> celebration of <u>independence day</u> brought pleasure to people of all ages. Of course, all was not fun and games; many important laws were passed during these years. One of the most influential pieces of legislation in the early 1900's was the <u>pure food and drug act</u> passed in the summer of 1906. Advertisements of many "quack" medical cures came to a quick halt. All this began in those first few years of the twentieth century as <u>america</u> boldly entered the 1900's—the time period <u>labeled</u> by some as the <u>progressive era</u>.

Exercise 3　Using Capitalization with Proper Adjectives

1. African-American
2. correct
3. Shaniel
4. pro-American
5. Photoflex

27　Rules for Capitalization (for Titles, in Letters) (Page 161)

Practice 1

Exercise 1　Using Capitals in Titles

1. major adams
2. the ransom, red chief
3. queen, england
4. professor harold jenkins
5. the last supper
6. *arsenic, old lace*
7. father riley
8. mrs. pauling, dr. o'rourke
9. *undersea world*
10. handel's *water music*

Exercise 2　Using Capitals for Salutations and Closings

1. Dear Dr. Morgan,
2. With deep affection,
3. Gratefully,
4. My dear Cousin,
5. Very truly yours,
6. Dear Professor Atkins:
7. Yours sincerely,
8. Dear Sir or Madam:
9. My dear Marian,
10. With all good wishes,

27　Rules for Capitalization (for Titles, in Letters) (Page 162)

Practice 2

Exercise 1　Using Capitalization with Titles of People

1. Grandma
2. Reverend, Jr.
3. Mayor
4. President
5. correct
6. Miss, Mr., Sr.
7. Aunt
8. Rabbi
9. Queen
10. Senator-elect

Exercise 2　Capitalizing Titles of Things

1. Painting: *at the circus*
2. Poem: "lines composed a few miles above tintern abbey"
3. Short story: "before the wolves come"
4. School courses: german, business 312
5. Sculpture: *variation within a sphere*
6. Opera: *the siege of rhodes*
7. Book: *wellington : the years of the sword*
8. Periodical: *national pictorial*
9. One-act play: "the wonderful ice cream suit"
10. Song: "by the light of the silvery moon"

Exercise 3　Using Capitalization in a Letter

1. yes
2. no
3. yes
4. yes
5. yes
6. no

7. yes
8. yes
9. yes
10. no

28.1 End Marks (Page 163)
Practice 1
Exercise 1 Using End Marks for Sentences and Phrases
1. (!)
2. (?)
3. (.)
4. (!)
5. (!) or (.), depending on level of emotion
6. (.)
7. (!)
8. (.)
9. (.)
10. (?)

Exercise 2 Using End Marks in Your Own Sentences
Sample sentences are given.
1. Bill's birthday is on May 6(?).
2. Dr. Young works very hard.
3. Kim lives at 23 Elm Street?
4. Watch out!
5. Did you mean to?

28.1 End Marks (Page 164)
Practice 2
Exercise 1 Using the Period and Question Mark
1. Who has more bones—a baby or an adult?
2. I have often asked in what country a person can expect to live the longest.
3. What was the name of Roy Rogers' horse?
4. Which state has produced the most Presidents?
5. How many? Who?
6. The scientist questioned how long a queen termite can live.
7. Who knows what Lawrence Welk's license plate said?
8. Of all the animal personalities, who was first named to the Animal Hall of Fame?
9. Where can you find the tallest living thing in the world?
10. I wondered where the name Typhoid Mary came from.

Exercise 2 Using the Period and Exclamation Mark
1. Please bring me that pin cushion.
2. His voice is fantastic!
3. Don't step on the cat!
4. Darn!
5. A child is caught in that burning building!
6. Do it this minute!
7. The house looked fresh after its new paint job.
8. Well, I have never been so insulted in my entire life!
9. Try to finish those essays for tomorrow, class.
10. I just won the Boston Marathon!

Exercise 3 Using All End Marks
(1) Hey! Get your fresh, hot, buttered popcorn right here! (2) The cry of the vendor selling popcorn has been heard for years at circuses, ball games, and county fairs. (3) But some may wonder who first learned about this delicacy. (4) Even before Columbus sailed to this continent, the Indians of Central and South America were popping little kernels of corn. (5) They ate them, made popcorn soup from them, and wore them during religious ceremonies. (6) Today popcorn is one of America's favorite snack foods. (7) Just how much popcorn do Americans eat in a year? (8) According to statistics, they eat an average of two pounds per person each year. (9) For the popcorn industry that figure is larger than it sounds. (10) As a group, Americans eat an incredible amount of popcorn—almost half a billion pounds each year!

28.2 Commas (With Compound Sentences, With Series and Adjectives) (Page 165)
Practice 1
Exercise 1 Using Commas Correctly
1. The actor delivered the soliloquy in a clear, strong voice.
2. My sister goes to college in Ohio, and my brother goes to college in Maine.
3. Parsley sprigs, lemon slices, and tomato wedges formed an attractive border on the platter.
4. The hot, tired campers headed straight for the lake.
5. Janice may bake a cake, or we can order one at Farella's.
6. none
7. Our trip was far from perfect, but at least we got home safely.
8. Elmer saw a large, lumpy figure moving through the shadows.
9. Jeremy had planned a special meal, but it was ruined.
10. Will you fly, take the train, or drive to California?

Exercise 2 Understanding Rules for Commas
1. equal adjectives
2. compound sentence
3. series
4. equal adjectives
5. compound sentence
6. adjectives in order
7. compound sentence
8. equal adjectives
9. compound sentence
10. series

28.2 Commas (With Compound Sentences, With Series and Adjectives) (Page 166)
Practice 2
Exercise 1 Using Commas in Compound Sentences
1. The drummers beat the rhythm, and the band marched the parade route.
2. The photograph shows your feet, but your head is cut off.
3. Neither did we visit the aquarium, nor did we watch the show at the planetarium.
4. correct
5. correct
6. The hateful mosquito bit me, and I have had a huge welt ever since.
7. My mother lost her favorite earrings, so I will get her another pair for her birthday.
8. correct
9. The student saved time for the last essay question, yet he found the time was not sufficient.
10. The TV blared, but the child slept on.

Exercise 2 Separating Items in a Series
1. correct
2. I carefully watered the philodendrons, the ivy, and the African violet.
3. The crowd sat on the edge of their seats, listened

with awe, and absorbed the speaker's powerful words.
4. The politician answered with great patience, diplomacy, and knowledge.
5. I looked under the bed, in the closet, and through my desk to find my homework.
6. Cloris Leachman, Henry Fonda, and other well-known stars performed in the play.
7. I described the symptoms to the doctor: a temperature, aching bones, nausea, and a rash on my legs.
8. Send that letter to the President, the Secretary of State, and the Ambassador to France.
9. correct
10. The sun shone brightly, the clouds drifted lazily overhead, and we waded in the warm water.

28.2 Commas (After Introductory Material, With Parenthetical and Nonessential Expressions) (Page 167)

Practice 1

Exercise 1 Recognizing Introductory Material
1. Yes,
2. To win the game,
3. Shrugging her shoulders,
4. Before we knew it,
5. Exhausted,
6. Although he works hard,
7. As soon as we got your call,
8. Alice,
9. To get to work,
10. Frankly,

Exercise 2 Using Commas with Parenthetical and Nonessential Expressions
1. It was Bill, not Bob, whom I met at the concert.
2. The novel *All the King's Men* is set in Louisiana.
3. We agreed, of course, that the party should be a surprise.
4. Mr. Palmeri, our next-door neighbor, grows beautiful roses.
5. T. S. Eliot, who was born in St. Louis, adopted England as his home.

28.2 Commas (After Introductory Material, With Parenthetical and Nonessential Expressions) (Page 168)

Practice 2

Exercise 1 Using Commas After Introductory Material
1. Though we probably do not think about it often,
2. In fact,
3. According to old legends,
4. On top of Sapo Hill in Rome,
5. Soon after,
6. Working with caustic soda in the 1700's,
7. To have soap in the early days of American history,
8. When the 1800's arrived,
9. However,
10. In 1933,

Exercise 2 Setting Off Parenthetical Expressions
1. We have enough paper plates left over, I think.
2. The suit, nevertheless, needed drastic alterations before I could wear it.
3. When does your ship sail, Mr. Harville?
4. I will type up the letter, Kim, if you get it written by tomorrow.
5. I, therefore, went out shopping for a bathing suit.

Exercise 3 Distinguishing Between Essential and Nonessential Expressions
1. Pirates, those colorful, legendary plunderers of the ocean, made many spectacular heists on the high seas.
2. Bartholomew Roberts, who allowed no drinking or gambling on board his vessel, caught and pirated over 400 ships.
3. Long Ben Avery, beginning his pirating career at age twenty, captured two million dollars worth of booty—the largest amount of loot ever stolen.
4. The pirates, who possessed a very strong code of honor within their own ranks, had strict rules for dealing with problems on board.
5. essential

28.2 Commas (Other Uses) (Page 169)

Practice 1

Exercise 1 Adding Commas to Sentences
1. That family has moved to 721 Barker Street, Jefferson, Missouri.
2. John ordered swordfish; Paul, fried clams.
3. The station's goal is 1,235 new subscribers.
4. Jed asked, "Is February 13 a good day for the party?"
5. Sarah Marsh, L.P.N., prefers hospital work to private duty in homes.
6. Without Ellen, Ann was lonely.
7. On June 12, 2001, my grandfather celebrated his sixtieth birthday.
8. The new hotel has 1,354 rooms.
9. "Whenever you are ready," Pat called, "we can leave."
10. After dinner, entertainment will be offered.

Exercise 2 Punctuating a Letter
629 West 4th Street
Montpelier, Vermont 05602
December 4, 2001

Dear Paulette,
Your letter was waiting for me when we arrived home on Friday, November 30, after a short trip. We had gone to Boston, Massachusetts, to spend Thanksgiving with my grandparents.
It was odd that you should have asked for Margie's address. I just got a letter from her, too—the first one since her family moved on August 1, 1999. Her address is Margaret Bayard, 289 South Caxton Place, Gettysburg, Pennsylvania.
Your plan for a reunion this summer sounds wonderful! I wonder if Beth will be able to come 1,700 miles for it though. But as you always used to say, "Let's go for it!" Keep me posted on the plans.
Your old friend,
Sonya

28.2 Commas (Other Uses) (Page 170)

Practice 2

Exercise 1 Using Commas in Other Situations
1. The drive from Seattle, Washington, to Portland, Oregon, is a pretty one.
2. He was elected on Tuesday, November 5, and inaugurated in January of the next year.
3. There were 52,500 people watching the parade.
4. "Please move into the left lane," the officer patiently instructed.
5. My brother asked, "Have you eaten dinner yet?"

6. Our class will have Martin Deardorf, Ph.D., as our guest.
7. I read the address on the business card: R.P. Mendosa, 615 Taggert Lane, Cupertino, California 95041
8. The irate customer spoke belligerently; the public relations officer, gently.
9. "When I reached the age of eight," the woman recalled, "I decided to become a dental hygienist."
10. During the afternoon, tea and pastries were always served.

Exercise 2   Correcting Careless Use of Commas
Words from between which commas were removed are underlined.
1. During the initial training period, the falcon sits on a gloved hand with a hood covering its head.
2. Bees have existed for about fifty million years and live everywhere but the North and South Poles.
3. An interesting fact about the buffalo is that it was once on the nickel coin.
4. Bill, don't forget to clean the garage and the deck.
5. The cost of World War II in deaths and suffering was enormous.
6. She bought shoes and presents for her grandparents.
7. If eaten, the beautiful Christmas poinsettia is poisonous.
8. The crayfish is the freshwater counterpart of the lobster and is found in freshwater springs and lakes.
9. The queen bee really does not rule the colony but only serves to reproduce the bees.
10. When new seedlings begin to grow, they need water and sunshine.

28.3   Semicolons and Colons (Uses of the Semicolon) (Page 171)
Practice 1
Exercise 1   Using Semicolons Correctly
1. Since childhood, Amy has loved animals; therefore, her career as a veterinarian is hardly surprising.
2. Cucumbers, carrots, tomatoes, and onions are common in salads; for a change of pace, have you ever tried adding broccoli, eggplant, or corn?
3. When Anna is home from college, all the bedrooms are full; but we can always put up a guest in the playroom, a room that is seldom used.
4. Just put the packages on the porch; we'll have to wait here until someone gets home with the key.
5. Penny had just come off a twelve-hour shift; she was exhausted.
6. We are to supply paper goods, beverages, and snacks; but Tom will provide the main dish, the vegetables, and the salad.
7. The house needs to be painted; in addition, it needs a new roof.
8. This is an ideal time to start out; the roads are not yet crowded.
9. Jason, whom I have known all my life, was a very serious youngster; but he has, surprisingly enough, become the life of every party.
10. Grandma has lived in that old house all her life; no wonder she doesn't want to move.

Exercise 2   Understanding Uses of the Semicolon
1. conjunctive adverb
2. items that already have commas
3. items that already have commas

4. independent clauses
5. independent clauses
6. items that already have commas
7. transitional expression
8. independent clauses
9. items that already have commas
10. independent clauses

28.3   Semicolons and Colons (Uses of the Semicolon) (Page 172)
Practice 2
Exercise 1   Using the Semicolon with Independent Clauses
Yo-yos have been enjoyed for years; in fact, people in ancient Greece played with toys like yo-yos for entertainment. In France, the popularity of the yo-yo grew quickly; for instance, the nobles in seventeenth-century France played with yo-yos in the royal courts. Napoleon's soldiers played with them while waiting to fight; France's prisoners supposedly played with them while waiting for the guillotine. Even King George IV is pictured with a yo-yo; a cartoonist satirically drew him spinning his top. In Europe they played with yo-yos; in the Philippines they used them for more serious purposes. In the sixteenth century, the people of the Philippines hunted with yo-yo-like weapons; they sat in trees and sent the yo-yos hurtling down to stun the animals below. History reports that Donald Duncan first promoted the yo-yo in America in 1926; however, recent evidence shows Lothrop Llewellyn selling a metal yo-yo as early as 1906. He sold his yo-yos in Gloucester; Llewellyn even took out a patent on his invention. The latest yo-yo craze occurred in the 1960's; indeed, Duncan reportedly sold fifteen million in 1961 alone. Today, the most difficult yo-yo trick is the whirlwind; it requires performing inside and outside loop-the-loops.

Exercise 2   Using Semicolons with Internal Punctuation
1. When the milk carton fell, it split; but I picked it up before all the milk flowed onto the floor.
2. Joe, Maria, and I drove into the city last night; and we went to a delightful concert in the park.
3. As I watched, the tall, thin man reached into the pedestrian's pocket, removing his wallet; but before I could even protest, the pickpocket was lost in the crowd.
4. As she tried to lay out the pattern on the material, she finally concluded that she was short of fabric; and so she switched to another pattern, one requiring less material.
5. My grandmother knew more about people, places, and life in general than many world travelers; yet she never left the state of Nebraska.
6. When the cast was posted, you should have seen the look of joy on Martin's face; for to get a lead in the play was his dream.
7. Walking home from the store, I found an injured, frightened cat; and I knew, at that moment, he was meant to be mine.
8. I peeked out of my sleeping bag and saw a squirrel, who was busily gathering his winter food; a bird, who was welcoming the morning in song; and a doe, who was surveying her peaceful domain.
9. During this morning's practice, we have to master the routine; or the coach says we will work, work, work all day.

10. I am certain that you will enjoy this class, which is interesting and challenging; and the teacher, Mr. Gray, is excellent.

28.3 Semicolons and Colons (Uses of the Colon) (Page 173)

Practice 1

Exercise 1   Using Colons Correctly

1. Jeremy unfolded the note: "Meet me in the gym after school."
2. The express, which was due at 8:14, did not arrive until 9:00 PM
3. Two actors have refused Academy Awards: George C. Scott and Marlon Brando.
4. The three magazines with the largest paid subscriptions last year were these: *TV Scene, Reader's Review,* and *National Reflections Magazine.*
5. Warning: This cabinet contains dangerous electrical equipment.

Exercise 2   More Work with Colons

1. The text of the sermon was Matthew 10:8.
2. I am reporting on a biography titled *Gandhi: Fighter Without a Sword.*
3. Caution: Read this manual completely before using your power sled.
4. Flight 401 leaves LaGuardia Airport at 8:40 AM each weekday.
5. The president banged the gavel: "Let the meeting come to order."

28.3 Semicolons and Colons (Uses of the Colon) (Page 174)

Practice 2

Exercise 1   Using Colons as Introductory Devices

(1) This man was born December 5, 1901, and until his death in 1966, he carried one of the best-known names in the world: Walt Disney. (2) Of course, he is best remembered as the creator of some of our most beloved cartoon characters: Mickey Mouse, Pluto, and Donald Duck. (3) Walt Disney studied one subject with diligence: he concentrated on art. (4) Walt Disney felt he had to go to the one city where he could possibly become successful: he headed to Hollywood. (5) In Hollywood, he made money from his drawings, but he finally hit success with a now-classic Mickey Mouse cartoon short: "Steamboat Willie." (6) Disney went on to create many of the following famous films: *Snow White and the Seven Dwarfs, Fantasia,* and *Mary Poppins.* (7) In 1955, he started something that was to change family entertainment: he opened Disneyland. (8) Parents appreciated Walt Disney: "Our children can explore the worlds of Frontierland, Fantasyland, Tomorrowland, and Adventureland in a clean environment." (9) Several years later, Disney directed his efforts in a new direction: television. (10) Yes, Disney has left us the kind of memorials that will continue to be enjoyed by millions: Mickey Mouse, Snow White, Bambi, and the rest of the Disney gang.

Exercise 2   Using Colons for Special Writing Situations

1. Warning: Pull the plug after you finish using the iron.
2. School ended at 2:35 P.M., and we were expected to be ready for the presentation at 3:00 P.M.
3. *The Readers' Guide* listed *Green Garden Magazine* 16:23, but I could not find that issue.
4. "Dear Mr. Nelson:" is the way I started my business letter.

5. The Old Testament reading came from Psalms 13:05. (or 130:5)
6. I read *Caring for Livestock: A Guide for Beginners.*
7. I should be finished with my homework at 10:00 P.M.
8. Danger: This water is polluted. No swimming is allowed.
9. Note: The meeting will begin one hour late.
10. The movie starts at 7:30 P.M.

28.4 Quotation Marks with Direct Quotations (Direct Quotations) (Page 175)

Practice 1

Exercise 1   Distinguishing Between Direct and Indirect Quotations

1. I
2. D
3. D
4. I
5. D
6. D
7. I
8. I
9. D
10. I

Exercise 2   Using Quotation Marks Correctly

Sample rewritten indirect quotations are given.

1. "Can you tell me how to get to the World Trade Center?" asked the tourist.
2. Marcia began her letter: "Dear Santa, Please bring me a new sled."
3. "Have you chosen your topic for the report?" Darryl inquired.
4. Bruce said, "Please don't tell anyone about the party."
5. "We could go roller skating," Dana suggested, "or would you rather see a movie?"
6. "The garden really needs weeding," Mom observed.
7. I called the waiter over: "May I please have another fork?"
8. "We could organize a scrap paper drive," Amanda suggested.
9. "Ouch!" Lou cried. "That pan is hot!"
10. "Our entire card catalog," the librarian said, "will soon be on a computer."

28.4 Quotation Marks with Direct Quotations (Direct Quotations) (Page 176)

Practice 2

Exercise 1   Indicating Direct Quotations

1. "Hain't we got all the fools in town on our side? And ain't that a big enough majority in any town?"—Mark Twain
2. correct
3. "Among mortals," Euripides commented, "second thoughts are wisest."
4. Her favorite saying was "To each his own."
5. James Martineau once said, "Religion is no more possible without prayer than poetry without language or music without atmosphere."
6. "Wit has truth in it; wisecracking is simply calisthenics with words."—Dorothy Parker
7. correct
8. correct
9. "I rode this bicycle," Felipe gasped, "at least two miles up the hill."
10. "Maybe I can go shopping with you at the mall this afternoon," Carolyn said.

Exercise 2 Indicating and Capitalizing Quotations

1. "It is better to wear out than rust out."—Bishop Cumberland
2. In one of her poems, Mary Lamb referred to a child as a "young climber-up of knees."
3. Sympathy was once described by Charles Parkhurst as "two hearts tugging at one load."
4. "The greatest powers of the mind are displayed in novels," Jane Austen wrote.
5. "Better late than never" has become a favorite proverb for those who never get anything done on time.

28.4 Quotation Marks with Direct Quotations (Other Punctuation Marks with Quotation Marks, Quotation Marks in Special Situations) (Page 177)
Practice 1
Exercise 1 Punctuating Direct Quotations

1. Didn't the travel agent say, "All tips are included in the package price"?
2. Jeffrey remarked, "She should be here any minute." Then the doorbell rang.
3. I wonder," Phyllis mused, "if we have taken the right action."
4. "Who ordered the pizza?" Kelly asked.
5. The patient winced, "That felt like more than just the prick of a pin!"
6. "I remember," Grandma reminisced, "the day when you were born."
7. "Do you think," Mom asked, "that we need more cookies?"
8. "Have you ever wondered," the teacher asked, "who first said, 'Eureka'?"
9. Carmen announced loudly, "I'm starved"; just then the waiter arrived.
10. "Perhaps," Phil suggested, "we should postpone the party."

Exercise 2 Paragraphing Dialogue
Check students' dialogues for appropriate paragraphing as well as use of the quotation marks.

28.4 Quotation Marks with Direct Quotations (Other Punctuation Marks with Quotation Marks, Quotation Marks in Special Situations) (Page 178)
Practice 2
Exercise 1 Adding Quotation Marks and Other Punctuation Marks

1. "The car keeps overheating," she explained to the mechanic.
2. "We enjoyed perfect skiing weather," my friends told me. "The sun came out and the wind died down."
3. We watched the principal on the closed circuit TV: "I am pleased to announce that one of our own teachers will be on the school board this year."
4. "Watch that child!" a driver called out.
5. "Will you go to the Senior Ball with me?" asked my friend.
6. "Ouch!" Archie yelped. "I'm having a few problems with this project."
7. "Doesn't that kite look beautiful floating in the air up there?" the father asked his young child.
8. She explained, "I got the job at Mervyn's. I start working there tomorrow morning."
9. "I sent the package first class," the secretary reported.

10. "Since the milk has turned sour," the clerk apologized, "let me get you a new quart right away."

Exercise 2 Punctuating and Capitalizing in Longer Selections
"Today we are lucky to have Dr. Margaret Sherman to discuss the subject of dreams."

"It is a pleasure to be with you today," Dr. Sherman began. "As I talk, please feel free to interrupt and ask questions."

Someone in the audience raised a hand: "Will you cover the interpretation of dreams?"

"Yes," the doctor replied, "but first let me talk about the importance certain cultures place on dreams. For instance, the Cheyenne Indians sent their boys out to dream a vision that would reveal their destinies. In the Ibans tribe in Borneo they believe that a secret helper comes in a dream to provide advice."

"I have heard that people have gotten inspirations and inventions from their dreams. Can you verify this?" an individual asked.

"The doctor turned to the questioner: "Mozart reported that he saw whole musical pieces composed in his dreams, and Friedrich Kekule solved the structure of benzene based on his dream."

"And did Einstein discover the theory of relativity through a dream?" someone in the back of the room challenged.

"As a matter of fact," the lecturer explained, "he had been sick from overwork. He worked out his theory while experiencing a feverish dream."

"I find this fascinating," a girl in the front row whispered.

Ten minutes later the speaker concluded: "We should welcome our dreams—not fear them. Let me leave you with these words from William Wordsworth: 'Come blessed barrier between day and day.' "

28.4 Underlining and Other Uses of Quotation Marks (Page 179)
Practice 1
Exercise 1 Punctuating Different Types of Works

1. correct
2. "Inferno", Divine Comedy.
3. "The March of the Toys", Babes in Toyland.
4. Queen Elizabeth 2, "God Save the Queen"
5. "The Land of the Dead", News Review Magazine

Exercise 2 Choosing the Correct Form

1. Hamlet
2. Genesis
3. "Happy Birthday"
4. Magna Carta
5. Nutcracker Suite

28.4 Underlining and Other Uses of Quotation Marks (Page 180)
Practice 2
Exercise 1 Underlining Titles, Names, and Words

1. The movie Vertigo was very popular.
2. Many books such as Gone with the Wind have been made into movies.
3. Margot Fonteyn, a famous ballerina, appeared in the production Marguerite and Armand.
4. My favorite CD album is We Are the World.
5. Renoir depicts a summer outing in his painting Luncheon of the Boating Party.
6. The word nice is too often used in place of a more descriptive word.
7. She reads The Daily Tribune every day.

8. correct

9. In 1830, the people held a race between a horse and a railroad steam locomotive, the <u>Tom Thumb</u>; the horse won.

10. I thought I heard the clerk say the number <u>fifteen</u>, but she apparently called out the number <u>fifty</u>.

Exercise 2 Using Quotation Marks with Titles

1. I read the assigned chapter: "Building the Affirmative Case."

2. Our foreign visitor had learned "The Star-Spangled Banner."

3. The short poem "Ozymandias" by Shelley conveys the theme that no one can achieve immortality.

4. Woody Guthrie wrote the famous song "This Land Is Your Land."

5. I tried out for a part in the one-act play called "The Veldt."

6. "Road to the Isle" is my favorite Jessamyn West story.

7. "A Modest Proposal" is a satirical essay written by Jonathan Swift in 1729.

8. This month's issue had an interesting article about elephants called "What Do You Do with a 300-Pound Nose?"

9. Henry David Thoreau's famous essay "Civil Disobedience" was first published in 1849.

10. "The Open Window," a short story by H.H. Munro, has a surprise ending.

Exercise 3 Punctuating Different Types of Titles

1. I just finished the chapter called "Life with Max" in the book <u>Agatha Christie: An Autobiography</u>.

2. The magazine <u>Short Story International</u> published "Before the Wolves Come" by Hugh Munro.

3. I would much rather read short poems like "Poe's Dream Within a Dream" than long ones like Lord Byron's <u>The Prisoner of Chillon</u>.

4. "Waltz of the Flowers" is often a featured excerpt from <u>The Nutcracker Suite</u>.

5. correct

28.5 Dashes and Parentheses (Dashes)
(Page 181)
Practice 1
Exercise 1 Using the Dash

1. In the first presentation—it was just an illusion, of course—a small ball was passed through a solid mirror.

2. One of the exhibits—you would have loved it—depicted colonial baking in a hearth oven.

3. The justices of the Supreme Court, the complete Senate, and the members of the House of Representatives—all assembled to hear the State of the Union message.

4. The librarian—you know Mrs. Norman—was very helpful in finding the information I needed.

5. I know I have that paper somewhere—oh, never mind.

6. Whitney Jones—an interesting man who has spent most of his life in Saudi Arabia—is teaching a course at Rutgers this fall.

7. Reggie Jackson, Ted Williams, Mickey Mantle, Willie Mays—all were famous baseball players.

8. They are serving strawberry ice cream—your favorite—for dessert.

9. The storm seems to be over—no, the sky is darkening again.

10. Joe Smith—a golfer with a handicap of two—is fifty years old.

Exercise 2 More Work with Dashes

1. Actors take particular pride in receiving major awards—the Oscar for motion pictures, the Tony for Broadway plays, and the Emmy for television—because they are chosen by their peers.

2. I wonder what could be keeping Elena—hey, there's her car now.

3. Yesterday's football victory—the crowd was ecstatic—guarantees us a chance at the state title.

4. The woman I met at the museum—I think her name was Barker or Barkus—used to work with Mom at the bank.

5. Turkey, stuffing, cranberry sauce, pies—all are traditional dishes for an American Thanksgiving dinner.

28.5 Dashes and Parentheses (Dashes)
(Page 182)
Practice 2
Exercise 1 Using the Dash

1. The marching band—which has been, I might point out, practicing for weeks—won a blue ribbon at the competition.

2. Our new gardener—she is a genius with all plants!—pruned the roses recently.

3. The scenery—long, sandy beaches, desolate lava beds, and fiery sunsets—brings many tourists to Hawaii.

4. Cats are lovable and—hey, stop eating my plant, you bad cat!

5. To be able to see exotic fish in their natural habitat—that provides one of the greatest joys of snorkeling.

6. That runner—what was his name?—looked tired after his race.

7. We ordered Valentine arrangements—carnations, daisies, and roses—to be sent to our relatives.

8. The family bookkeeping system—which just looks like a jumble of numbers to me—is designed to keep me on a budget.

9. Some ski resorts—for example, Lake Placid in New York—provide for a variety of skiing activities.

10. Baseball, basketball, football, and tennis—these probably represent America's favorite sports.

11. Lavender—she just loved that color—was her choice for the walls.

12. The movie—have you seen it yet?—has been nominated for several awards.

13. With the arrival of our cousins—one never knows how many will come—confusion reigns.

14. Sometime in April 1564—no one knows the exact date—William Shakespeare was born.

15. Several essays by Thoreau—we read them last year in class—have been widely quoted.

16. Aunt May—or Crankie, as my brother and I always called her when we were children—has not been feeling well.

17. The stock market—see Chapter 10—has really been climbing lately.

18. The first two years of my life were spent in Germany—my father was stationed there.

19. Her enthusiastic—I should say fanatic—devotion to the singer is almost frightening.

20. Elaine prepared quite a feast of Mexican food—tamales, burritos, rellenos, and enchiladas.

Exercise 2 Using the Dash in Paragraphs

(1) The party—it's been in the planning stages for several weeks now—will take place on Saturday. (2) I hope you can be here a little early—I'll need help setting up the buffet table. (3) The clown—Bojingles Entertainment, Inc., is sending him out—will arrive at about four o'clock. (4) By then, all the guests should be here. (5) I've invited the Johnson twins—you remember them, don't you? (6) I've also invited Susan Campbell—I haven't seen her in months. (7) The extra chairs, which I ordered from a party supply house, will be delivered in the morning. (8) In addition to the clown, we'll have other live entertainment—a guitar player, a singer, and a magician. (9) This—the third party I've ever given—will be the best one ever! (10) In a way, I'll be glad when it's over—the preparations have really been exhausting.

28.5 Dashes and Parentheses (Parentheses) (Page 183)
Practice 1
Exercise 1 Using Parentheses

1. As soon as we had finished dinner (it was about 6:30), I started my homework.
2. We considered several plans for raising funds: (a) a bake sake, (b) a bottle drive, or (c) a plant sale.
3. In the Battle of Hastings (1066), William of Normandy defeated the English.
4. Jason's favorite pet (he has several unusual ones) is a boa constrictor.
5. Considering the distance between the two cities (3,124 miles, to be exact), driving seems impractical.

Exercise 2 More Work with Parentheses

1. Beth's party (What a wonderful party it was!) lasted till midnight.
2. Benjamin Franklin (1706–1790) was an extremely versatile man.
3. The coral reefs (What a beautiful underwater sight they make!) have meant destruction for many unknowing ships.
4. I watered the plant (which has a water indicator that shows when it needs moisture). Then, I added some fertilizer to the soil.
5. My alarm watch stopped (Could the battery be dead already?) and made me late for school.

28.5 Dashes and Parentheses (Parentheses) (Page 184)
Practice 2
Exercise 1 Using Parentheses

1. We watched the second one-act play ("The Devil and Daniel Webster"), but then we had to leave.
2. The skater looked confident (perhaps more confident than the judges liked) as he left the ice.
3. Our new exchange student (German) speaks English well.
4. Mopeds (motorized bicycles) first became popular in Europe.
5. Check the boat for the following safety supplies: (a) extra gas; (b) life preservers; (c) flares.
6. Claude Engles (1911–1983) was a wonderful neighbor to us for many years.
7. I must remember to do my homework in these classes (1) algebra; (2) speech; and (3) history.
8. This painting by Picasso (see the picture on page 75) is considered one of his best.

9. My report card came today. (I've been checking the mail every day.)
10. The grades will please my parents.
11. While the lion was completely out (the effects of the tranquilizer), the vet entered the cage confidently.

Exercise 2 Using Capitals and Punctuation with Parentheses

1. Helmers Electronic firm (Did they open up in 1974?) showed a 25-percent increase in profits.
2. The sale went well (over one thousand dollars profit), and we now have room for the new merchandise.
3. After the fashion show (held at 11:00 A.M.), a lunch was served.
4. correct
5. The cowboy hat (I planned to wear it skiing) fit perfectly.

Writing Application
Using Dashes and Parentheses in Sentences
Sample sentences are given.

1. What an incredible event occurred yesterday!—I can't put it into words.
2. Railroads—whose tracks stretch across the continent—are the most efficient means of transporting large shipments of freight.
3. To see a hummingbird in my garden—This is a sight I will never forget.
4. I saw the following animals: (1) chipmunks, (2) foxes, and (3) deer.
5. Mark Twain (1835–1910) was a famous American writer and humorist.

28.5 Hyphens (Page 185)
Practice 1
Exercise 1 Using Hyphens

1. The sergeant-at-arms asked the demonstrators to leave the meeting.
2. Alison's half-hearted response disappointed us.
3. Of the twenty-four bottles in the case, three were broken.
4. You will need five-eighths yard of fabric for the sleeves alone.
5. correct
6. Even as a young child, Paul was very self-sufficient.
7. Several anti-government demonstrators were jailed.
8. That hand-carved mantel is a masterpiece.
9. We will have several out-of-town guests with us for the holidays.
10. Twenty-seven students in our school were nominated to the National Honor Society.

Exercise 2 Hyphenating Words

1. mis-spell
2. Athenian
3. cre-ate
4. Scandinavian
5. above

28.5 Hyphens (Page 186)
Practice 2
Exercise 1 Using Hyphens in Numbers, Word Parts, and Words

1. My mother's yoga class is part of her self-improvement plan.
2. We had forty-three senior citizens on the bus trip.
3. correct

4. The happy-go-lucky child played contentedly.
5. The miniature elephant measured only one-quarter inch.
6. correct
7. correct
8. The all-important decision will be handed down tomorrow.
9. At the art gallery, we saw free-form sculptures.
10. During the post–World War II days, the United States experienced a baby boom.

Exercise 2   Using Hyphens to Avoid Ambiguity
1. The clay head that I had modeled needed to be re-formed.
2. Eager for the game to start again, he watched the half-time clock.
3. The stairs to the walk-up I saw in the ad were tiring.
4. The six foot-soldiers walked across the bridge; one fell off and then there were five.
5. The dress my mother made was a re-creation of an older one.
6. She gave him five-dollar bills to pay for the book.
7. They had barely enough money to decorate their new co-op.
8. Liking food well done, he refused the half-baked potato.
9. Re-coiling the hose took more time than they had expected.
10. We were told to wait for the express-mail clerk.

28.6   Apostrophes (With Possessive Nouns, With Pronouns) (Page 187)
Practice 1
Exercise 1   Writing Possessive Forms
1. the children's toys
2. two weeks' salary
3. the elephant's trunk
4. my sister-in-law's birthday
5. Elinor and her sister's apartment

Exercise 2   Using Apostrophes Correctly with Pronouns
1. their
2. someone else's
3. neither's
4. ours
5. anyone's

28.6   Apostrophes (With Possessive Nouns, With Pronouns) (Page 188)
Practice 2
Exercise 1   Using Apostrophes with Single-Word Possessive Nouns
1. kittens'
2. lass's
3. skater's
4. taxis
5. town's

Exercise 2   Using Apostrophes with Compound Nouns
1. Sierra Club's
2. great-uncle's
3. National Honor Society's
4. Snack-in-the-Box's
5. Director of Transportation's

Exercise 3   Using Apostrophes to Show Joint and Individual Ownership
1. Rhonda's and Emily's
2. sororities and fraternities'

3. Fred and Marilyn's
4. Laura's and Marcello's
5. Doug's and Hy's

Exercise 4   Using Apostrophes with Pronouns
1. correct
2. Someone else's
3. correct
4. his
5. one another's

28.6   Apostrophes (With Contractions, Special Uses) (Page 189)
Practice 1
Exercise 1   Writing Contractions
1. They'd
2. we're
3. he'd
4. We've
5. I'm
6. won't
7. aren't
8. you're
9. you'll
10. haven't

Exercise 2   Using Apostrophes Correctly
1. g's
2. '66
3. o'clock
4. can't, e's, i's
5. 7's

28.6   Apostrophes (with Contractions, Special Uses) (Page 190)
Practice 2
Exercise 1   Using Apostrophes with Contractions
1. isn't
2. do not
3. it's
4. didn't
5. didn't
6. wasn't
7. who'll
8. that is
9. won't
10. They've

Exercise 2   Using the Apostrophe in Special Cases
1. Hearing all those *Happy New Year*'s from people has put me in a holiday mood.
2. I think you are leaving the *s*'s and *ed*'s off the ends of your words.
3. We sing eight *do-da*'s in a row before we get to any lyrics in the song.
4. Ten *,*'s in one sentence make the sentence too choppy and confusing.
5. Europeans put an extra line in their *7*'s to show they are different from the *1*'s.
6. We both had *H*'s for our first and last initials.
7. The girl said twenty *however*'s during the course of her short speech.
8. I always get carried away writing *I*'s in my letters.
9. He always forgets the *r*'s in those words.
10. The Emporium stores use *E*'s in various sizes as a symbol of their name.

Diagraming Basic Sentence Parts (Subjects, Verbs, and Modifiers) (Page 191)

Practice 1

Exercise 1   Diagraming Subjects, Verbs, and Modifiers

1.

2.

3.

4.

5.
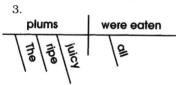

Diagraming Basic Sentence Parts (Subjects, Verbs, and Modifiers) (Page 192)

Practice 2

Exercise 1   Diagraming Subjects, Verbs, and Modifiers

1.
play | does begin

2.
I | will study

3.

4.
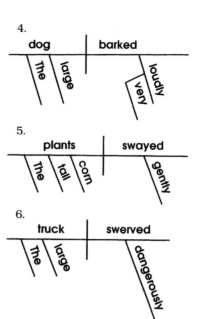

5.
plants | swayed

6.
truck | swerved

Diagraming Basic Sentence Parts (Adding Conjuctions) (Page 193)

Practice 1

Exercise 1   Diagraming Sentences with Conjunctions

1.

2.

3.

4.

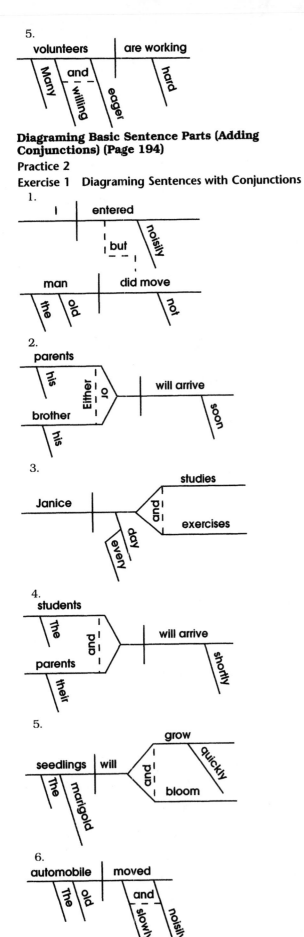

5.
volunteers | are working

Many / and / willing / eager / hard

Diagraming Basic Sentence Parts (Adding Conjunctions) (Page 194)

Practice 2

Exercise 1 Diagraming Sentences with Conjunctions

1.
I | entered
but | noisily
man | did move
the / old / not

2.
parents
his / Either / or
brother
his
will arrive / soon

3.
Janice
every / day
studies
and
exercises

4.
students
The / and
parents
their
will arrive / shortly

5.
grow / quickly
seedlings | will
The / marigold / and
bloom

6.
automobile | moved
The / old / and / slowly / noisily

Diagraming Basic Sentence Parts (Complements) (Page 195)

Practice 1

Exercise 1 Diagraming Complements

1.
police | offered | immunity
The /
informers
the

2.
referee | declared | champion | winner
The / the / former / the

3.
children | show | respect
Those /
parents
their / great
and
adults
other

4.
single | became | hit
Their / new / quickly / a

Diagraming Basic Sentence Parts (Complements) (Page 196)

Practice 2

Exercise 1 Diagraming Complements

1.
girl | crossed | street
The / young / carefully / the
very

2.
teacher | plays | chess
My / history / well
very

3.
brother | was elected | president
Her / class

4.
sun | melted | snow
The / warm / quickly / the

5.

6.

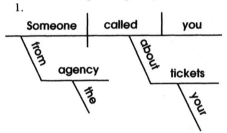

Diagraming Phrases (Prepositional Phrases, Appositives, and Appositive Phrases) (Page 197)

Practice 1

Exercise 1   Diagraming Prepositional Phrases

1.

2.

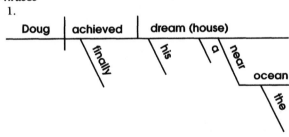

Exercise 2   Diagraming Appositives and Appositive Phrases

1.

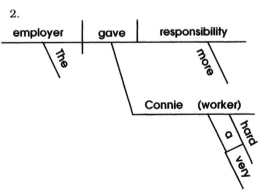

2.

Practice 2

Exercise 1   Diagraming Prepositional Phrases

1.

2.

3.

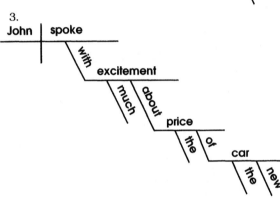

Exercise 2   Diagraming Appositives and Appositive Phrases

1.

2.

3.

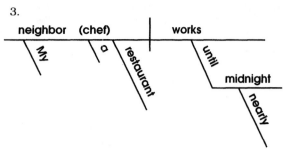

Diagraming Phrases (Participles and Participial Phrases, Gerunds and Gerund Phrases) (Page 199)

Practice 1

Exercise 1   Diagraming Participial Phrases and Nominative Absolutes

1.

2.

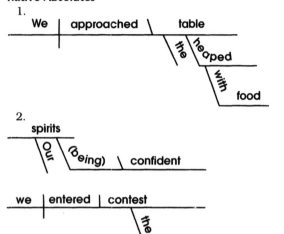

Exercise 2   Diagraming Gerunds and Gerund Phrases

1.

2.

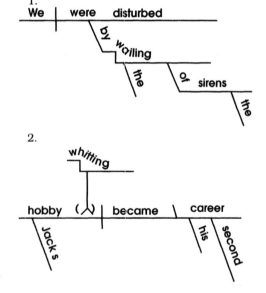

Diagraming Phrases (Participles and Participial Phrases, Gerunds and Gerund Phrases) (Page 200)

Practice 2

Exercise 1   Diagraming Participles and Participial Phrases

1.

2.

3.

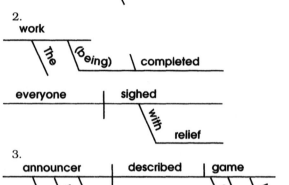

Exercise 2   Diagraming Gerunds and Gerund Phrases

1.

2.

3.

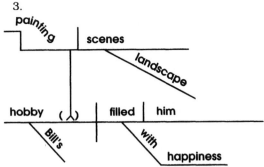

Diagraming Phrases (Infinitives and Infinitive Phrases) (Page 201)

Practice 1

Exercise 1   Diagraming Infinitives and Infinitive Phrases Used as Nouns

1.

2.

Exercise 2   Diagraming Infinitives and Infinitive Phrases Used as Adjectives and Adverbs

1.

2.

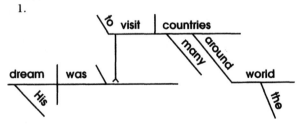

Diagraming Phrases (Infinitives and Infinitive Phrases) (Page 202)

Practice 2

Exercise 1   Diagraming Infinitives and Infinitive Phrases

1.

2.

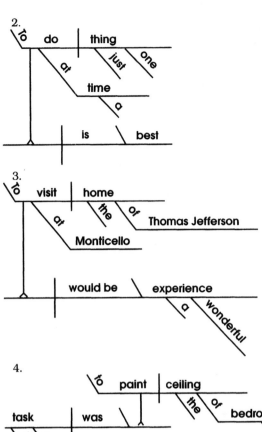

3.

4.

5.

6.

Diagraming Clauses (Compound Sentences) (Page 203)

Practice 1

Exercise 1   Diagraming Compound Sentences

1.

2.

Exercise 2   Diagraming Compound Elements and
Compound Sentences

1.

2.

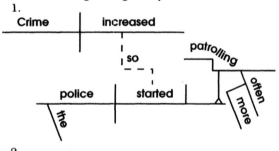

Diagraming Clauses (Compound Sentences)
(Page 204)

Practice 2

Exercise 1   Diagraming Compound Sentences

1.

2.

3.

4.

5.

6.

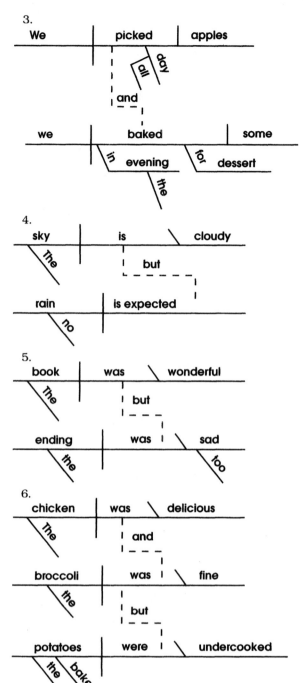

Diagraming Clauses (Complex Sentences)
(Page 205)

Practice 1

Exercise 1   Diagraming Adjective and Adverb Clauses

1.

2.

Edna | prepared
for day
the

she | would have | job
her *own*
when

Exercise 2   Diagraming Noun Clauses

1.
we | would mow | lawn
that *today* *his*

We | promised
Mr. Hillyer

2.
we | decide | Whatever

is | likely
to
displease | someone

Diagraming Clauses (Complex Sentences) (Page 206)
Practice 2
Exercise 1   Diagraming Complex Sentences

1.
attorney | is | person
That *a*

Betty | knows | whom
well
quite

2.
restaurant | is \ place
That *the*

they | ate | dinner
usually *on* nights *where*
Saturday

3.
Andrea | moved
because

job | required | relocation
her *new* *a*

4.
They | sing
as if

they | were
in chorus
a

5.
parents | would buy | puppy
his *that* him *a*

boy | suspected
The *little*

Diagraming Clauses (Compound-Complex Sentences) (Page 207)
Practice 1
Exercise 1   Diagraming Compound-Complex Sentences

1.
We | unloaded | car
the

and

guide | led | us
the *through*
until woods
the

we | found | campsite
a *good*

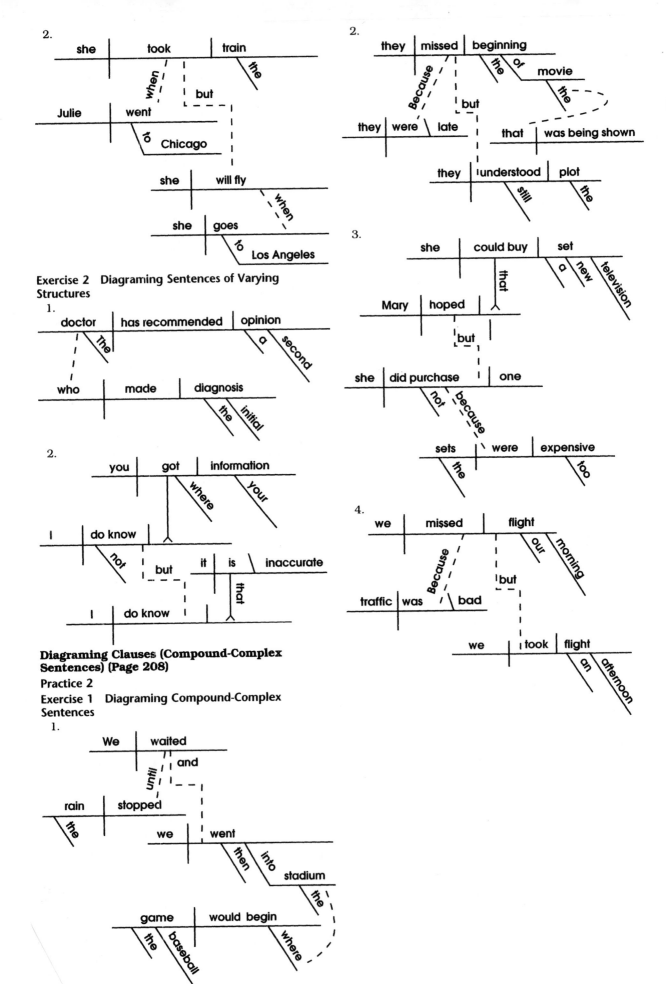

2.

Exercise 2   Diagraming Sentences of Varying Structures

1.

2.

Diagraming Clauses (Compound-Complex Sentences) (Page 208)

Practice 2

Exercise 1   Diagraming Compound-Complex Sentences

1.

2.

3.

4.